# The Extratempestrial Model

Dr. Michael P. Masters

*This book is dedicated to the brave women and men who endured truly remarkable and often lamentable events, but who showed great courage in sharing their experiences with the world.*

# Acknowledgments

I would like to acknowledge the help and support of those who took the time to read and critique this manuscript throughout its long-term evolutionary process, and for their insightful and influential comments and suggestions that helped shape it along the way. These include Daniel Blais, Greg Bishop, Cheyenne Crooker, Chad Okrusch, Nick May, Dean Alioto, and perhaps most notably, Keira Masters, whose spiritual open-minded energy and patient and carefully crafted critiques consistently contribute to the development and refinement of new ways of thinking about the complex mysteries that circumscribe our current reality.

# Table of Contents

*So many people today—and even professional scientists—seem to me like somebody who has seen thousands of trees but has never seen a forest. A knowledge of the historic and philosophical background gives that kind of independence from prejudices of his generation from which most scientists are suffering. This independence created by philosophical insight is—in my opinion—the mark of distinction between a mere artisan or specialist and a real seeker after truth.*

– ALBERT EINSTEIN

# Chapter 1

# The Extratempestrial Model

*UFO reports are not necessarily caused by visits from space travelers.... If time and space are not as simple in structure as physicists have assumed until now, then the question 'where do they come from?' may be meaningless: they could come from a place in time.*[1]

– JACQUES FABRICE VALLÉE

My fascination with the UFO enigma began when I was eight years old, after learning that my father once saw a strange light in the night sky while working in a rural area of northeast Ohio. Seeking answers to this odd occurrence, he, like most sensible people of the mid-1980s, bought Whitley Strieber's book, *Communion: A True Story*.[2] My curiosity was catapulted forward one afternoon when I happened to glance up at the living room shelf and noticed the eerie image of an archetypal "grey alien" looking back at me from the front cover of Strieber's book.

Upon seeing this obscure alien figure, with its broad forehead, small face, narrow chin, and large haunting black eyes, I remember being moved by an ephemeral image that entered my mind. It encompassed three humanoid creatures visualized together. On the left side was something like a chimpanzee, or an early hominin form, in the middle was a nondescript modern human, and on the right was that odd, yet entirely familiar alien creature from the book's cover. Even at a young age, and knowing nothing of phylogenetic relationships, it was evident that the human in the center of this mental image resembled both the "chimpanzee" to the left, and the "alien" to the right, which led me to wonder if they could somehow be related.

This experience, along with the fact that I've always been easily bored by the banality of reality, was the impetus for my deep dive into the UFO phenomenon. The striking similarity between this "alien" and ourselves caused me to question whether our distant descendants could be using backward time-travel technology to visit and study their past. With further research into human biocultural evolution, procured while pursuing a PhD and subsequent career in biological anthropology, the scope of this potential paradigm expanded.

An important component of this concept centered on how long-term biological and cultural trends in human evolution, if they persist into the future, may ultimately result in us becoming them. This is noteworthy considering how often these beings are described as human, or with unique derived traits characteristic of the hominin lineage. It is also improbable that extraterrestrial aliens elsewhere in the universe would evolve to be bipedal, and generally look and act so much like us. Furthermore, most UFOs seen in association with these beings have a form consistent with what we would expect to see in a craft capable of manipulating spacetime, which suggests these are the very devices that allow our future progeny to venture backward across the landscape of time.

Seeking a locution to encompass this time-travel approach, I eventually coined the term extra*temp*estral. By replacing the Latin root *terr*, meaning *Earth*, with the Latin root *temp*, meaning *time*, we retain a semantic similarity to the more conventional extra*terr*estrial lexis, while alluding to their future human origins. Furthermore, if these visitors are our descendants, they may also live here on Earth, just in a time or times that lie to the future of our current present. In essence, the term is meant to convey that they are us, following many millennia of continued evolutionary change in our culture and biology.

It is fun to speculate about what might happen between now and the disparate points in our future from which they come. However, there is currently no way for us to know what social, political, economic, atmospheric, nuclear, planetary, celestial, or subterranean forces may contribute to the expression of any future human characteristics.

We can only surmise how different environments on Earth, in space, or elsewhere might shape our impending appearance, though without the aid of hindsight, such conjecture is unjustified.

Although we can't know how ensuing forces will impact our physiology and culture, examining dominant trends throughout the hominin past may provide some insight into our future form. For instance, among the most overt and enduring changes were an increase in size and roundness of our upper skull, and a concomitant reduction and retraction of our mid and lower facial anatomy. These craniofacial changes arose in association with our ancestors becoming habitually bipedal, which initially occurred 6–8 million years ago.

These most marked changes to our craniofacial architecture persisted, and accelerated, throughout the entirety of hominin evolution, regardless of where we lived on this planet, or what our environmental conditions were like at any given time. Considering the enduring nature of these and other past trends, what is observed in the appearance and behavior of the visitors, while alien to what we are now, is entirely consistent with what has occurred throughout the human past, and what may be the human future.

Moreover, the majority are described as symmetrical, four-limbed, pentadactyl, bipedal, large-brained, humanlike, or entirely human beings, with large round heads, enlarged eyes, small faces, and relative hairlessness who are capable of communicating in our languages, breathing our air, and who possess technology advanced beyond, but seemingly built upon, our own. These accounts, coupled with a thorough understanding of the past and modern human condition, point to the continuation of established biological and cultural trends here on Earth, long into the distant human future.

## TEMPORAL CONVERGENCE

The notion that UFOs and aliens may be our distant human descendants has been around for some time. After publishing *Identified Flying Objects* in 2019, I had the honor of meeting numerous authors, screenwriters, producers, and fellow scientists who also espouse this time-traveling humans idea as an explanation for at least part of the UFO phenomenon. It was fascinating to see that so many other people, with such a diverse set of skills and experiences, had reached the same conclusion, and that many were also working to get this idea out there in some capacity.

While there are bound to be others I have missed, some notable individuals I've met, collaborated with, or simply heard of who are also striving to make this a more conventionally understood concept include Diane Tessman, who published *Future Humans and the UFOs*;[3] an author writing under the pen name Chris J. Simpson, who in 2014 published a science fiction book called *The Chrononaut*;[4] and Leon Kirkbeck, cofounder of the Augusto Group production company and co-host of the *Cryptid Factor* podcast,[5] produced in association with comedians and actors Rhys Darby, David Farrier, and Dan Schreiber.

Dr. Jack Sarfatti, an American theoretical physicist who studied at the Cornell Space Science Center and Max Planck Institute for Physics, among other notable institutions, also advocates for this time-travel model. Additionally, Sarfatti has put forth a theory about how our descendants may achieve backward time travel in the physical sense, which will be discussed later in this text. John Ventre, former state director for the Pennsylvania Mutual UFO Network (MUFON) also posited that unidentified aerial phenomena (UAPs/UFOs) are future human military aircraft. In a live interview with KDKA Radio out of Pittsburgh, Pennsylvania, Ventre states, "I think what we're dealing with is maybe interdimensional. It could be us from the future, it could be something coming through a dimension. What we're seeing here is most likely just military advanced crafts."[6]

Notable military personnel have also suggested that time travel may explain the origin of UFOs, including Sergeant Jim Penniston, USAF, Ret., whose encounter will be detailed later in this text.[7] Distinguished US Navy Commander George W. Hoover, toward the end of his life, and after holding top-secret clearance throughout much of it, revealed that the 1947 crash in Roswell, New Mexico, involved time traveling humans.[8] Additionally, Philip J. Corso and William J. Birnes's 1998 book *The Day after Roswell*, explains how Dr. Hermann Oberth, a German physicist and engineer who is considered a founding father of rocketry and astronautics, suggested that the craft recovered from Roswell, New Mexico, in 1947 was "not a spacecraft but a time machine."

> The other explanation Dr. Hermann Oberth came up with was that this was a time/dimensional travel ship that didn't traverse large distances in space. Rather, it 'jumped' from one time/space to another or from one dimension to another and instantly returned to its point of origin.[9]

Renowned computer scientist, astronomer, author, and Ufologist, Jacques Vallée, whose quote began this chapter, has long advocated in many of his writings and interviews that UFOs could be the result of intertemporal/interdimensional beings. Richard Hoffman, former defense contractor, MUFON state director, and current executive board member of the Scientific Coalition for UAP studies in Huntsville, Alabama, also considers time travel a strong candidate to explain much of the UFO phenomenon. In fact, Rich Hoffman, Jack Sarfatti, and myself were all guests on an episode of *Coast to Coast AM* titled, "UFOs: Theories & Technology," which aired on June 23, 2019, with renowned journalist George Knapp, where we each offered different but complementary views on this time-travel model.[10]

I recently came across a well-written 1992 book by Marc Davenport titled, *Visitors from Time: The Secret of the UFOs*.[11] Similar to this section of the book, Davenport also lists works written by those who had independently arrived at this same time-travel conclusion. While too numerous to catalog here, a comprehensive summary of these authors and their contributions can be seen beginning with page 218 of Davenport's book. Other published works on the subject include a 2001 book by Jenny Randles called *Time Storms: Amazing Evidence for Time Warps, Space Rifts and Time Travel*, which examines "whether UFO's may in fact be time travelers from our own future";[12] a 2010 book by David Fair called *UFO: Uninvited Future Observers*;[13] a 2012 book by Alan Butler called *Intervention*;[14] and a 2018 book by Nathan Bollio titled *Aliens Are Humans from the Future, UFO is a Time Machine*.[15]

Other written works include a series of short articles by Jeff Barris (*Chrononauts – An Evolutionary Angle*); Clayton Rumley (*Humans… Among Us!*); and David Anderson, PhD (*Time Travelers from the Future*).[16] Whitley Strieber also briefly acknowledged time travel as a possible explanation for UFOs in his 1987 book *Communion*, and though it was a somewhat censorious analysis, the Extratempestrial Model was thoroughly scrutinized in two different papers by Dr. Michael D. Swords, whose thoughtful critiques are considered throughout this tome.

This idea has also made its way into popular culture in various forms, which includes a 2012 song titled "Aliens (Are Only Us from the Future)" by Squackett, which featured Chris Squire (from Yes) and Steve Hackett (from Genesis) on the only studio album they ever produced titled, *A Life Within A Day*;[17] a 1993 science fiction film called *Official Denial*, which depicts a person inside a "rubbery alien suit" who came from the future;[18] and almost immediately after publishing my first book in 2019, several people began telling me about a scene from an even earlier film from 1984 called *Repo Man*, where Miller, played by actor Tracey Walter, tells Otto, played by Emilio Estevez,

> **Miller:** There ain't no difference between a flying saucer and a time machine… Where'd all these people come from? I'll tell you where, the future. Where'd all these people disappear to?
> **Otto:** The past?
> **Miller:** That's right! And how'd they get there? Flying saucers. Which are really? Yea, you got it, time machines![19]

I have also been contacted by countless people over the last few years who have expressed to me that at some point in their lives, they too had postulated that UFOs and aliens may simply be us from the future. Among my favorites was a comment written in response to an article about my book, which was posted on the website Above Top Secret, in which one sagacious reader, who goes by the alias *burntdogg*, commented,

> I used to postulate this back in my late teen yrs while partaking of the sacred herb down at the local creek. Part of my argument was that the human body would evolve around our dependence on technology and less on manual labor: we would lose muscle mass, fingers become elongated to perform button pushing (or maybe jazz guitar), our eyes widen due to working in darkened rooms, staring at computer screens (or trying to focus on the content of our smart phones), etc.
>
> Then a friend would argue 'so, with all this grand technology, we come back from the future to mutilate cows?'
>
> And I reply 'yes, the future is udderly ridiculous [sic]'[20]

## COLLECTIVE CONSCIOUSNESS

Numerous instances exist throughout the human past where little bursts of innovation or insight independently creep into our collective consciousness, then spread more widely through two other cultural processes: migration, and diffusion. This appears to have been the case with the origin of agriculture during the Neolithic revolution. Beginning around 12,000 years ago, plant and animal domestication arose independently, and at nearly the same time, in six major geographic regions. It then spread rapidly from these original agricultural centers and has since become the primary subsistent strategy for nearly every society throughout the world.

Another notable instance of independent invention occurred when both Charles Darwin and Alfred Russel Wallace came to the same groundbreaking conclusion that nature selects for certain traits over others, thus directing the process of biological evolution. This novel notion arose independently for both naturalists around the same time. While conducting research across different continents, each scholar became keenly aware that natural selection causes organisms to become better adapted to their environment. Furthermore, it was clear to them that differences among closely related species are the result of evolution occurring over many generations, and when viewed in reverse, these variants can all be traced back to an earlier common ancestor.

Since Wallace and Darwin published their pioneering works in evolutionary biology nearly 170 years ago, the speed with which technology and knowledge evolves has accelerated immensely, to the extent that new ways of making, doing, or thinking now arise in tandem in a much narrower timeframe. It is possible that chrono-consistency concerning the Extratempestrial Model (chrononauts, temponauts, or whatever we decide to call these time traveling humans), is nothing more than co-incidence. However, as more people postulate about this increasingly prevalent paradigm, one can't help but wonder if a shift in our collective consciousness is occurring.

There are many reasons why serious consideration should be given to this time-travel model. Not least among them are the advanced capabilities of UFOs and the nearly ubiquitous description of human and humanlike individuals associated with them, although far more information is required before any concrete claims can be made. It was not the intent of my last book, nor is it the intent of this one, to proclaim any insight beyond what can currently be known through scientific study and how it may be applied to understanding the more tenuous topic of UFOs. However, examining what we know of our pasts, what we see happening today, and what we will seemingly someday be capable of may bring us closer to a comprehensive comprehension of this concept and an eventual ability to measure its merits once granted the vantage of hindsight.

The aim of the current study is to offer a critical analysis of conventional contactee case studies as they relate to the Extratempestrial Model, the Extraterrestrial Hypothesis, and other interpretations of UFO encounters. Assessing the similarities and differences among these reports could be crucial to our understanding of the phenomenon and potentially reveal much about what is happening now, as well as across countless cases in the human past. In this context, the distinction between the terms *abductee* and *contactee* should also be noted. In a published book chapter titled "Alien Attraction: The Subculture of UFO Contactees and Abductees," Christopher D. Bader, professor and chair of the Sociology Department at Chapman University, clarifies the distinction:

> The contactee/abductee distinction is key withing the UFO sub-culture. Someone who calls himself or herself a 'contactee' is signaling an entirely different type of experience, and perspective on that experience, than someone who calls himself or herself an 'abductee.' Contactees enjoy their experiences and look forward to the next adventure. They feel privileged to have been selected for contact by the aliens.... Although their stories continue to develop, abductees generally fear their experiences. They are not contacted, but *captured*.[21]

By examining consistent patterns across reliable reports provided by those who have interacted with unusual entities as abductees, contactees, and as part of other contact modalities, we may begin to understand the nature of these experiences, as well as the potential origin of the visitors involved. When the same things happen to a diverse group of people throughout the world and through time, we are obliged to pay attention. There is much we can learn from these encounters, and it is high time we vanquish the synthetic stigma that surrounds this subject and foster a future where open minds prevail, with the hopes of someday obtaining an unfettered understanding of the UFO phenomenon.

# Chapter 2

# The Paradigm Predicament

*To really begin to perceive the visitors adequately it is going to be necessary to invent a new discipline of vision, one that combines the mystic's freedom of imagination with the substantial intellectual rigor of the scientist.*[22]

– Whitley Strieber

*We wish to find the truth, no matter where it lies. But to find the truth we need imagination and skepticism both. We will not be afraid to speculate, but we will be careful to distinguish speculation from fact.*[23]

– Carl Sagan

The most conventional explanation for the UFO phenomenon has long been the Extraterrestrial Hypothesis (ETH), which is the idea that UFOs, and the beings who operate them, hail from a different planet in a separate region of the universe. There are logical reasons why the ETH arose and persisted as the dominant model for so long. First and foremost, UFOs are primarily seen in the sky. The aerial proclivities of these craft would naturally lead any human group, past or present, to postulate that these objects must have come from the bright lights in the heavens above.

This "things-coming-down-from-outer-space" explanation is an intuitive one. Though simple as it may be, there are some glaring issues with the ETH. For instance, how might an intelligent lifeform find a distant civilization living amongst the countless stars in the vastness of space? How might life elsewhere arise, endure, and evolve to become an upright walking humanoid species like ourselves, especially considering how rare it is here on Earth?

Although the oxygen in our atmosphere has been discoverable for about 3 billion years, we only began advertising our existence as an advanced lifeform in 1974. That year, to celebrate a major upgrade to the recently collapsed Arecibo Radio Telescope, we sent the most powerful broadcast ever deliberately beamed into space. Presently, this 1,679-bit radio message, which looks like a screenshot from an old Atari game, has only traveled about 50 light years from Earth—or about 0.19% of the way to its destination in the M13 globular star cluster near the edge of the Milky Way galaxy, roughly 21,000 light years away.[24]

In addition to the proximity problems we face, and particularly regarding the limited amount of time that has passed since our radio and deep-space satellite communications were sent out from Earth, there is the issue of equal coincidence of existence among us and other intelligent species. We often take for granted that we live now. But how does this now compare to that of past and future nows for other lifeforms throughout the 14-billion-year history of the universe? Any advanced civilization would not be expected to exist at the same or even a similar level of technological development, and at the same time, as any other civilization in their celestial neighborhood.

Additionally, if advanced alien races are visiting us from other planets, we would expect to constantly see them coming and going in the space around our tiny planet. Instead, they seem to just pop in and out of our existence here and now, and often in areas of high electromagnetic anomalies. Rather than being a characteristic of spacefaring people, this behavior is consistent with future human visitors employing an intertemporal or interdimensional means of travel. According to UFO investigative researcher Steve Mera, in a 2020 interview with the *Leak Project,*

> We can now comfortably say a UFO is seen at least every 10 seconds. It's ridiculous…. That would constitute a huge amount of UFOs. And, we have to ask, well where are they all coming from. Now if we do stand by the theory that these things are interplanetary craft, interstellar, and traveling the distances to Earth, then we would

expect to see some type of superhighway going backwards and for-wards. And when we interview the SETI scientists... they said 'space is unusually quiet,' which means, if we had a superhighway out there, we'd be seeing noise in the electromagnetic field of the ionosphere as they're going backwards and forwards, and we're not seeing that... we're not seeing this superhighway....

Where are they actually coming from? The evidence over the last 10 years points toward that these things are materializing and dema-terializing at will. In, and out. But they're actually doing it at key loca-tions.... Over the years, we have managed to get hold of the imaging and scanning from two satellites of planet Earth, of electromagnetic and geomagnetic anomalies. And when you start to cross-reference the electromagnetic anomalies against the significant UFO instances over the last 200 years, you're seeing a ridiculous correlation.[25]

In addition to spatial and temporal limitations of the Extraterrestrial Hypothesis, there is the issue of whether we would be capable of com-municating with beings who evolved on a separate planet but who hap-pened to attain a similar level of intellect at the same time. For instance, what if the extraterrestrials buzzed and danced like bees, used infra-sound like an elephant, ultrasound like a tarsier, seismic communica-tion like the demon African mole rat, or any other form of vibrational communication observable among the various species here on Earth?

We should still be able to hear, feel, or use devices to detect commu-nicatory vibrations made by extraterrestrial aliens. However, ascertain-ing symbolic substance from them so we can decipher meaning and es-tablish mutual understanding is an improbable prospect. Additionally, because almost every close encounter involves vocalized or telepathic speech that takes place in the contactee's native language, our shared means of communicating is far more similar than what we would ex-pect of extraterrestrial entities.

As I have stated numerous times, I do not see the Extratempestrial Model as mutually exclusive with other interpretations of the UFO phenomenon, including the Extraterrestrial Hypothesis, though there are numerous issues with the latter that are often overlooked. One problem has to do with the immense space that separates solar systems, but perhaps more important is the often-overlooked time factor. By all accounts, UFOs can travel incredibly fast, so darting between stars may not be an issue. But what about the rate at which time passes for space travelers relative to those who stay home? The issue of time dilation is rarely considered in the context of us, or an extraterrestrial species, traversing vast distances to visit other civilizations.

This is an aspect of Einstein's theory of Special Relativity, which is often depicted in the context of the Twin Paradox. Relative to the twin who stays home and remains in a rest frame, the fearless spacefaring sibling who jets off from their home planet at incredible velocity will experience time moving at a slower speed by comparison. Depending on how fast and for how long the space twin travels relative to the speed of light, hundreds, thousands, or tens of thousands of years may have passed back on Earth.

According to Skip Newhall, who received a PhD in applied mathematics in 1972 from the California Institute of Technology and who worked at the Jet Propulsion Laboratory (JPL) for 36 years, the time it would take for someone to traverse the entire Milky Way galaxy, while traveling at nearly the speed of light, is vastly different for the people inside the ship relative to those who stayed behind on Earth. More specifically, for astronauts traveling in the spaceship (rocket time), it would take 11.2 years to reach the galactic center, and to reach the opposite edge of the galaxy it would take 22.4 years in rocket time. However, for those who remained in a rest frame back on Earth, this same trip across the galaxy would take 100,002 years.[26]

As an even more extreme example of this time dilation effect, imagine if we wanted to travel to the Andromeda galaxy. According to Newhall,

The Andromeda galaxy is about 2,500,000 light-years away. It depends on your flight strategy. The most obvious is to launch a rocket from earth, accelerate at 1 *g* [the acceleration of the Earth's gravity]

16

for half the trip, and then decelerate equally for the remainder. From the theory of relativity, we find that the travel time for the rocket crew would be 28.6 years [but 2.5 million years for observers on Earth].[27]

Any astronaut who commits to a voyage like this will inevitably be required to bid farewell to their family, friends, and the entire society they grew accustomed to at that time. For when they arrive home, after traveling near the speed of light for even a relatively short duration of rocket time, everyone they had known will be long dead, and the language and culture they once knew will have evolved into something entirely unrecognizable, if it still exists at all.

However, if these space travelers also developed backward time-travel technology, it would be possible for them to return home to the same relative place, and time, as their societal cohort, while still reaping the benefits of deep-space exploration. Without the ability to return to their home time, it may be difficult to recruit people for interstellar missions, if it means they must say goodbye to everyone and everything they had ever known. In essence, we may need to develop backward time-travel technology to accomplish interstellar space exploration, and if we do, what will stop us from using that capability to also visit the past?

Another potential problem related to time dilation and interstellar exploration—and an interesting thought experiment in general—was pointed out in a 2020 article by Trevor Mahoney. Because time moves more slowly for astronauts traveling through space at a high rate of speed, those who remain on Earth will continue to advance their space exploration technology at a much fast rate. This could mean that the astronauts zipping through space in what they believe to be the most advanced technology of their time are quickly overtaken by new astronauts piloting even more advanced ships developed in the older astronaut's relative future. In this way, the rapid rate of time's passage back on Earth, and the increased speed with which new materials and technologies evolve, could mean we are constantly catching up to and surpassing the spacecraft and astronauts who left years earlier. According to Mahoney,

Whether it be gravitational time dilation or normal time dilation, humans of the far future may have technology that travels so fast it would make any mission today pointless.... Sending deep space missions now is futile because, in the far future, our technology will overshadow what we have now. Maybe we will be able to go light speed and catch up with one of our ships within 10 minutes.

Wouldn't that suck? You've been on a 25-year voyage and a fresh set of astronauts just roll up next to your ship; stomachs still full from Earth breakfast.[28]

## Phylogenesis

As mentioned above, it is improbable that extraterrestrial aliens would evolve to look or act like us. The odds are very low that another two-legged, upright walking hominin, with two eyes, a nose, a mouth, five digits on each hand and foot, and an enlarged brain and neurocranium, would evolve again in a separate solar system. It is even less likely when considering the specific environmental and biocultural factors that culminated in our complex condition, making our species unique among the plethora of other organisms on this planet.

Taking into consideration countless consistent reports provided by sound-minded individuals who assert that they have seen or interacted with these beings, both they and us seemingly share numerous derived characteristics unique to the hominin lineage. Among the most recognizable of these is our bipedal form of locomotion, or upright walking, which is the trait that defines our hominin lineage.

It is important to note that bipedalism is incredibly rare among all animals here on Earth, and it is undoubtedly even rarer on earthlike exoplanets elsewhere in the universe, considering most are far more massive by comparison. In fact, according to data obtained from the Exoplanet Catalog of the Planetary Habitability Laboratory at the University of Puerto Rico at Arecibo, only 46 of the 2,023 confirmed exoplanets (2.27%) have a mass less than or equivalent to that of Earth.[29] Additionally, despite living on a relatively small planet with gravity of only 9.8 m/s², bipedalism is extremely uncommon here, to the extent that we are the only mammal that does it full time.

Our bipedal form of locomotion is also to blame for such discomforts as neck and back pain, knee problems, complicated births, hemorrhoids, hernias, fainting, and fractured hips, among others.[30] The myriad effects that gravity alone has on shaping the physical and behavioral characteristics of an organism suggest that even if intelligent extraterrestrial beings do exist, we may be the only advanced *bipedal* beings in the galactic neighborhood.

Reports of close encounters also indicate that we and the visitors share traits like bilateral symmetry, relative hairlessness, dexterous hands, sexual reproduction, the lack of a tail (which is also rare on Earth), a large and globular brain, big eyes, and a small nose and mouth. These shared derived traits (or synapomorphies) are unlikely to arise in alien creatures that underwent a separate evolutionary trajectory on a different planet elsewhere in the universe. Other scientists are also skeptical about the universality of intelligent life on other planets, or that extraterrestrial beings would evolve to look anything like us. According to legendary cosmologist Carl Sagan,

> The sure lesson of evolution is that organisms elsewhere must have separate evolutionary pathways; that their chemistry and biology, and very likely their social organization will be profoundly dissimilar to anything on Earth.[31]

Douglas Vakoch, president of Messaging Extraterrestrial Intelligence (METI), and editor of a NASA-sponsored research paper titled "Archaeology, Anthropology and Interstellar Communication" states,

> Moreover, any civilization we contact will have arisen independently of life on Earth, in the habitable zone of a star stable enough to allow

its inhabitants to evolve biologically, culturally, and technologically. The evolutionary path followed by extraterrestrial intelligence will no doubt diverge in significant ways from the one traveled by humans over the course of our history.[32]

According to Snyder-Beattie et al. (2020), in an article titled "The Timing of Evolutionary Transitions Suggest Intelligent Life is Rare," which was published in the journal *Astrobiology*,

On Earth, the emergence of complex intelligent life required a preceding series of evolutionary transitions such as abiogenesis, eukaryogenesis, and the evolution of sexual reproduction, multicellularity, and intelligence itself. Some of these transitions could have been extraordinarily improbable, even in conducive environments.... Using a simplified Bayesian model that combines uninformative priors and the timing of evolutionary transitions, we demonstrate that expected evolutionary transition times likely exceed the lifetime of Earth, perhaps by many orders of magnitude. Our results corroborate the original argument suggested by Brandon Carter that intelligent life in the Universe is exceptionally rare, assuming that intelligent life elsewhere requires analogous evolutionary transitions.[33]

In the article "Extraterrestrial Intelligent Beings Do Not Exist," renowned American mathematical physicist and cosmologist Frank Tipler takes a staunch stand against the probability of any advanced extraterrestrial species ever arising at all:

The biologists argue that the number of evolutionary pathways leading from one-celled organisms to intelligent beings is miniscule when compared with the total number of evolutionary pathways, and thus even if we grant the existence of life on $10^9$ to $10^{10}$ planets in our Galaxy, the probability that intelligence has arisen in our Galaxy on any planet but our own is still very small... the probability of the evolution of creatures with the technological capability of interstellar communication within five billion years after the development of life on an Earth-like planet is less than $10^{-10}$ and thus we are the only intelligent species now existing in this Galaxy.[34]

Lastly, according to anthropologist Garry Chick, in the article "Biocultural Prerequisites for the Development of Interstellar Communication,"

Somewhere between 1.5 and 2 million living species have been cataloged on Earth.... When 20 species of hominoids are included in that total of 2 million extant species, primates constitute only 0.001 percent (0.00001) of the living species on Earth. Moreover, only 1 of these 20 species has developed a technology capable of interstellar communication. In sum, the development of high intelligence on Earth has been extremely rare, and there is little evidence to support the idea that its development is inevitable. Even if some forms of intelligence do evolve on other planets, there is no good reason to believe that at least one of them must be human-like.[35]

Our search for habitable exoplanets continues to demonstrate the uniqueness of Earth. Discovering other planets has also brought to light numerous characteristics of our planet and solar system that are conducive to life. For instance, life on Earth benefits from being in a singular rather than a binary star system, having a liquid core and geomagnetic field to protect us from harmful ultraviolet radiation, and from having two gas giants and an unusually large moon that help divert asteroids away from us. Our tides, atmosphere, low gravity, orbit, distance from the sun, chemical composition, abundance of carbon, and DNA as the coding system for all life on Earth are additional factors that make it highly unlikely extraterrestrial beings would look, walk, eat, drink, mate, sense, think, communicate, or be anything like us.

## CLANDESTINE CREATURES

If extraterrestrial beings did happen to locate us, and traverse vast distances to get here, we might expect some formal introduction upon their arrival. Still, the approach of the visitors thus far has been etic in nature, with no formal contact or announcement of their presence in our times. It is hard to fathom why extraterrestrials from a distant star system would zip around our skies and oceans and occasionally perform covert medical examinations on us, then return home without introducing themselves. This scenario seems far more paradoxical than one in which our distant descendants return to investigate their own past, while avoiding overt contact for fear of disrupting our social order, or the entire timeline.

While we would expect that life, and even other intelligent lifeforms, exist elsewhere in the universe, the Extratempestral Model remains the more parsimonious explanation, or the one with the fewest assumptions. There are numerous problems with the notion that humanlike beings would evolve on a different planet in a distant solar system, that they could find us here among all the other stars in the universe, or that they could, or would ever, traverse exceptionally long distances to stalk primitive Earthlings in utter secrecy for thousands of years.

To the contrary, it is easy to understand why time-traveling humans from the future would look like us, how they would find us, how they would get here, why they would care, and why they might refrain from ostentatious encounters with past persons, or at least until their status as future versions of ourselves becomes widely recognized as such. In a 2020 interview with *Space.com*, I was asked by author and space journalist Leonard David, "But why not argue that ET is actually a traveler from across the vastness of space, from a distant planet? Wouldn't that be a simpler answer?"

I would argue it's the opposite. We know we're here. We know humans exist. We know we've had a long evolutionary history on this planet. And we know our technology is going to be more advanced in the future. I think the simplest answer is that it is us. I'm just trying to offer what is likely the most parsimonious explanation.[36]

Paul Hynek, a CFO, board member, business consultant, and son of celebrated astronomer, professor, and ufologist, J. Allen Hynek, often makes note of two important questions he feels we should all be asking about these beings: "How would they know about us?" and "Why would they care?" In a 2020 interview with *Dr. J Radio Live*, Hynek points out that the time-traveling humans explanation helps answer both questions, which he considers "two of the biggest enigmatic questions in this whole conundrum-rich field."[37]

If these visitors are from the future, as our direct human descendants, they would undoubtedly know about us. Also, as their ancestors, they would be expected to care, the same way we care about our own historic and prehistoric past. However, when assessing these two questions in the context of the Extraterrestrial Hypothesis, it is harder to make the case that space aliens from a distant solar system or a different galaxy would know about us, given the vastness of the universe, or that they would care, considering we have no shared species status or common history on this planet.

Opposing Perspectives?

Beyond the Extraterrestrial Hypothesis, other explanations for the UFO phenomenon also exist. One interpretation is the *Interdimensional Hypothesis* (IDH), which centers on the notion that these beings are visiting us from a different dimension or parallel universe. It should be noted, however, that these interdimensional beings may still be future humans, just from a different "world" or "timeline," and particularly if the many worlds interpretation of quantum mechanics (MWI) is someday, and somehow, shown to be the correct elucidation of space and time.

The first version of the MWI was put forth by physicist Hugh Everett in his 1957 PhD thesis. In it, he presents an interpretation of quantum mechanics, which holds that there are many separate "worlds" that exist in parallel to our own.[38] In this model, the universal wave-function is real, but there is no wavefunction collapse. Instead, when quantum experiments with various outcomes are performed, all are realized, and although we are only capable of observing one specific result, every other potential outcome is also manifested, just in different and newly created worlds. In this sense, UFOs and their occupants could be arriving from one of these parallel worlds in the multiverse, though the question of their earthly human or extraterrestrial origins in this alternate universe remains.

It is also possible that our future human descendants use additional dimensions to pilot their UFOs through time and space to get here and now. Yet, if the claim is made that the beings visiting us evolved in a different universe with extra dimensions, much like the Extraterrestrial Hypothesis, they would not be expected to look or behave like us, given that these added spaces and times would produce divergent evolutionary conditions, if other dimensions exist at all, that is. When asked what he thinks of higher dimensions, Carlo Rovelli, a physicist at the University of Marseilles in France, states,

> I do not think they exist... It is just a space where you can go up-down, left-right, ahead-back, but also in one other dimension, something like leftB-rightB. It is a bit like having many arms, like an Indian god.[39]

We have yet to prove the existence of higher dimensions or parallel universes, which is problematic for the Interdimensional Hypothesis. Though even if the multiverse or additional dimensions do exist, there are other issues with how the interdimensional interpretation is applied to the UFO phenomenon. For instance, when someone invokes an interdimensional or alternate universe argument to speculate about the origin of the visitors, are they referring to the woven, brane, expanding, or quantum model? Each of these versions of the multiverse present their own set of problems related to evolution within and travel between worlds.

While *interdimensional* and *extra-dimensional* have become buzz-words of late, they are often expressed with a high level of ambiguity when used in reference to UFO origins. Beyond these linguistic limitations, some logistic issues with the higher dimension and parallel universe paradigms also exist. For instance, in addition to the pervasive problem of homology and how interdimensional entities could ever evolve to look like us under entirely different circumstances in their disparate and disconnected world, how could beings in alternate universes or other dimensions find and visit us in this world? How could they get through, especially since these parallel worlds aren't detectable on our side? How could their interdimensional craft and other technologies function in our universe if they were developed using a different set of physical laws that probably don't exist here? And like extraterrestrials, why wouldn't they acknowledge their presence if they did happen to break through the barriers that divide our worlds?

The entities seen in association with UFOs are unquestionably more advanced than us. Perhaps they have figured out how to test whether higher dimensions exist, whether we live in a block universe or a multiverse, and how to move between parallel universes if the latter interpretation is correct. Despite some limitations, the Interdimensional Hypothesis (IDH) seems a plausible explanation for the UFO phenomenon. In fact, when considering similarities in the physiology and technology between us and the visitors, one must wonder if the Interdimensional Hypothesis and the Extratempestrial Model are one and the same.

It is possible that the only difference between these interpretations rests with how we conceptualize spacetime. For instance, do these human and humanlike beings originate in a different world or timeline in the multiverse (i.e., The Interdimensional Hypothesis)? Or are they part of our same timeline in the context of the block universe (i.e., The Extratempestrial Model). In both scenarios, these visitors could be members of our more advanced human future; it is only a matter of whether they are coming here and now from a divergent timeline in the multiverse or a self-consistent timeline in our own universe, respectively. In either case, the highly human attributes of these ubiquitously bipedal beings strongly suggest shared ancestry and a common Earthly origin of these visitors.

*Ultraterrestrial beings* are also occasionally invoked as an explanation for the UFO phenomenon, which views these encounters as interactions with spiritual or higher power entities who are capable of taking on whatever form they desire and who occasionally attempt to deliberately deceive us. Popularized in the 1970s by John Keel, in his book *UFO's: Operation Trojan Horse*, this idea disavows the Extraterrestrial Hypothesis in favor of a theory that links UFOs and aliens to a variety of supernatural and paranormal phenomena.[40] In this view, the observed beings and their technology are just the material manifestation of a transcendental consciousness that reveals itself in UFO/alien form, where these ethereal entities adopt a physical shape to interact with us, only because we exist in a material world.

It has also been posited that a fifth-dimensional all-pervasive consciousness exists, and much like the residents of Edwin Abbott's *Flatland*,[41] we lowly 4-D humans are incapable of fully appreciating this ethereal consciousness and the ultraterrestrial entities who hail from these higher dimensions. It should be noted that because the ultraterrestrial explanation involves a higher consciousness that is thought to exist in additional dimensions, it is occasionally considered in association with the Interdimensional Hypothesis.

Intense meditation and CE-5 protocols are often considered ways of bridging this divide between the material and spiritual world so that contact and communication with the visitors becomes possible. According to noted contactee and UFO researcher Cheryl Costa,

> The method for contacting extraterrestrials is called the close encounter-5 protocol, or CE-5. In a formal sense, CE-5 is defined as human-initiated, bilateral communication with extraterrestrials. Since CE-5 is a consciousness-based technique, people can use thought, meditation, visualization, prayer, ritual and even remote viewing to accomplish the connection.[42]

A related paradigm, at least in the sense that we are the smaller of the Russian dolls in the set, is the *Simulation Hypothesis*. This model, popularized by Swedish-born philosopher Nick Bostrom in the early 2000s, advocates that nothing is real; instead, we are all living in an artificial computer simulation.[43] Regarding the UFO phenomenon specifically, the idea is that a technologically mature posthuman civilization manufactured this fabricated reality, and we occasionally see them popping in and out of the digital universe they created.

It is worth noting that because Bostrom's simulation argument involves a posthuman society running "ancestor simulations," this theory may also be extratempestrial in nature, since future humans could be the ones running these high-fidelity ancestor simulations. However, a 2020 paper published in the journal *Entropy*, which builds upon this simulation model, excludes any technologically mature civilization responsible for developing and running the computer simulation. Instead, these researchers argue that the physical universe is a "mental self-simulation" that generates itself from information and pure thought without the aid of advanced beings.[44]

A favorite explanation among skeptics, debunkers, and the uniformed, is that UFOs are simply everyday objects that are mistakenly labeled as something extraordinary, when in fact they are not. This Illiberal mindset guided much of the deliberate debunking campaign carried out over the last 75 years. However, even while researchers at Project Bluebook were doling out every conventional explanation they could come up with to dispel UFO sightings and to dissuade people from talking about them, behind the scenes, they and other government organizations continued to take them seriously. Today, this "conventional objects" explanation holds far less water, and most notably since April 2020, when the Pentagon acknowledged the authenticity of three US Navy cockpit videos, which captured advanced craft that cannot be confirmed as ordinary objects.

While mistaken identity may be true of some cases, many heavily scrutinized UFO reports, examined by top experts over the last 75 years, remain unexplained. This includes more recent investigations carried out in a time when better equipment can aid in analyzing the legitimacy of cases, and after developing a better understanding of what is typical of advanced aircraft, seagulls, lens flares, weather balloons, and swamp gas. Furthermore, some of these studies focused on reports provided by highly trained military pilots, who arguably have the best ability to differentiate between the exceptional and the banal.

For example, the unclassified "Preliminary Assessment of Unidentified Aerial Phenomena" by the Office of the Director of National Intelligence was released on June 25, 2021.[45] It examined 144 UAP reports, using far more sophisticated technology than what was available during Project Bluebook investigations carried out between 1947 and 1969.[46] However, despite advances in our technology and understanding of ordinary objects, this investigation was only able to provide a conventional explanation for a tiny percentage of these reports.

> The Pentagon task force's preliminary assessment is based on the review of 144 UAP reports involving observations made by military aviators between 2004 and 2021, but mostly from the last two years. The task force also considered but opted not to focus on 'a range of information on UAP described in U.S. military and IC (Intelligence Community) reporting,' since it 'lacked sufficient specificity.' Of the 144 reports, the task force could only determine an explanation for one (a deflated balloon). The rest remain unexplained.[47]

The "conventional objects" explanation is also problematic because it does not account for the contactee and abductee aspect of the UFO phenomenon. Arguably, such accounts are harder to substantiate and evaluate compared to videos recorded using sophisticated military surveillance technology. Though given the colossal number of abductee reports, and marked consistency among them, they too are worthy of consideration.

While more conventional explanations have been put forth to explain abductions, like sleep paralysis, fantasy, schizophrenia, and drug use, for example, these are not consistent with what happens to those who are captured. I have never been abducted, but it is unintelligible how anyone could confuse the experience with something entirely ordinary, like smoking a joint or having an elaborate dream. If someone is levitated through the treetops by a beam of light and into a massive metallic ship where they are physically examined and have sperm and eggs extracted from their person, and they are later returned to the place where they were taken hours and occasionally days after disappearing, it is hard to imagine how this could be confused with any ordinary experience.

Lastly, there is the common claim that UFOs are the result of contemporary military research and development. In this interpretation, instead of something otherworldly, or objects that come from our more advanced human future, the magical craft seen in our skies and oceans are merely the modern machines of some sovereign nation, but which are not yet recognized as such. Despite some glaring problems, this too is often touted by skeptics, debunkers, and those with strong opinions but who never put any time or effort into researching the phenomenon.

One of the biggest pitfalls of this paradigm is that these same advanced objects have been observed in our atmosphere doing the same physics-defying maneuvers for well over 80 years, at a time when propeller airplane technology was the most sophisticated aeronautic technology we had. It is ludicrous to assume that any nation possessed craft that could hover silently, then perform 100g accelerations, in the year 1925; yet this hypothesis persists.

Regardless of which model one favors, it is difficult to dismiss the fact that close encounters generally involve the same types of beings, doing the same types of things, in mostly the same types of craft, regardless of where or when they are observed. These accounts are ageless, but unfortunately, we continue to occupy a time when they remain gallingly difficult to comprehend. Despite accelerating progress in our proficiency with physics, material sciences, technology, and time, we still lack the expertise necessary to fully grasp what is going on. This phenomenon manifests in a capricious manner, which has been conceptualized and conveyed by different people across disparate periods and places, who do their best to understand what is happening, despite living in a time that has always predated when we are truly capable of doing so.

# Chapter 3

# Enduring Stigma

*Thus, even if visitor experiences are an essentially mental phenomenon, to laugh at them or dismiss them as some known form of abnormal behavior when they obviously are not is in effect to be silent before the presence of the new. Science should bring its best efforts to this, which means good studies that proceed from open and skillfully drawn hypotheses.*[48]

— Whitley Strieber

## Intertemporal Incredulity

The Modern Military, Conventional Objects, Extraterrestrial, Simulation, Ultraterrestrial, Intertemporal, Interdimensional, and other models to explain the UFO phenomenon should be weighed on their merits, evaluated with logic, and, as always, in the context of what is known and what is currently unknowable. Despite accelerating progress, our primitive minds cannot be expected to fully comprehend highly advanced future technology, as past peoples couldn't possibly fathom our proudest achievements today. Whether the visitors are a product of time, space, a higher consciousness, or something else entirely, until we achieve a similar level of progress, these craft and their occupants will persist as profoundly magical.

Among his many accomplishments, famed writer, inventor, and futurist Arthur C. Clarke is well-known for three adages, referred to as Clarke's Three Laws, which he published in an essay titled "Hazards of Prophecy: The Failure of Imagination." Of these, the third law, which was added to the revised version of his 1973 book *Profiles of the Future*, is the best known and most widely cited, particularly as it pertains to the UFO phenomenon.

31

1. When a distinguished but elderly scientist states that something is possible, he is almost certainly right. When he states that something is impossible, he is very probably wrong.[49]
2. The only way of discovering the limits of the possible is to venture a little way past them into the impossible.[50]
3. Any sufficiently advanced technology is indistinguishable from magic.[51]

Early anthropologists defined magic as "how primitive minds perceived the world, qualitatively distinct from rational thinking."[52] While our knowledge and perception of magic has since evolved, this early explanation seems appropriate when applied to how humans interpret many aspects of our reality in relation to religion, political perception, and our view of UFOs through time. This becomes more relevant if the phenomenon is indeed a glimpse into the lives of our advanced human descendants, who innately exist in a more magical futuristic realm.

A technologically sophisticated human species that has unraveled the mysteries of time, and who puts on display the incredible accomplishments of our ensuing future, would be expected to exhibit seemingly magical abilities. However, we are approaching a stage in our own edified evolution when the miraculous means of these travelers no longer needs to be cast as magic but may instead be understood as the tools of an even more advanced society. When viewed through the lens of our own accelerating achievements, we can see how compounding cultural continuity culminates in a communal time, as a type of technological phylogeny.

We should also cease in defining those who witness and attempt to describe their speciously magical experiences as crazy, drunk, drugged, or delusional. In fact, the outmoded stereotype of a half-baked tippler stumbling around the forest fictitiously envisioning UFOs and aliens is indecorous and offensive. As mentioned above, this stereotype was largely manufactured by those tasked with creating stigma surrounding the subject of UFOs. It was also evidently perpetuated by people who have never been extremely drunk or high on drugs, since what is described in alien abductions does not occur, regardless of how mullered one might be.

There is no basis for equating what abductees and contactees experience to what happens to the human body and mind when under the influence of alcohol and the majority of drugs. This is especially true when considering that many contact events last multiple hours and occasionally days, so these events are still happening long after the effects of any drugs have dissipated. Furthermore, the overwhelming majority of contactees and abductees are not high or on drugs when these interactions occur.

In the grand scheme of things, the technologies observed in association with UFOs are not that far removed from our own. To the contrary, and as we'll see throughout this text, many elements of our current culture are observable in the form and function of these outwardly alien tools. Though to see these consistencies, we must first open our eyes and remove the diaphanous veil of shame that was laid before them long ago.

## The "un" Issue

Partly due to the inherent enigmatic and clandestine comportment of these visitors, many questions about UFOs remain unanswered. Intentional intellectual roadblocks have also been erected, largely in the form of fabricated stigma, which has acted to quell conversations about this subject, though the issue is undoubtedly worthy of our attention. As shown in the previous chapter, a multitude of accounts from Project Bluebook, the UAPTF, and other investigations over the last 70 years have demonstrated that some percentage of UFO reports remain officially unidentified and unexplained; but do not be deceived. This does not mean they are unexplainable, or that because they are currently unidentified, we should never attempt to formally identify the origin of these objects and their occupants.

Since 2017, the US Navy and Pentagon have openly acknowledged the existence of previously secret programs set up to investigate UFOs.[53] [54] Additionally, on April 27, 2020, the Navy declassified, and shared on their Naval Air Systems Command website, three authenticated UFO videos.[55] Much of this progress toward acknowledgment of the reality of UFOs is due to Helene Cooper, Ralph Blumenthal, and Leslie Kean's 2017 *New York Times* article, "Glowing Auras and 'Black Money': The Pentagon's Mysterious U.F.O. Program."[56] Among other revelations, this landmark publication brought to light information about the US Advanced Aerospace Threat Identification Program (AATIP), which had a 22-million-dollar budget specifically dedicated to the study of unidentified aerial phenomena.

It is important to reiterate that the US government's 2017 acknowledgment of previously classified programs to investigate UFOs, the Navy's 2020 verification of three UFO cockpit videos, and the June 25, 2021, release of the unclassified "Preliminary Assessment of Unidentified Aerial Phenomena" by the Office of the Director of National Intelligence, genuinely happened. Although, possibly due to our society's short attention span, political strife in many developed nations throughout the world, and a virgin-soil pandemic that began in late 2019, these monumental disclosures were largely ignored by the general populace.

According to a tweet by Santiago Mayer, which went viral soon after the Defense Department publicly acknowledged these UFO cockpit videos, "2020 is so fucking wild that the Pentagon just confirmed UFOs and it's barely news."[57] It was arguably tough for any meaningful information to break through in the year 2020, as we were endlessly bombarded with new and often unsettling developments. Nevertheless, in the sense that this could potentially be one of the greatest mysteries and biggest questions of our time, official acknowledgment of these videos is in fact a big damn deal.

Over the last 60-70 years, and particularly during the war on minorities and dissenters (read: the war on drugs) perpetuated by the Nixon and Regan administrations, people have been harassed, intimidated, and incarcerated by police and federal agents for marijuana possession and use. Throughout this time, most US citizens never would have thought that someday this plant would be legal to grow, possess, and use in moderate amounts, though it is now decriminalized or fully legal in most states. Similarly, those with a long-standing interest in the UFO phenomenon never would have thought the US government might someday acknowledge the existence of UFOs, so for many of us, this recent revelation is tremendously impactful.

These developments are also noteworthy because the rally cry of self-proclaimed skeptics and debunkers has long centered on the notion that "UFOs don't exist," and if they do, "Where are all the photos and videos?" For decades, a lack of authenticated images of UFOs made it easy for people to ignore the reality of this phenomenon, including members of the scientific community. However, over the last few years, this *ad ignorantium* argument has become much more tenuous.

We now have official verification of images and videos captured by accredited naval pilots, which show advanced machines performing maneuvers beyond the abilities of contemporary aircraft. It is true that in every iteration of the UFO/USO/UAP acronym, they remain "unidentified," but this should not prevent us from trying to identify what they are. Scientists should also be leading the way, as we arguably occupy the best position to progress knowledge of this issue. One would expect, given the stated mission of science, that substantiation of the reality of an enigma this perplexing would garner the attention of scientists and researchers worldwide, whose job it is to investigate strange and mysterious aspects of our natural world.

Confirmation that aircraft capable of incredible maneuvers far beyond the abilities of any modern nation are whizzing around our skies would be expected to light a fire under every academic, driven by an unrelenting desire to discover the undiscovered, to know the unknown, and to identify the unidentified. However, even seemingly sensible scientists routinely default to instant dismissal of anything involving UFOs. This includes pop-culture science icons, who commonly claim that because "these are 'un'-identified objects, we don't know what they are," which implies we can't ever know what they are and we shouldn't waste our time trying to figure it out.

As mentioned in the first chapter, producer and podcast host Leon Kirkbeck also advocates for a time-travel model to explain the UFO phenomenon. In 2018, American astrophysicist Neil deGrasse Tyson had the opportunity to sit down for an interview with Kirkbeck, though things got a bit awkward when he brought up the extratempestrial idea. During an "Expert Interview" segment in an episode of their *Cryptid Factor* podcast, which he hosts with actor and comedians Rhys Darby and Dan Schreiber, Kirkbeck played the recorded interview from when he asked deGrasse Tyson about the possibility that UFOs could be piloted by time-traveling humans from the future.[58]

**Tyson:** What was your question?

**Kirkbeck:** Ahh, just about, whether UFOs, could be, uhh, just time traveling humans from the future?

**Tyson:** No! They're lights in the sky that you don't know what they are. That's what the 'U' stands for. Un-*fucking*-identified! O.k.?! You don't know what it is… Period! And you cannot invoke not knowing what it is as reason to say that it's intelligent aliens visiting from another portal or another dimension. One does not lead to the other. There's no logical connection between you not knowing what you're looking at and intelligent aliens coming from another dimension, there is no thread connecting this. Your *ignorance* of what you see in the night sky, to this other thing, that you *pulled* out of your ass!

I have great respect for Neil deGrasse Tyson and his work, though when I first listened to this interview, I was horrified by his response to the question. Not because of the language used, or the palpable rage in his voice, but because of his unabashed repudiation of scientific inquiry. He acknowledges that there are objects and lights in the sky, but he immediately dives straight into the deep end of dismissal, focusing solely on the "un"-identified aspect of UFO nomenclature. There was no mention of how mysteries have always inspired new scientific pursuits, or how there have always been unidentified aspects of our reality that we work tirelessly to identify by asking questions and conducting research. Furthermore, if Kirkbeck had used the term *Tic-Tac*, *disc*, or *flying saucer*, would the same rant focused exclusively on the prefix "un" have ensued?

Not investigating something baffling because we don't yet know what it is may be the worst approach to gaining knowledge about it. What if Nicolaus Copernicus had said, "It sure looks like the Sun goes around the Earth, so... let's just go with that, and nobody should ever look into it further... or I'll yell at them." Or when we started to realize that some yet-unidentified microbes were making us sick, but because we couldn't see them with our primitive technology of the time, we just threw up our hands and said, "Well, it seems like there's something there, but it's unidentified, so forget it, I guess we'll never know, and your theories about microscopic pathogens and handwashing are stupid."[59]

If we had applied this mentality and approach to investigating the unknown and unidentified aspects of our existence along the path to scientific enlightenment, we might still be going to the doctor for bloodletting procedures and to be covered in leeches as our preferred means of treating pathogenic infections. Though if we acknowledge what the Pentagon already has, that there are countless credible cases of close encounters certified by respected military personnel, police, scientists, industry leaders, celebrities, and ordinary citizens, then we may begin to work toward gaining a better understanding of what they are, with the hopes of someday removing the "un" from "unidentified" altogether.

## SENSIBLE SKEPTICISM

A bastion of the scientific method is hypothesis testing, and an important prerequisite for any valid scientific hypothesis is that it must be testable, falsifiable, and repeatable. Unfortunately, questions like, "Are extraterrestrial humanoids traveling here from another solar system?" or "Are intelligent aliens visiting from another portal or another dimension?"

are not testable. However, it is possible to develop testable and falsifiable hypotheses related to the UFO phenomenon.

In fact, as crazy as it may sound, the "UFOs are piloted by time-traveling humans from the future" hypothesis is both testable and falsifiable, and in a causal loop context, it is also repeatable. Even if we temporarily disregard the many logical connections and threads that connect our human past to present, coupled with informed ideas about what the human future may hold based on enduring 6-million-year trends in our evolutionary past, this theory checks all the boxes necessary for hypothesis testing.

The continued existence or extermination of humankind innately allows this hypothesis to be tested and falsified. Whether we survive or die, the passage of time itself will reveal the true nature of this notion. In other words, if this interpretation of the UFO phenomenon is correct, at some point in our evolutionary future we will become the ones piloting these cylindrical, triangular, spherical, and predominantly, disc-shaped craft. In the worst-case scenario, if we annihilate ourselves, or are eradicated by some outside force, the hypothesis has still been tested and unequivocally falsified.

Like UFOs, artificial intelligence, gene editing, cryptids, and consciousness, the question of backward time travel is also a tad taboo. Advocates and detractors make convincing cases for its plausibility and impracticality. However, the general consensus is that nothing in the laws of physics, philosophy, or logic prohibits time travel to the past;[60] [61] and as Arthur C. Clarke stated above, when a distinguished scientist states that something is impossible, he is very probably wrong.[62] Furthermore, if we continue to make it through successive stages of the great filter to persist as a species, and if we eventually develop the technology, materials, and engineering necessary to achieve backward time travel, we would expect to see our distant descendants at some or many points in their past.

In 1950, during a casual lunchtime conversation about a cartoon in *The New Yorker*, which showed bubbly aliens emerging from UFOs to steal trash cans from the streets of New York City, physicist Enrico

Fermi famously asked, "Where is everybody?"[63] In that moment, it occurred to Fermi that if there are billions of stars, with a certain percentage possessing earthlike planets, and a high probability of life arising on at least some of them, then there should be aliens here, whether they're stealing our trash cans or not.[64] While Fermi was focused on the question of extraterrestrial life and interstellar travel, the same enigma exists in the context of backward time travel. More specifically, scholars have questioned why we are not inundated with tourists from the future if backward time travel will someday be achieved.

Physicist Stephen Hawking often iterated this Fermiesque question as it relates to the future possibility of time travel to the past. However, while Enrico Fermi was open to the idea of intelligent life on other planets, Hawking took a much more critical approach to the time-tourist dilemma. Most notably, he was fond of saying that because we are not overrun by future human time tourists coming back to observe events of their past, this should be taken as evidence that backward time travel will never be possible at any point in the human future.[65]

Paul Davies, another accomplished physicist and leading scholar on the study of time, takes a more judicious position, drawing attention to the dubious nature of Hawking's argument. In his book *About Time: Einstein's Unfinished Revolution*, Davies writes,

> A shaky argument that is often used against time travel is that if our descendants ever discover how to do it they will come back and visit us. As we don't see these temponauts, we can conclude that they will never come to exist.[66]

Davies's critique demonstrates how a lack of evidence should not be considered evidence that a time machine will never exist, and he goes on to list physical and logical reasons why this is a convenient, but flawed dissent. Hawking's disdain for the notion that humans could ever achieve backward time travel can also be seen in his Chronology Protection Conjecture, which advocates that the laws of physics are such that they will not allow backward time travel on all but a submicroscopic scale.

It also states that the intrinsic properties of nature would prevent any alteration to the past that could result in time paradoxes.

Hawking's opinion that humans will never accomplish backward time travel is itself paradoxical, considering he also champions our species' many incredible achievements. For instance, in a poignant 1994 television advertisement for the BT Group, which was later used as the intro for Pink Floyd's song "Keep Talking," Hawking offered a "message of hope," advocating for the continued advancement of innovation and technology through unrestricted communication and unfettered human dialog. The last few lines of the message read,

> Our greatest hopes could become reality in the future. With the technology at our disposal, the possibilities are unbounded. All we need to do is make sure we keep talking.[67]

Despite Hawking's strong belief in the incredible abilities of our species, and the prospect for further advancement in the future, he remained incredulous about whether we will ever develop the knowledge, technology, and machinery necessary to achieve time travel to the past. However, to advocate that humans will never come to possess a deep enough understanding of time, nor the mechanisms with which to alter our position within it, is to deny millions of years of cerebral, cognitive, and cultural advancement across the collective whole of hominin evolution.

Furthermore, if UFOs turn out to be time machines, and the human and humanlike beings so often seen in association with them are in fact our distant descendants, then this cross-temporal contact provides a resounding response to Hawking's Chronology Protection Conjecture. For if historical and modern reports of UFOs and "aliens" are indeed true, and these travelers are from deep time rather than deep space, then clearly the laws of physics do not prohibit backward time travel. We may also be obliged to consider this form of intertemporal interaction in the context of the Fermi paradox, Davies's *temponauts*, and Hawking's *time-tourist dilemma*—where a candid comeback to the question "Why don't we see travelers from the future if backward time travel will someday be possible?" may simply be "We do, and we have throughout antiquity."

I can think of few areas of inquiry within the scientific community that have been blackballed to such an extent as the UFO phenomenon, though there is finally hope that the tides are turning and a sea change is nigh. For those who have studied this subject for some time, there have been frequent false horizons, and countless hopeful moments that fade as quickly as they come. Perhaps it will be different this time around, and contemporary developments suggest a modicum of new hope is warranted. Though regardless of what, if anything, changes, we should continue striving to acquire deeper insight into this mystifying spectacle while combating any lingering stigma that stands in the way.

# Chapter 4

# Abduction

*A combined historical and scientific approach is applied to ancient reports of what might today be called unidentified flying objects (UFOs). Many conventionally explicable phenomena can be weeded out, leaving a small residue of puzzling reports. These fall neatly into the same categories as modern UFO reports, suggesting that the UFO phenomenon, whatever it may be due to, has not changed much over two millennia.[68]*

– Richard Stothers

## A Worthwhile Pursuit

Like most academics, I take my teaching, service, and scholarship work seriously. I also have many hobbies, interests, sporting activities, events with family and friends, and countless other ways I could spend my time. I wouldn't allocate any amount of effort to researching and writing about the UFO subject if I didn't think there was something truly remarkable happening. I feel compelled to investigate this mysterious and yet-unidentified phenomenon, which I would never do unless I was sure this is both real and potentially one of the most important questions of our time.

I have not personally seen a UFO, nor have I had any type of encounter with unusual nighttime lights, orbs, aliens, spirits, or conscious manifestations of any kind. Despite a lack of personal experience, I keep an open mind about cases involving close contact with entities that appear to exist beyond conventional reality. There are always outliers, and the human imagination can run wild, though we should critically consider the accounts of those who have had an odd experience and acknowledge the recurrent patterns that exist across cases.

Anyone conducting an in-depth investigation into where, when, and how UFO incidents occur, regardless of how skeptical they are to begin with, are sure to eventually recognize the reality of these events. Additionally, it is apparent from descriptions provided by US Navy pilots and other military personnel that the appearance and aptitudes of UAP craft are entirely consistent with what is described in civilian close encounters, as well as in cases of alien abduction, which are arguably the closest type of encounter one can have.

Contemplating the many parallels between military and civilian sightings, it is logical to assume that these UAP interactions are holistically intertwined, which may be due to their common origins. It seems improbable that these are separate things, especially considering the incredible consistency across contactee reports regarding what is seen, how, when, and where. Whether it is a US Navy pilot watching a UFO from the cockpit of a McDonnell Douglas F/A-18 Hornet in 2015, or a Brazilian farmer lying on an examination table inside a UFO in 1957, we are likely dealing with the same phenomenon.

The common core of contact cases should be considered, and especially in abductions, since striking similarities exist in how people are taken, what happens while they are in captivity, how long they are gone, and how, where, and when they are returned following their interaction with the visitors. The phenomenon has been with us for a long time, and the marked similarity across cases should be critically examined for clues about what is and has been happening throughout the ages.[69][70][71]

Reports provided by sound-minded individuals who convey events, emotions, screen memories, descriptions of the captors and their craft, awkward sexual feelings, and a slew of other sensations and experiences ought to be examined with the same level of deference and scrutiny we apply to the military cockpit videos that have come to dominate the conversation. Although these eyewitness accounts do not constitute scientific evidence, they would be admissible as evidence in a court of law, and they should be included in any attempt at deciphering the UFO enigma.

We must also recognize limitations inherent in investigating contact experiences and note that intangible personal accounts are the primary source of information. Although they contribute a wealth of observational data, it is not the same as having one trained observer collecting these data across UFO contact cases as they happen in real time. Instead, we are left to summarize the experiences of untrained observers whose own personalities, feelings, memories, and emotions, among other cofactors, introduce additional points of bias, which innately reduces the reliability of any in-depth analysis, regardless of how methodical it may be.

Despite some drawbacks, we should cautiously consider the accounts of rational people who recount real experiences, since there is potentially much we can learn from them. Generally speaking, contactees are willing to tell their story out of a sense of duty, or to disseminate information told to them, which they feel is significant and worth reporting. In contrast, abductees are most often taken against their will and do not have the same desire or sense of obligation to speak openly about what happened to them.

In both cases, we should be open and empathetic to their experiences and emotions, especially since many endure mental and physical hardship during these encounters, which occasionally results in post-traumatic stress (PTS). Although not everyone is willing to tell their story, there is comfort and solidarity in knowing others have experienced similar things. Furthermore, as the stigma surrounding this subject continues to diminish in time, more might be willing to openly discuss what happened, and those who do should be commended for their bravery, not victimized and shamed.

Abductee and contactee experiences are also important for people like myself, who have never had an encounter but who wish to understand this aspect of an already anomalous occurrence. From a research standpoint, these testimonials represent a valuable source of data that facilitates an abductive approach, which unlike deductive reasoning, yields a plausible conclusion based on an amalgamation of evidence, even if it can't yet be positively verified. Abductive conclusions are qualified as having a remnant of uncertainty or doubt, which naturally applies in analyses of abduction accounts. Though when considered in association with countless other coherent encounters, abductive reasoning can be understood as inference to the best explanation, or at least the best we can hope for at this moment in time.[72]

## ART, ARTIFACTS, AND ORAL HISTORY

The long history and prehistory of this phenomenon would seem to indicate that the same or similar things have been happening to people throughout the ages. This is also something we would expect to see if our future progeny are visiting various periods throughout their past. It could be argued that cave paintings, carvings, geoglyphs, petroglyphs, and other art, artifacts and features that appear to show UFOs and large-headed humanoid beings are instead depicting something more conventional, or something specific to the culture from the time they were created. Though because they can be found in so many different places that date to different times, and because people paint and create what they see, we must wonder if these pieces are suggestive of a common experience.

Unfortunately, people's intentions and the symbolism behind their artistic works do not preserve in the archaeological record. We are left only with the material remains of past actions and behaviors and must make informed guesses about the meaning behind these creations. This can lead to tenuous interpretations that are difficult to substantiate, and more recently, wild speculation about how past feats were accomplished has become commonplace. Although some artifacts, features, and past practices do suggest people have seen UFOs and been in contact with these visitors for thousands of years, I would never argue that extraterrestrials, future humans, or any other outside group was responsible for building the pyramids or any other ancient relics, since the people of those times were certainly capable of these achievements.

Over the last decade, many publications, podcasts, documentaries, and radio and television shows have been guilty of "ETing the gaps," or ascribing an "alien" explanation to ancient innovations that appear overly advanced for the people of those times. However, these claims are overstated and largely stem from a lack of understanding about the toolkit and complex system of social organization characteristic of earlier groups. Such assertions also have racist undertones that need to be addressed, since they imply past people in those places were incapable of such feats, and because artifacts and features that were built by Europeans are rarely if ever attributed to aliens.[73]

While remaining cognizant of implicit imperialist inferences—and mindful of other interpretations—art, artifacts, and features that depict images consistent with what is described in modern UFO encounters are worthy of further scrutiny. For instance, it may be worthwhile to consider the 10,000-year-old rock paintings in Madhya Pradesh, India; the 5,000-year-old Wandjina cave paintings of "sky beings" in Australia; the Nazca "Owlman" geoglyph in the desert of southern Peru; jade stone carvings from Veracruz, Mexico; and encephalized bipedal beings seen in various forms of rock art in Kondoa, Tanzania.

Intentional cranial modification should also be considered in this context, in part because it creates craniofacial characteristics consistent with the archetypal "grey alien." Artificial cranial deformation also arose independently throughout the world and dates back thousands, and potentially tens of thousands, of years. This long history of independent invention is noteworthy given that certain scholarly explanations for the global prevalence of this practice center on how prehistoric groups were attempting to look like "the gods," or that they were specifically instructed to modify their crania by those they perceived as gods. According to a 1995 paper by Gerszten and Gerszten, published in the journal *Neurosurgery,*

> Many living people who have undergone intentional head deformation claim that their gods instructed their ancestors to perform the practice and that they are simply fulfilling the desires of their gods.[74]

There are many reasons to consider future human time travel in the context of UFO encounters. But conspicuous consistency in the portrayal of contact throughout the ages and into modern times ranks high among the most logical reasons why inference to the best explanation may favor an intertemporal interpretation. We currently cannot know if our descendants were abducting our ancestors—as they appear to be doing to people in our own time—since the direct experiences of past groups aren't preserved in the archaeological record. However, consistency across ancient images, petroglyphs, geoglyphs, and countless other examples of art and artifacts through the ages suggests the same types of beings are doing the same types of things across extensive periods of their past.

It is important that we critically consider this time-travel model along with all other possibilities, particularly since numerous examples of art, artifacts and features are suggestive of past contact with similar visitors. We should also examine indigenous myths and oral legends, which occasionally describe situations almost identical to what is recounted in modern abduction reports. Such accounts should be weighed alongside other evidence, especially since some seemingly outlandish stories have been shown to be the product of true events.

For instance, similar tales have been told for centuries about three massive waves that cast huge stones toward terrified villagers on Makin Island, in the Republic of Kiribati. Although the details of these accounts vary to some degree, in each narrative, two enormous stones were cast ashore to punish the villagers, but the third and biggest stone was stopped before reaching them on shore. In 2012, after hearing this story for the first time, James Terry, a geoscientist at Zayed University in the United Arab Emirates, decided to investigate.[75]

Just of the south shore of Makin atoll sit three massive rocks, named Tokia, Rebua, and Kamatoa. Their presence is mysterious, since no one knows how they got there, and because no other rocks like them can be found anywhere else nearby. James Terry believes that the fable he heard, about an angry king who was mad about receiving rotten fruit and retaliated by sending huge waves to cast boulders at the villagers, may represent a *geomyth*, or a legend that chronicles true information about the geologic past in an area.

After visiting the island, and hearing a similar iteration of the account, he grew even more curious. Terry did a uranium/thorium analysis on corral in the boulders and discovered that they were deposited offshore about 445 years ago, or around the year 1576 CE. This date happens to correlate with a powerful tsunami that struck Makin Island that same year. This finding supports Terry's geomyth claim, where villagers who survived the tsunami event created a narrative to capture this monumental moment in their history, which was passed down through the ages and into modern times. By seriously considering the odd oral legend of the indigenous people of this region, James Terry was able to unravel the mystery of how these enormous rocks appeared on Makin Island in the South Pacific.

Another recent example of how legend and oral history can help inform scientific knowledge of real events is evident in the search for a long-lost ship, the HMS Erebus. This is one of two ships that disappeared during the ill-fated Franklin Expedition, which set sail from Greenhithe, England, on May 19, 1845. These two vessels, the HMS Erebus and Terror, were tasked with sailing through the Canadian Arctic across the Northwest Passage, which had been charted, but never navigated in its entirety.

In August of 1845, the ships were seen passing by an area to the west of King William Island, which is part of the Canadian Arctic Archipelago in the Kitikmeot Region of Nunavut. This was the last reported sighting of these vessels, as the ships would soon disappear, along with the 130 crewmen aboard. It was later discovered that all died from exposure, starvation, and disease, in what is still regarded as the Arctic's worst maritime disaster.[76]

The area near King William Island was assiduously searched soon after the crew went missing; however, nothing was ever found there. This is because the two ships became trapped in sea ice and drifted for nearly 19 months until they were eventually dropped in their final resting place off the Adelaide Peninsula, far to the south of King William Island. Remarkably, early indications that the ships may have drifted south came from Inuit legends and specific placenames that grew out of odd encounters their ancestors had.

For instance, the English translation for some sites in and around this part of the Adelaide Peninsula are *White Man Footsteps*, *The Boat Place*, and *The Place of the Bearded Seal*. Along with numerous indigenous oral histories that developed around the Franklin Expedition, these toponyms provided an important line of evidence that aided researchers in their search for the two ships, which had inadvertently drifted toward this more southerly region of the Arctic Circle.[77] Certain Inuit oral histories also describe instances of rampant starvation, pestilence, bloated corpses (the origin of the bearded seal placename), cannibalism, and other indications of the terrors faced by members of this ill-fated expedition in their final days. These accounts, which must have sounded insane to those they told of this encounter, have since been substantiated by further historic, ethnographic, and archaeological research.[78]

Largely thanks to this early ethnographic research, on September 2, 2014, nearly 170 years after its disappearance, the HMS Erebus was finally located by team leaders Ryan Harris and Marc-André Bernier, who carried out their exhaustive search in association with Parks Canada, an agency of the Canadian government. Members of the team were keen to acknowledge the contribution of this cultural research, led by indigenous Inuit and non-native anthropologists and historians, who helped reorient the search more toward the south where the ships had come to rest.

> Ryan Harris, the Parks Canada marine archeologist who led the ship's search, said both Franklin ships, HMS Terror and HMS Erebus, appear in the [Inuit] oral tradition. The Inuit, however, provided a more detailed description of one ship said to have been found south of King William Island off Grant Point on the Adelaide Peninsula in an area known as Ootloo-lik 'the place of the bearded seal.' And Ootloo-lik is the name of the place where she grounded...The latter also told that the body of a man was found on board the ship, and he must have been a very large man and had long teeth.[79]

Another source states,

> Witness accounts from Inuit who spoke to early searchers in the 19th
> century offered tantalizing clues of at least one ghost ship, with a big,
> dead white man aboard, drifting south on the ice. They claimed it was
> far from the point where an 1847 ink note, concealed in a tin can, re-
> ported the ships had been abandoned, imprisoned in heavy ice. Many
> so-called experts thought it was hogwash. The Inuit had to be telling
> tall tales. Turns out the Inuit were right all along. But it took more
> than a century of searching, and a serendipitous series of events over
> the past several weeks, to prove it.[80]

Incidents associated with the final days of the Franklin Expedition,
and the future fate of the HMS Terror and Erebus, became locked away
in the mistrusted oral history of the indigenous Inuit. Details pertaining to where the ships were and what happened to the crew remained
a mystery, until anthropologists and historians began seeking insight
from a seemingly unlikely source, the tall tales of those whose ancestors had witnessed what transpired firsthand. This ethnographic data
proved to be an asset in solving the riddle of the Franklin Expedition
and demonstrates the importance of considering oral histories in the
context of modern mysteries. It also highlights how easy it is to dismiss
such accounts as "hogwash," or as primitive groups telling tall tales, if
they aren't directly in line with conventional cultural knowledge.

The disconnect between early rescuers and the Inuit observers of
the mid-19th century was largely due to the massive cultural divide that
existed between these two groups at that time. For instance, the clothing, ships, and material culture of those in the Franklin Expedition,
while completely normal from the standpoint of British and Canadian
society, were entirely alien to the Inuit inhabitants of that region, which
is reflected in the peculiar names given to represent these people and
things in their oral histories.

This intercultural rift represents a good metaphor for how we, and
people in the recent, historic, and prehistoric past, may view our distant

descendants returning from a far more advanced human future. The vessels, clothing, technology, and morphological traits of those who reside in a time that is hundreds or thousands of years ahead of our own would innately reflect a more enhanced state of human biological and cultural evolution. Our descendants and their advanced toolkit, despite being built upon that which exists today, would be progressively more difficult to understand, and their presence in past periods would be conceptualized and chronicled in increasingly rudimentary ways, the farther back in time they go.

Past groups are only capable of understanding events in the context of what is conventionally recognized among members of their temporal cohort, and this is no different today, as we too struggle to make sense of the seemingly magical attributes of UFOs and their occupants. It is easy to dismiss modern reports of unidentified aerial phenomena as hogwash, and most notably ones involving accounts of abductions and anthropomorphic examinations, considering the degree to which they deviate from our conventional conception of reality. However, if taken seriously, we may be able to garner some insight into the imminent state of our species from these ephemeral glimpses of them, as they occasionally descend upon us from the future.

## THE TAKEN

Although some variation exists regarding the details of individual abductions, each tends to follow the same basic narrative. Most abductions take place while people are driving or while they're asleep in their bedrooms at home. In the latter case, abductees often report seeing a light outside their window or notice movement, or a humanoid form in their room. They report feeling immobilized, then being carried by a beam of light outside, and often through windows and occasionally solid walls. They are transported by this energetic beam of light into a craft where physical and psychological tests are performed, and body tissues, fecal matter, and gametes are collected.

Some abductees communicate with the visitors vocally or telepathically, which always takes place in their native language. Depending on their level of cooperation, the better-behaved are occasionally offered a tour of the ship. Lastly, the abducted individual is returned near to where, and occasionally when, they were originally captured, and often with a sense of missing time, screen memories, or temporary amnesia about what transpired.[81] [82] [83]

These encounters are also far more common than most people realize. In fact, survey research suggests that the number of people who have been abducted by UFOs could potentially be as high as five or 6 percent of the overall population.[84] Admittedly, studies carried out using surveys are prone to sample bias and other methodological issues, so this statistic should be approached with caution. Though even if this is a slightly inflated statistical result, accounts of alien abductions are exceedingly common and comprise a substantial number of authentic UFO reports.

A principal focus of the current research, which is primarily a case study of case studies, is to examine the reports of those who claim to have had direct contact with the visitors and to assess these and other contact modalities in the context of the Extratempestrial Model. As stated above, caution is warranted when examining abductions, as they remain an unproven aspect of the UFO phenomenon. Additionally, more conventional explanations like hallucinations, sleep paralysis, schizophrenia, fantasy proneness, false-memory syndrome, masochistic fantasy, escaping the self, hypnotizability, the Psychocultural Hypothesis (PCH), and others should also be considered in the context of close encounters.[85] [86] [87] [88] [89] [90] [91]

As we will see throughout this text, the type and amount of interaction people have with these visitors, as well as consistency across their accounts, strongly suggests that each of the above explanations is hard to justify as the root cause of their experiences and memories. However, these more orthodox explanations should be critically considered since we tend to anthropomorphize the unknown. Regarding the Psychocultural Hypothesis specifically, people may falsely impose the commonly described humanoid alien form on things that are not actually aliens. This propensity to anthropomorphize the visitors may simply be because the human form is familiar, recognizable, and easily understandable, being that we ourselves are human beings.

This psychosocial tendency can also involve the misappropriation of an actual event, in which real things are falsely imposed on something less understandable. For instance, it is sometimes argued that the beginning of human spaceflight on this planet may have caused us to imagine that other advanced civilizations elsewhere in the universe were also entering a new phase of spaceflight, which caused us to begin looking for evidence of these expat extraterrestrials who were further along in the process, whether they exist or not. We should be aware of enigmas like these, but also recognize that there are far too many unexplained abduction accounts for any of these explanations to be the root cause of them all.

Considering the credentials, status, expertise, and experiences of countless individuals who have had a close encounter, and the fact that most remain unexplained following heavy vetting, there is reason to believe these constitute real events. Because so many credible witnesses have observed these craft and their occupants at close range, it is hard to dismiss this phenomenon as merely the manifestation of a feeble collective consciousness. Although UFO stigma continues to keep people from sharing their stories, the shame is waning, and abductees and contactees are coming forward to communicate their experiences. As they do, the consistency among their accounts grows ever clearer, which further speaks to the communal nature of these encounters.

An interesting and vaguely paradoxical argument both for and against the Psychocultural Hypothesis centers on the notion that during projects Grudge and Bluebook, the typical images of flying saucers and grey aliens were intentionally promulgated across various forms of media as part of a psychological operation (PSYOP). This was carried out so when people saw actual disc-shaped craft and humanoid aliens in real life, it could be dismissed as a biproduct of these deliberately placed mainstream cultural memes. Considering that projects Sign, Grudge, Bluebook, and others were tasked with quelling interest in the UFO phenomenon, this scenario doesn't seem too farfetched.

It is important to note, however, that many people had sightings and other close encounters long before UFOs became integrated into the ethos of our global society. In fact, the first three case studies examined in this text [Dworshak, Wartena, and Villas-Boas] took place in times and places when and where common knowledge of UFOs did not yet exist, though each of these and the other witnesses' descriptions of the visitors and their craft are remarkably similar. Because they predate broad knowledge of UFOs, or any widespread public depiction of advanced humanlike beings, which could have inadvertently shaped the observer's recollection of events, the psychocultural and PSYOP justifications are less valid.

Many of the case studies examined below also originated with upstanding citizens who occupied respected roles when their interactions occurred. This includes numerous military personnel, attorneys, parents, business owners, and others, who by all accounts, are trustworthy sources with no record of mental illness or a history of deceptive behavior. We have every reason to believe these witnesses and we should take into consideration their account of events, including incidents observed by multiple individuals at the same time, which tend to carry more weight. This included the USS Nimitz "Tic-Tac" encounter, which was documented concurrently by pilots, radar operators, and aircraft carrier personnel. Because we have reverence for those in uniform, and considering their adept ability to distinguish unidentified from identifiable objects, these encounters tend to be held in higher regard.

Regardless of the achieved status of those who see them, eyewitness accounts provided by multiple individuals and large groups are more believable. These also ranked higher on the Strangeness and Probability Scale, developed by esteemed astrophysicist Dr. J. Allen Hynek, who rated on a scale from one to ten how odd or unexplainable (strangeness) an encounter was, and how reliable and trustworthy (probability) the witnesses were. Over the past six decades, Hynek and others have effectively applied this scale to differentiate among reports that are easily understood, versus those that defy logic and thus remain unexplained.[92]

Hynek's probability rating was instrumental in helping to differentiate between fake or embroidered accounts and those given by credible people who witnessed something that couldn't be explained with a contemporary understanding of technology, space, and time. For Hynek, attempting to assess how reliable and trustworthy someone was based on their account and personal disposition was seen as a more subjective part of the scientific inquiry, given that it was essentially a short-term character assessment of a complete stranger. This hasn't changed either, as it remains a challenging but important aspect of evaluating the validity of an eyewitness and their account, which becomes more difficult in instances where they were the only one who saw anything.

In addition to the personal credibility assessment, Hynek considered other factors that could help in determining the veracity of experiencer testimonies, including internal consistency of the account, uniformity across several separate reports of the same incident, how the report was made, the conviction of the individual as they recounted events, as well as a general assessment of how it all fit together.[93] Hynek's work was important in that it established a foundation upon which we could begin to build a better understanding of UFO encounters. The standardized quantitative system he developed was and continues to be critical for assessing the validity and credibility of eyewitness accounts, as it aids our understanding of events, regardless of how odd or otherworldly they may seem.

It is important to be skeptically openminded in examining perinormal phenomena; a term I prefer over *paranormal* as the prefix in the former alludes to something that exists all around us, as opposed to that which is beyond, aside from, or runs parallel to our conventional reality. It's also critical that we do not simply "believe" every account but instead be mindful and cautiously consider the experiences of others who may have raised a periscope to briefly glimpse the unorthodox realm that circumscribes us. In this sense, I echo the sentiments of Jeffrey J. Kripal, the J. Newton Rayzor Chair in Philosophy and Religious Thought at Rice University, where in his 2010 book *Authors of The Impossible*, he acknowledges the importance of an etic approach to examining and conveying the odd experiences of others.

I do not "believe" all the tales I will tell you in the pages that follow, however convinced I may sound in this or that passage. Indeed, as a professional scholar of religion, I consider it my job *not* to believe, and I take that professional commitment very seriously. Which is not to say, at all, that I discount these stories as unimportant, as simply fabricated or completely false. I do not. What I am trying to do is recreate for the reader what the field researcher calls "unbounded paranormal conditions," that is, a place in space and time, in this case a text recreated and realized in your mind, where–to speak very precisely now–really, really weird shit happens.

## COMMON CONTACT EXPERIENCES

The Dr. Edgar Mitchell Foundation for Research into Extraterrestrial and Extraordinary Experiences (FREE) was cofounded by the late Apollo 14 astronaut Dr. Edgar Mitchell. In 2018, this foundation published a comprehensive analysis of contact experiences, carried out in association with prominent scientists and researchers with an interest in the UFO phenomenon. Their report was edited by Rey Hernandez, Dr. Jon Klimo, and Dr. Rudy Schild, the latter of whom was the FREE executive director and emeritus research astronomer at the Harvard/Smithsonian Center for Astrophysics at Harvard university.

Boasting an impressive sample of 3,256 individuals, the FREE Experiencer Research Study was the first and largest worldwide multi-language investigation of people who report having had contact with UFOs and ETs.[94] The results of the FREE study revealed numerous thought-provoking and informative patterns across this large sample of contactees and abductees, especially regarding the types of beings observed and how people felt about their overall contact experience.

When asked "Do you believe you have observed a physical Non-Human Intelligence (NHI)?" 1,534 individuals answered in the affirmative. This group, who responded that they had indeed observed a "non-human intelligence" was then asked, "Can you describe what group of NHI you observed?" and "How would you describe your experience?" The subject responses to these questions yielded fascinating results, which are highly consistent with the experiences detailed across the 15 case studies examined in the current text. Furthermore, when considered holistically, these survey results support an extratempestrial explanation for the origin of these entities.

For instance, despite obvious bias in the phrasing of the question, which specifically asked about a "non-human" intelligence, 52% of respondents described the beings they witnessed as "Human-Looking." It is also important to note that the individuals who interacted with human-looking beings reported having a far more pleasant experience than those who encountered actual alien forms. Specifically, 85% of respondents stated that their experience with the "human-looking" beings was either positive or neutral, while only 5% reported that it was a negative experience.[95]

"Human-looking" beings were the most common form described across the study sample, which lends credence to the Extratempestrial Model, since our ancestors, ourselves, and our descendants are all human. Further support for the ETM comes from the fact that the second, third, and fourth most reported entities were also bipedal hominins, who possess derived traits characteristic of the hominin clade, but which represent a slightly "more evolved" grade relative to us and our ancestors, suggesting they originate from a more distant point in our evolutionary future.

Specifically, after "human-looking," the next most commonly described forms were *short greys*, between 3 to 4 feet in height (51%), *tall greys*, who were between 5 to 9 feet tall (33%), and *hybrids* (26%), who had traits of both modern humans and the "grey aliens." Additionally, of the 708 individuals who stated that they had direct "contact with an ET (NHI) on a UAP craft," again, the most frequently reported form was "human-looking" (48%), with the *short greys* (45%) and *tall greys* (33%) representing the second and third most observed beings.[96][97] It should also be noted that these percentages do not sum to 100 because many experiencers observed some combination of these different forms on the same craft at the same time.

Other actual "alien" creatures were also occasionally reported, such as insectoids, mantids, reptiles, and spirits, for example. However, these represented only a small percentage of the entities observed, while the overwhelming majority of abductee and contactee reports describe physical beings, with quintessentially "human," "human-looking," or a "humanoid" form. Furthermore, as stated above, the physical characteristics of these *grey aliens* and *hybrids* are reminiscent of what we would expect to see in the physiology of our distant human descendants, if the same long-term morphological trends that characterize our own hominin evolutionary past persist into the future.

Some number of UFO reports will undoubtedly deviate from the events described in the 15 case studies selected for this analysis, and occasionally regarding the type of craft observed and descriptions of the beings encountered, including some with less hominin characteristics. However, looking closely at the details of contact experiences featured here and elsewhere, the overwhelming majority describe human and humanoid individuals, seen inside or in association with cigar-, triangle-, and most commonly, disc-shaped craft. The case studies examined as part of the current study conform to the typical encounter, and when viewed individually, or in association with other accounts, we should keep an open mind to the possibility that they may represent instances of intertemporal interaction among us and our future human descendants.

## The Case Study Sample

The principal purpose of the current study is to examine abductee and contactee cases in the context of the Extratempestrial Model. The close encounters selected for scrutiny occurred on five different continents and span a period of nearly 100 years. They were chosen in part because of this broad temporal and geographic representation but also because they have been thoroughly vetted and because they encapsulate much of the variation observable across contact experiences.

As stated above, marked similarity among abductee and contactee cases across the world and through time makes sense in the context of the ETM. If people from the human future are returning to various points in their past for the same or similar purposes, how they look, what they arrive in, the technology they possess, and what they are observed doing, would be relatively consistent across past periods. Although they remain essentially the same, some variation in how their presence is perceived by those they visit would be expected, since the religion, worldview, mores, folkways, myths, legends, and countless other culture-specific qualities of a group would contribute to how these visitors are conceptualized across time and space.

This makes sense in a prehistoric and historic context but should also be considered in cases that occurred prior to the 1940s, before the UFO zeitgeist began to materialize. Numerous close encounters predate our broad-based cultural knowledge of UFOs. These offer something of a virgin perspective, without being tainted by preconceived notions of what these craft and their occupants might be, and without the contrived stigma that has persistently pervaded the subject since the mid-20th century.

As mentioned previously, these early cases also help address certain critiques levied in response to the abduction aspect of the phenomenon, including hypnotizability and the Psychocultural Hypothesis (PCH). The relative PCH purity of these early encounters is noteworthy because they occurred decades before the media storm that grew up around the 1947 Roswell crash and the 1961 abduction of Betty and Barney Hill. These also took place long before the first satellites, human space flight, walking on the moon, and an ensuing stage of wonder about what else might be out there in the vastness of the universe. Prior to these monumental human events and broad awareness of UFOs, it is harder to argue that close encounters are simply a product of human psychology and the mythos that arose around our recent technological achievements.

The first two cases considered as part of the current study occurred prior to 1947 and are lesser-known events, though there is much we may glean from them. For instance, they appear to have been accidental encounters; they took place during the day; they include detailed descriptions of the visitors' technology; one consisted of multiple interactions with the same UFO occupants throughout the individual's lifetime; one involved telepathic communication and the other verbal speech; and each may offer insight into what is likely a more evolved state of human physiology, technology, culture, and cognition among humans in both the proximate and more distant future.

# Case Study 1

⌁

# 1932
# Leo and Mike Dworshak
# North Dakota, USA

*These men were so ordinary looking in one way and so exotic in another. They had light brown hair... their complexion was very light beige, resembling a good tan. Their eyes were blue with a dark pupil.... Their hands and feet were shaped like ours, but their shoes were totally unlike our own.... A top with slacks uniform replaced the coverall they had always worn before. These men were as alike as peas in a pod.[98]*

– LEO DWORSHAK

The first encounter examined as part of this series of case studies is that of two young boys named Leo and Mike Dworshak. They were the sons of German immigrants who lived near Killdeer, North Dakota, in the United States during the dust bowl period of the Great Depression. Further detail about their encounters, and Leo Dworshak's lifelong interaction with the visitors, can be found in his 2003 book *UFOs Are with Us: Take My Word.*[99] Additional information, along with a thoughtful analysis of this and the close encounter detailed in the following chapter, can be found in Joan Bird's 2013 book, *Montana UFOs and Extraterrestrials.*

Mike and Leo's adventure began in the summer of 1932, when they were out exploring an area near their farm and happened across a large, round, silver, metallic object that they could see from the top of a hill. At the time of this encounter, Leo was twelve years old, and Mike was seven. Because they were young children, the boys hadn't seen many things they could compare this strange object to, but they described it as a massive machine that was as big as their barn. Leo stated that it must have been a machine because of the complicated way in which it was spinning, with colored flashing lights rotating around the perimeter of the otherwise stationary craft.

Curious, the two boys tried to approach the craft but encountered an invisible shield that would not let them get any closer. As they stood and watched from this ethereal boundary, a ramp suddenly descended from its smooth underbelly and three "people" walked out and onto the ground below the craft. The boys watched for a short period but had to return home for supper, though they would often return to this spot in the hopes of catching a glimpse of the huge and highly mysterious machine.

Their efforts paid off, because about two weeks later, the brothers saw the machine again, and this time they got a much better view, since they happened to return as the aircraft was flying overhead on its way to the same landing spot in the valley below. There were twice as many people this time, who were all wearing more conventional clothes in the form of pants and shirts, as opposed to the coveralls they wore the first time the boys saw them. During a later visit to this UFO hotspot, the boys were again fortunate to have seen the silver metallic craft moving. Leo stated that it raised about 15 feet off the ground, emitted a low-pitched humming sound as the flashing lights continued to rotate around the outside, then suddenly accelerated away from them at tremendous speed, disappearing from sight in an instant.

Over time, the boys had many more interactions with the ship, including one where it moved overhead and trapped them in the aforementioned energy field. However, it released them suddenly the moment Leo had the thought that they might be in trouble if they didn't return home soon. As time went on, Leo began to have thoughts about these people and their flying machine, which he believed were placed there by the visitors.

Much like how the spacefaring boy tamed the fox in the classic tale of *The Little Prince*, the Dworshak boys and these visitors slowly began to grow accustomed to each other's presence, and they eventually began to form a sort of bond. On one of the earliest occasions, Mike and Leo observed the men doing what appeared to be exercises outside the craft. They decided to walk closer, and this time, not only was the forcefield not there, but the men were smiling at them, and they seemed genuinely happy that the boys decided to approach.

Now able to get a better look at their outfits, Leo noted that the men were dressed nicely, in nondescript uniforms with no patches or insignia that he could see. They also looked similar to one another, with the same light brown hair, tan skin, blue eyes, and a husky build. Leo noted that the men appeared healthier than anyone he'd ever seen, though this may have been due to where and when he lived, considering it was the height of the Great Depression. He was also struck by their eyes, describing them as having deep, tunnel-like characteristics, like that of an old soul who had seen much throughout their life.

Considering this contact in the context of the Extratempestrial Model, it is important to note that Leo's description of these visitors is remarkably human. In fact, since the first encounter, Leo had always referred to them as "people," and "men," specifically. Everything about his description of them is entirely human, and not just regarding their physical appearance, but also their style of dress and way of interacting with the two boys. Beyond their culture, clothes, and physiology, numerous other characteristics of the visitors' appearance and behavior suggests these men originated in a future time, as opposed to having come from a distant planet.

One notable trait was their capacity to communicate in the boys' native language. For instance, while in the presence of these men, Leo's little brother Mike began to speak to them in a mix of English and German. After spouting off some words in his creole dialect, two of the men walked into the ship. Soon after, a different man came out and spoke to the two boys, first in German, and then in English. The man told the boys that he was able to speak over 500 languages or, "all of the languages that existed on Earth at that time," as he stated.[100]

Whether it was a product of Leo's faulty memory or the man's error, this statement isn't accurate. Many linguistic groups had been wiped out during European colonialism and imperialism beginning around 500 years ago, but in the 1930s, there were still thousands of different languages spoken throughout the world. Despite this, the man's ability to speak 500 languages would allow him to communicate with most cultures in existence at that time, and it is incredibly impressive regardless of its historic accuracy.

This part of Mike and Leo's interaction may also suggest these people were from the human future. Comparatively, it would be much easier for our descendants to learn languages from their own past, and much harder for beings that evolved on a separate planet to learn one, let alone 500 languages. Among the millions of lifeforms here on Earth, we are only able to engage in complex communication with our most closely related great ape cousins. This interaction is also limited, since an ape's higher vocal tract anatomy doesn't allow them to vocalize speech in the same way, so we use symbols and sign language to communicate. This is also a somewhat one-sided, anthropomorphic form of interaction, considering we have only ever taught them our languages, but we have no idea what they are saying in their chimpanzee, orangutan, or gorilla languages.

Assuming an alien civilization happened to evolve something even remotely similar to what we use for vocalized vibration-based communication, it would take an inordinate amount of time in the beginning stages of contact to learn each other's languages. This learning curve becomes exponentially steeper if our initial linguistic instructions are only able to come via interstellar radio signals, considering there would be a decade-, century-, or millennia-long delay between transmissions. It could potentially take hundreds or thousands of years to learn even rudimentary elements of an extraterrestrial's language, depending on where their planet is in the galaxy and how much, if anything, could be garnered from each transmission.

There are challenges with learning the languages of past cultural groups on our own planet as well, including those who lived as recently as 3,000 years ago. Without any context, or shared words or phrases between modern and ancient languages, it is almost impossible to know what a culture's arbitrarily chosen symbols were meant to represent. In fact, without the Rosetta stone, we would have only a vague idea about what was being communicated in Egyptian hieroglyphics. However, because we have more ways of archiving culture and language in modern times, our descendants should have far more information to work with if they wish to learn the languages of their past.

Mike and Leo's first attempt at communication is also telling, considering the first two men they encountered went into the ship once the boys started talking, then one specific individual came out to greet them, speaking in both German and English. Specialists with different but complimentary knowledge and skills often collaborate on the same research projects or at the same field sites. We might also expect variation in the occupational specialization of our extratempestrial descendants, as they work together to perform research at their field sites of the past.

In 2007, I worked as an archaeologist at the Middle-Paleolithic Neanderthal site of Chez-Pinaud à Jonzac, near Bordeaux, France, where we had a broad range of experts who all contributed in various capacities. There were biological anthropologists like myself, who specialized in skeletal biology and hominin evolutionary anatomy, who we jokily dubbed the "Boners." There were also archaeologists with broad knowledge of the different lithic tool types indigenous to that region and time, called the "Stoners."

In addition to the Stoners and Boners, there were paleontologist, entomologist, paleobotanists, geologists, and countless others who worked together to help advance our knowledge of Neanderthal lifeways in this region of southern France, where they lived from about 150,000 years ago up until they were replaced by our *Homo sapiens* ancestors around 35,000 years ago. Further indication of occupational specializations can be seen in other case studies as well, including the abduction of Betty and Barney Hill, which will be discussed in a later chapter.

Although there is much about Mike and Leo's interaction with the visitors that seems to support the Extratempestrial Model, like the Betty and Barney Hill case, the Dworshak boys were told by these men that they were from a different galaxy. Such statements should be acknowledged and assessed, and they should not be arbitrarily dropped from the narrative just because they don't neatly conform to the ETM. However, it is also important to skeptically consider such claims, and similar other statements made by the visitors regarding their origins.

In his book *UFOs Are with Us: Take My Word*, Leo Dworshak states that the men told the two boys they had come from a different galaxy and that they traveled to our planet for over 5,000 years. Despite this interstellar claim, Leo also remembers the men telling he and his brother that they came from a place far beyond our world, by millions of years in time.[101] Looking at these two seemingly contradictory descriptions of their origins, in the context of the men's appearance, ship, tools, and behaviors, it seems more likely that they traveled through time rather than space.

If these visitors came from the future, and possibly 5,000 years in the future if this was a coy sidestep of the question, we might expect them to remain incognito to avoid disrupting the timeline, as per the many worlds interpretation of quantum mechanics. Or if viewed in a block universe context, to avoid adding uncertainty and confusion to a period that predates broad knowledge of our future time-travel capabilities. Conducting research in rural North Dakota in the 1930s, and allowing two young boys to occasionally interact with them, who no one would believe anyway, seems logical in a time-travel scenario. Although, if these visitors traveled from a different galaxy, we might expect a more formal announcement of their arrival, and meetings with the leaders of some sovereign nations.

Another reason these men may have lied to Mike and Leo Dworshak could have been because they didn't want to give too much away about who specifically was visiting from the future. I recently received an email from an abductee who was given the opportunity to speak with her captors. These entirely human-looking visitors explicitly stated that they were humans from the future. However, they refrained from advertising this fact for fear that if people know what "races" will come to dominate the geographic and technological landscape, it may cause wars, where different nations fight to become the dominant group in those future times. In concert with other logical reasons why our descendants may wish to avoid overt contact prior to us becoming them, this should also be considered.

Another reason I feel these men may have lied to Mike and Leo Dworshak about their origins has to do with where they said they were from specifically. Although Betty Hill and Leo Dworshak both claim the visitors said they came here from a different planet, each were told very different places. The likelihood that bipedal humanlike beings evolved on another planet is very low, but the probability that hominins evolved the same way on three separate planets, with one in an entirely different galaxy, and that these other two interstellar human species happened to converge on Earth within 29 years of one another, is effectively zero.

It is doubtful that we would ever be discovered by beings who live in a different galaxy, or that they could or would spend 5,000 years traveling here on a spaceship, just to study grasshoppers and do jumping jacks in rural North Dakota during the Great Depression. Furthermore, considering how little we understand about time and time travel today, let alone in the 1930s, maybe our distant descendants find it easier to utter that they are from outer space. They may believe, now and in the past, that this is a simpler concept for their primitive ancestors to comprehend when we inevitably ask *where* they're from. Although, the visitors do occasionally confess that they are us from the future, so the outer space explanation is not exclusive to these encounters. This includes a 16-year-old boy who was abducted from Greymouth, New Zealand, in 1980.

> Later he would remember being inside a huge object with a line of about 20 people, behind and in front of him. They went through a compartment that was apparently a waterless shower. The occupants of the craft, apparently human like beings, told the witness that they

were from the 'future,' that many were historians trying to learn from the past. They also told the group that the human race disrespected other living creatures and was immature and not ready for contact.[102]

Another revealing aspect of Mike and Leo's interaction, and another indication that these men may have come from the future, involves the visitors telling the boys that no one would believe their story until they were old men. This seems to suggest the men were aware that prior to the late 1940s, there was no broad-based cultural awareness of the UFO phenomenon, though the reality of their presence in our times would eventually become more conventionally understood, and within the boys' lifetimes.

There are other indications from Leo's account that these travelers knew the future. For instance, after a number of increasingly informal interactions, the boys finally get the chance to go inside the barn-sized disc-shaped craft. Onboard the ship, the men told Mike and Leo that they would begin to see things that would happen over the next 30 years. The boys were also told that the people of their time brought many of the depression-era problems upon themselves, and they were about to enter a period of great wars and even greater suffering. This suggests the men came from or at least possessed knowledge of the ensuing future, especially considering World War II was set to begin later that same decade.

Another indication that these were extratempestrial humans may be seen in the methods they used to conduct their research, along with what they were studying and why. For instance, Leo's little brother Mike once asked the men why they kept coming back to the same spot. They replied that they were studying life patterns in that valley, and they would continue monitoring it and other places as our world "gets deeper into trouble."[103] Based on his interactions and observations of the men's behavior, Leo came to believe they were collecting and analyzing insects to monitor environmental toxins in that area.

As Paul Hynek previously pointed out, we must ask, "How would they find us?" and "Why would they care?" Monitoring life in various places across the world over a specific period that predates our planet getting deeper into trouble is something we would expect of people poised to inherit this planet, but not necessarily of extraterrestrials who already have someplace to live. Leo's observations, in association with the visitors' constant concern about war, pollution, nuclear and chemical weapons, and how we treat the Earth, suggest they are not only studying us and our impact on the environment but that they are also stakeholders in the future of this planet.

This type of longitudinal method is indicative of a cross-temporal research objective. It is also interesting to consider, and Leo's lifelong interaction with these people indicates, that they are the same researchers traveling through time to collect samples over multiple Earth years. In this context, the study could have been carried out over the course of only a few days or weeks to them, if they did indeed possess the capacity to move through time. In other words, what appeared to have been multiple years or decades in Leo's frame of reference may have only been a few days to these researchers. With the ability to pop in and out of different points along the fourth dimension, it would be possible to collect longitudinal data, in the same place, across long periods of Earth time, but to the researchers themselves, the study could be carried out over a much shorter period.

This is also indicated by the fact that Leo consistently saw the ship land in the same area around Killdeer for years to come, and because each time he saw these people throughout his life, they didn't appear to age at all. Leo met and spoke with these same men again in the summers of 1936 and 1939. During this later interaction, the visitors commented on how much Leo had changed over the previous seven years. After they commented on his appearance, Leo began to take notice of the fact that these men had not changed at all. When he asked about this, the men stated that they were several thousand years ahead of Leo's time, but also that they were pathogen free and had a different life expectancy than what people of his time experience.

There are multiple aspects of this interaction that are indicative of their intertemporal abilities and origins in the human future. For instance, a divergence in the way time passed for the visitors and visited could account for the difference in their rate of aging. It could also be because humans will age more slowly in the future, as the visitors suggested. In fact, a prolongation of our life history cycle, meaning a delayed onset and longer duration of each stage of growth and development, has been a dominant trend throughout hominin evolution.

The visitor's explicit focus on patterns of change in Earth's ecosystem and the goings-on of humans throughout our collective history is palpable from Mike and Leo's interactions. This is again indicated by Leo's very last onboard interaction with the men, which took place in the autumn of 1963, just west of Bozeman, Montana. During this encounter, they reiterated the horrors of war, which Leo had now experienced firsthand after fighting in World War II, and after losing his little brother Mike in the Korean War.

The materials, supplies, and technology Leo observed onboard the ship also indicates these visitors were researchers from our future. For instance, during their first visit, Mike and Leo were given a tour, which included a look around the ship's kitchen, where the boys could see food and cooking equipment. They were also shown the men's sleeping quarters and a bathroom with fully automated toilets and no towels or toilet paper in sight. These are again indicative of intertemporal continuity, considering this is lavatory technology we currently possess, and which is already common in Japan, to the extent that hotels, restaurants, rest stops, bus stations, and 80% of homes have them.[104] The purpose of these various rooms inside the ship, as well as the tools and technology seen in them, are almost identical to what we use for the same purposes in modern times.

If these visitors evolved on a different planet, in a separate galaxy no less, they wouldn't be expected to look, act, or be anything like us, and therefore, shouldn't have the same kitchen, bathroom, and bedroom facilities. These amenities and their use represent *cultural universals*, which are customs, beliefs, and behaviors that exist in every human society throughout the world. Because they were also observed on the visitors' ship, it again suggests a human connection and cultural continuity with the ensuing future.

Eating, sleeping, and excreting are common acts among all animals on this planet, and these basic functions might be performed by extra-terrestrial beings as well. Although, from Leo Dworshak's encounter, the composition of rooms on the craft, the function of their cultural implements, the specific physiological form of these men, and their behaviors, where they were observed engaging in things like exercising and collecting data, are entirely consistent with modern human spaces, tools, appearances, and activities.

Other advanced utilitarian technologies were also on display. For instance, Leo and Mike were shown what they described as a magnetic laser beam, which could put living animals in a state of suspended animation so they could be collected, studied, and later released unharmed. There was also a screen showing various images, which, while confusing to Mike and Leo, seemed to show pictures relevant to human life at that time. The ship could also be made translucent, which allowed the people inside to observe what was taking place outside in all directions when enabled. A common characteristic of these craft we will see again in ensuing case studies.

A final indication of our shared species status can be seen in the visitors' insistence that Mike and Leo undergo a decontamination process before coming onto the ship, which is also a common theme among the case studies considered, and in other accounts of onboard interaction. This was done to reduce the possibility of germ transmission between the two parties, which is more likely to occur among members of the same species. Parasites, bacteria, and viruses can also be transmitted to humans from other species, which are known as *zoonoses*. This is readily apparent from the Middle East respiratory syndrome (MERS), severe acute respiratory syndrome (SARS), and most recently, the SARS-CoV-2 virgin-soil pandemic. Each of these are zoonotic viruses that moved from bats to a humans, with the latter being transmitted in the Wuhan province of China in late 2019.[105] [106]

Although pathogens can move between different animals, there is a far greater probability of transmission among conspecifics, meaning members of the same species. This may be why Leo and Mike had to undergo a decontamination process and were told to put on new clothes that were provided to them each time they entered the ship. This may have been of greater significance to these visitors because they boasted about being "germ-free." Since modern humans are not, nor were we between the 1930s and 1960s when Leo interacted with them, this decontamination procedure was probably to prevent the transmission of pathogens from us to them, not the other way around.

The physiology, facilities, language, behavior, technology, material culture, and overall interaction Mike had as a child, and Leo had throughout much of his life, suggest these visitors were people, just like us, but from a different time. The marked similarity between us and them also indicates they returned from a relatively proximate period in the future, after our society has advanced, but prior to our morphology evolving too far beyond its current form.

As mentioned above, more detail about the Dworshak case can be found in Joan Bird's fascinating book *Montana UFOs and Extraterrestrials: Extraordinary Stories of Documented Sightings and Encounters*. Bird's work also includes interviews from Leo Dworshak's later life, including some seemingly contradictory views he held about war and society.[107] This deeper dive into Leo's recollection of events and aspects of his personal life, which Bird brought to light through intensive investigation and numerous instances of informal interaction, helps frame the context of his account. It also highlights the lasting effect these exchanges had on his life, while providing a glimpse into how abductee and contactee encounters impact people in similar ways, regardless of how, where, or when they occurred.

# Case Study 2

~

# 1940
# Udo Wartena
# Montana, USA

*He was a nice looking man, seemingly about my age. He wore a light gray pair of overalls, a [hat] of the same material on his head, and on his feet were slippers or moccasins.... His English was like mine, but he spoke slowly, as if he were a linguist and had to pick his way.*[108]

— UDO WARTENA

Throughout much of the 19th and early 20th centuries, countless European immigrants came to the United States and often headed west to the Appalachian or Rocky Mountains to find work in the booming mining industry. This was the case where I currently reside in Butte, Montana, as a massive influx of people made this one of the largest metropolises of the early 1900s. In fact, upon moving to Butte about 12 years ago, I learned that my great-grandfather and great-uncle, both of Welsh descent, also lived and worked here in Butte nearly a century earlier.

About two hours northeast of Butte, up the Confederate Gulch drainage near the state capital of Helena, Montana, is Diamond City, which, while lacking in diamonds, was one of the richest gold strikes in Montana history. In early May 1940, while working near a glacial deposit showing signs of gold-bearing ore, a 37-year-old miner of Dutch ancestry named Udo Wartena, discovered something potentially much more valuable than gold. While clearing some boulders for his small-scale mining operation, Wartena came across a large airship hovering over a dam he made in a stream for sluice-mining gold.

Like many other UFO reports, what first caught Wartena's attention was the low humming sound the craft emitted. After hearing the noise for a while and wondering if it might be an Army airplane or a car on the desolate mountain road, he climbed higher to investigate, and was shocked to see the ship hanging in the sky above his sluice stream. In a 1976 letter to John Glenn, an astronaut who had recently been elected Senator of Ohio around that time, Wartena described the craft as similar to a large blimp, but less thick and more pointed on the sides.[109] In an article by Australian UFO researcher Warren P. Aston, which was published in the March/April 1998 edition of *UFO Magazine*, Wartena described it as,

> a large disc-shaped object, measuring about thirty-five feet high and over a hundred feet across… like two soup plates, one inverted over the other. It was stainless steel in color, though not as bright and shiny.[110]

Upon cresting the hill and seeing this odd object floating near the ground, it was instantly apparent to Wartena that this was not a car or an airplane. While standing there ruminating on what the strange aeronautic device may be, a stairway suddenly descended from the bottom of the otherwise solid-looking ship, and "a man" descended the stairs and started walking toward him. Interested, Wartena also began walking toward the man, who he described as nice-looking, about 35 years of age, with white hair and clear, almost translucent skin. The man approached Wartena, shook his hand, and apologized because they had not known anyone was in the area. He also told Wartena that "it was not their custom to interrupt or allow themselves to be seen."[111]

After a brief formal introduction, the man asked Wartena if he would mind if they took some water from the stream he dammed for his mining operation. Wartena approved but asked why they were getting water from his stream and not the large lake nearby. The man replied that the water was good, convenient, and free of algae. Later, during a detailed tour of the ship, where he was taught much about its inner workings, Wartena learned that the fuel source for these aircraft came from hydrogen extracted from water, which helps explain why its relative cleanliness was important.[112] Their stated intent to avoid being seen also helps explain why they sought fuel from this high mountain stream and not Canyon Ferry Lake, which sits in a more open and inhabited area closer to Helena, Montana, just to the west of them.

During their early interaction outside the silvery disc-shaped craft, Wartena made note of the man's adept English-speaking ability, which he likened to how a linguist would talk, slowly picking his words to ensure proper grammar and pronunciation. As we saw in the previous case of Mike and Leo Dworshak, and as we will see in most of the ensuing case studies, it is extremely common for the visitors to speak in the contactee's mother tongue, both vocally and telepathically. In fact, according to the Dr. Edgar Mitchell FREE study, 75% of contactees reported that communication took place in their native language.[113]

In the previous case study, the human men the Dworshak boys encountered stated that they could speak over 500 languages, or "all of the languages that existed on Earth at that time." This is intriguing, and revealing, because Udo Wartena was told by the man he encountered that "they know over five hundred languages and were learning ours and improving upon them all the time."[114] Although there were far more than 500 languages spoken in the 1930s and 1940s, it is curious that both groups of visitors, in these two separate encounters, claimed to have spoken exactly 500 languages specifically. This, along with countless other common features observable in these interactions, speaks to the consistency across reports, and indicates that many of these encounters may involve the same groups doing similar things across different periods of their past. It also enforces the notion that certain people onboard the ship may occupy the important role of linguist, translator, or ambassador while present in a particular time.

Further indication of this potential temporal ambassadorship role is apparent in how the man asked Wartena if he would be interested in coming onto the ship. After Wartena accepted, he was given a comprehensive tour of it, which is another common occurrence across contactee accounts. However, the Wartena case is unique in the sense that the man provided him with a wealth of esoteric information about how the ship operated. The man was also incredibly receptive to most questions he had, which gave Wartena a unique ability to convey detailed information about the form, function, and inner workings of the craft, or at least to the best of his abilities, considering he didn't hold an advanced degree in relativistic mechanics or electromagnetism and photonics.

Inside the ship, Wartena described being in a room about 12 by 16 feet across, with benches around the sides and indirect lighting that filled the space. He also saw another "man" on the tour, who was plainly dressed and who had very light, "snow white" colored hair. Once inside, Wartena noticed that the pervasive humming sound he heard outside was no longer audible. When he asked about the sound, the man not only told him what it came from and how it related to powering the ship, but according to Warren Aston's 1998 research, Wartena was given "what appears to be a full and open discussion of the key principle involved, in the following words."

> As you noticed we are floating above the ground, and though the ground slopes the ship is level. There are in the outside rim, two flywheels, one turning one way and the other in the opposite direction. He explained [that] this gives the ship its own gravitation or rather overcomes the gravitational pull of the Earth and other planets, the sun and stars; and through the pull of the stars and planets...to ride on like you do when you sail on ice.[115]

Wartena described the counter-rotating flywheels as about three feet wide and several inches thick. He also remembered that they were separated by motor-driven rods adjacent to transformer or battery-like boxes, which sat all around the inside edge of the disc-shaped craft. Wartena was told that the two rings spinning in opposite directions to one another develop an electromagnetic force, which was a term he was not familiar with at the time, but he would soon learn more about following the encounter.[116]

His tour guide went on to tell Wartena much more about their ship and the way it operated, while also speaking of advanced energy sources and interstellar travel. When Wartena asked where they were from, the man stated that they lived on a distant planet and pointed in its direction. However, Wartena was unable to remember the name of the planet they claimed to be from. It should also be noted that even though the man alluded to their extraterrestrial origins, he acknowledged that they look like us humans. He also claimed that they live among us from time to time, trying to learn from us while offering guidance when needed.

It is hard to tell from Wartena's account whether these travelers were indeed from a distant solar system, or if interstellar statements like this are just standard protocol when interacting with past human groups, as discussed in the previous case study. The fact that Wartena didn't remember what the man said about which distant planet they came from suggests it was not emphasized, even though the exact origination point of extraterrestrial visitors seems like it would be of great import during a rare interaction like this.

Beyond sharing the same physical form, and their knowledge of our culture and language, the man's claim that they have been observing us, but only minimally interacting, may also support an extratempestrial interpretation. This is further indicated by the fact that the only question the man refused to answer was about our religious figures and belief system. According to Warren Aston,

> When Udo asked if they knew of Jesus Christ and about religion he was told that they would 'like to speak of these things but are unable. We cannot interfere in any way.' The area of religion and belief systems was to be the only question the aliens refused to discuss.[117]

A common theme apparent across close encounters is an omnipresent attempt to limit overt interaction. This was also the case for Udo Wartena, as he inadvertently happened upon these visitors while they were trying to get water from a secluded location in the mountains of Montana. Similarly, the Dworshak boys found their eventual friends in a remote region of rural North Dakota, and they were kept away from the craft and men by an invisible force field during much of the early stages of their interaction.

This desire to limit interaction and direct or indirect influence could be considered in the same vein as the "Prime Directive" in Star Trek, where these interstellar space travelers were forbidden from interfering with the internal and natural development of other civilizations.[118] This concept was applied in the context of avoiding affecting separate interstellar societies. However, the same could be said for those attempting to prevent inadvertently influencing aspects of their own future, in more of a cross-temporal Prime Directive context.

We might expect that time travelers from the human future would be forbidden from interfering with the internal and natural development of past peoples, since this could affect them directly. This type of outward avoidance makes more sense under the ETM compared to the ETH, since an extraterrestrial race would care less about changing the course of history for a civilization on a distant planet, with whom they have no shared history. Although, we must again tease apart the impact, or non-impact, of such influence in the context of the block universe and the multiverse models, since you can have "change" with the latter but not the former.

When viewed in the context of the many worlds interpretation of quantum mechanics (MWI), simply visiting the past is expected to cause decoherence and the origin of new and different timelines. As such, avoiding overt interaction with past peoples may be irrelevant in the context of the MWI and the Quantum Multiverse Model because new timelines will form regardless of the level of interaction these time travelers have with past human groups. In other words, if a new timeline is created anytime someone or something comes back from the future, it doesn't matter how much interaction occurs, since your presence in that period has already caused a new timeline to form. Furthermore, if these are our future human descendants, because they do abduct us and interact in limited other ways, it may indicate that the Block Universe Model is correct, while the yet-unproven Multiverse Model is less accurate, since the visitors ostensibly persistent presence would constantly be creating a plethora of new timelines.

Although they claimed to have come from a distant planet, the travelers Udo Wartena encountered acknowledged their humanness, stated that they were involved in gathering information, said they help when needed, but they refused to speak about our religions and belief systems. These details tend to make more sense in the context of the Extratempestrial Model. However, the Prime Directive part of these encounters also fits with the Extraterrestrial Hypothesis, as well as the Simulation Hypothesis and any other interpretation of the phenomenon involving entities that observe us, regardless of their origins.

This is simply because non-interference is vital to the methodology of observational studies, where a researcher attempts to measure the actual behaviors of those they are observing, as opposed to what the study subjects do in response to outside influence. Though with that said, under the Simulation Hypothesis, we might expect that in certain iterations of our existence, where a multitude of computer models come about, outside stimulus is occasionally interjected so its effects can be quantified, as is the case with most agent-based computer models and simulations.

In later life, with the hope that it might help advance US technology in some way, Udo Wartena penned a letter to accomplished astronaut and senator John Glenn. In the letter, Wartena described his encounter and offered as much information as he could remember about the energy source and functional capabilities of the advanced disc-shaped craft he was shown some years earlier. Wartena considered this interaction important enough that he was willing to risk scorn and ridicule by a sitting senator, in the hopes that his incredible experience might help the US in some way.

Wartena's letter was ignored by John Glenn, or more likely, was ignored by one of Glenn's aides long before it ever got to him. Nevertheless, if taken seriously, this encounter could potentially reveal a great deal about the sophisticated technology of these travelers. Additionally, if these men were our distant descendants, it may provide a glimpse into how our current technology will advance beyond its present state and how we may someday develop aircraft capable of defying gravity and manipulating spacetime.

High electromagnetic fields are frequently detected in and around UFOs and places where they had recently been. It is also common for cars, radios, and other devices to become increasingly erratic and completely shut off as a UAP approaches. The prevalence of these reports suggests the electromagnetic force is integral to the operation of these machines. This fundamental force may also be a part of how these travelers manipulate spacetime to return to the past and how they withstand the tremendous g-forces generated in association with the incredibly fast accelerations and decelerations observed, as will be discussed later in this text.

There is already some indication that electromagnetism could be a valuable tool in our pervasive fight against gravity in aeronautic engineering. Its future significance in antigravity propulsion systems may be implicit in the immense difference between the electromagnetic and gravitational forces. In fact, according to Dr. Clifford Johnson, a professor in the Department of Physics and Astronomy at the University of Southern California,

> We tend to think of gravity as very strong–after all it's what binds us to the Earth. But actually, of all the forces we know in nature, gravity's the weakest…. Let me give you a number. It's 10 to the power 40 times weaker than electromagnetism, that's a one with 40 zeros after it![119]

The profound difference between gravity and the electromagnetic force points to the role the latter may someday play in helping us finally break free of the antiquated, Bernoullian, vector-based, combustion engine propulsion technologies of the modern era. If we are eventually able to develop aircraft capable of amplifying and directing the electromagnetic force against the weaker force of gravity, this could fundamentally transform the way we travel, and the speed with which we get around this planet, and perhaps to others as well.

Furthermore, a triangle, saucer, or disc shape seems ideal for opposing Earth's gravity once aircraft no longer require wings to fly. If antigravity accelerators were placed at each edge of a triangular craft, it would increase stability and help control pitch, roll, and yaw. A saucer or disc-shaped craft, much like a frisbee, could maintain lateral stability and counter the force of gravity more homogenously across its symmetrical base while rotating in the air, or by means of counter-rotating flywheels like the ones shown to Udo Wartena during his 1940 encounter.

Because electromagnetism is 10,000,000,000,000,000,000,000, 000,000,000,000,000 times stronger than gravity, it may also aid in constructing a device capable of bending and warping spacetime to allow time travel to the past. Manipulating the electromagnetic force could be a key component in creating closed timelike curves (CTC), by bending spacetime to the extent that light cones become reoriented toward the past. Amplifying the electromagnetic force could help create CTCs without having to maneuver masses equivalent to that of a black hole, which may otherwise be needed to achieve the same level of spacetime warpage using the force of gravity.

The form and observed capabilities of UAPs, considered alongside reports of close encounters detailing the components and inner workings of these craft, like that of Udo Wartena, indicate our species may eventually harness the awesome power of the electromagnetic force. This may allow our proximate descendants the ability to advance aeronautic propulsion, and our more distant descendants to eventually develop backward time-travel technology.

The Udo Wartena case is fascinating for many reasons, though one of the most intriguing aspects of this encounter is that he was able to query the visitors and learn a great deal from them. Most who enter a ship are taken against their will, examined, occasionally given bits of information or a short tour, then returned, often with retrograde amnesia, screen memories, and a sense of lost time. As seen in the previous case study, Leo and Mike Dworshak were also given a tour of the craft they entered, along with rudimentary explanations about how certain devices operated. Indeed, there are many common features observable in the Dworshak and Wartena cases, which could be an aspect of their proximity in both place and time.

Considering the temporal and geographic propinquity of Udo Wartena and Leo Dworshak's later encounters near Bozeman, Montana, the stated tendency for these visitors to return to the same area, the fact that they both claimed to have spoken exactly 500 languages, along with other similarities in their descriptions of the craft and men inside, it is conceivable that Wartena and Dworshak encountered the same visitors. If these were future human researchers tasked with examining changes to the ecology of this region in the mid-20th century, it is possible that the same time travelers could be seen by different people around that same time and place.

In fact, as the UFO flies, Diamond City in Confederate Gulch, where Wartena encountered these men, is only 21 miles to the northwest of Bozeman, Montana, where Dworshak commonly saw his friends throughout the '40s, '50s, and '60s. Although it could be a coincidence, it is possible that the visitors Leo Dworshak came to know identified Wartena's sluice stream as a good place to discreetly obtain water for fuel while working in this area throughout the mid-20th century.

Another correlate can be seen in how Udo Wartena, like Leo Dworshak, was told that he should not speak about the encounter since "no one would believe him at that time, but in years to come, he could tell about this experience."[120] This again speaks to the visitors' knowledge of the future, and rather precise knowledge no less, since it wouldn't be long after Wartena met this futuristic man in a remote region of southwest Montana that the entire world would suddenly become more aware of the UFO presence. Beginning with the 1947 Roswell crash, the 1952 Washington, D.C., UFO incident, the widely publicized 1961 abduction of Betty and Barney Hill, and continuing today with the formal declassification of documents, images, and videos, the UFO ethos has expanded considerably.

If the men Dworshak and Wartena encountered had come from a different planet, were observing us as part of a computer simulation, or they were from a separate timeline in a different universe, they wouldn't be expected to know what was to transpire in Earth's future, in a yet-to-be determined simulation, or in this specific timeline in our universe, respectively. Regarding the latter, because a new timeline would form as soon as these visitors arrived in our world, from that point on, no one could know what the future holds. However, when viewed in association with the Extratempestrial Model in the block universe, an ensuing awareness of UFOs is expected for those who have already seen this mysterious phenomenon become a part of their reality, as we slowly morph into them throughout our future, and their past.

Because stigma and blind dismissal of the reality of these craft remains, the man's suggestion that Wartena wait to tell of his account may mean there is still more disclosure to come, and an even broader acceptance of the reality of this phenomenon. We can't yet know what the state of UFO awareness will be in another 80+ years since Udo Wartena's encounter. But considering how much has changed since then, and how much more has been revealed in recent times, it is possible that we could be on the precipice of a global paradigm shift.

Wartena's 1976 letter to John Glenn revealed much about his experience, including a detailed account of novel energy systems and antigravity technologies that don't yet exist, or that are not yet conventionally known. Although the craft and tools of the visitors still seem magical in modern times, it is easy to understand how we may be poised to become these grey haired, pale-skinned, technologically progressed humans soliciting water from Wartena in the mountains of Montana, especially if our knowledge of physics, engineering, and material sciences continues to advance at an accelerating rate.

Udo Wartena was held in high regard throughout his life, and his family, friends, and others he knew had great respect for him.[121] There is little reason to doubt his integrity or the reality of his story. In fact, according to Warren P. Aston, who has researched Wartena and his account more thoroughly than anyone else,

The detailed and straightforward report of Udo Wartena is the most revealing, informative and totally credible of any claimed alien encounter that I have studied in some twenty years of research. There is not the slightest hint of any deception, evasion or fraud in his story, and the witness enjoyed the highest imaginable endorsement for his integrity and honesty – often given unsolicited – by those who knew him best over his lifetime.[122]

Wartena was fortunate to have received such support, considering he revealed his encounter at a time when most people were not overly open-minded or accepting of UFO experiences. Though as we continue to progress culturally, technologically, and in our awareness of these craft and the people piloting them, we may turn to reports like these for deeper insight into what has been occurring across time and space. Furthermore, acknowledging the differences, but also recognizing the commonality across accounts, may bring us closer to understanding the true origin of this mystical and mysterious phenomenon.

# Case Study 3

~

# 1957
# Antonio Villas-Boas
# São Francisco de Sales, Brazil

*I was flabbergasted, and not without good reason. The woman was stark naked, as naked as I was... moreover, she was beautiful, though of a different type from the women I had known.*[123]

— Antonio Villas-Boas

One of the best known, most credible, and sexiest accounts of an early abduction event is the 1957 case of reputable Brazilian lawyer Antonio Villas-Boas. At the time of his abduction, Villas-Boas was a 23-year-old farmer, and while many abductees experience multiple visits throughout their lives, much like the Udo Wartena encounter, this was a singular event. However, on a few different occasions leading up to his abduction, Villas-Boas remembered seeing an ominous and inexplicable bright light in the sky.

He first saw the light on October 10, 1957, after everyone had gone home from a party at his house. Late that night, he opened a window to let in some fresh air and noticed a bright white light illuminating the ground beneath it. Startled, Villas-Boas awoke his brother and roommate, João, but after seeing how ambivalent he was about the strange light, Villas-Boas also decided to ignore it and return to bed. He awoke later that night to check if the light was still there, and to his astonishment, it was not only there, but it was moving toward his window. This time, his brother was more intrigued, and the two of them watched in awe as the light continued to move toward them, before it suddenly disappeared.

Four days later, at around 10:00 p.m., the two brothers saw the light again, but this time it was so bright it hurt their eyes to look at it. Despite its agonizing luminosity, Antonio Villas-Boas was curious what it was, so he began to walk closer. As he approached, the light suddenly darted away at tremendous speed toward the other end of the field. He turned and followed it, but the light zipped away from him once again. They continued this spat of cat and mouse for a while longer, until the bright light abruptly disappeared in the sky.

The following night, at approximately 1 a.m., Villas-Boaz was working alone in the field, which was common that time of year since it was often too hot to work during the day. From his tractor, he once again saw a light appear in the sky, though on that particular night it was red, as opposed to the brilliant white light he had seen throughout the previous week. Also, in contrast to the hide and seek game they played the night before, this time the light shot straight toward him and stopped about 50 meters directly overhead. According to a deposition given by Villas-Boas on February 22, 1958,

> I was able now to see for the first time that it was a strange machine, rather rounded in shape, and surrounded by little purplish lights.... On the upper part of the machine there was something which was revolving at great speed and also giving a powerful fluorescent, reddish light. At the moment when the machine reduced speed to land, this light changed to a greenish color.[124]

Villas-Boas watched in amazement as three protrusions emerged from the underside of the ship. Now frightened, he attempted to flee on his tractor, but like most vehicles during this stage of an abduction, the machine suddenly turned off. Vehicles and other electronic devices losing power could be related to the strong electromagnetic field produced in association with a UAP's propulsion system, as indicated in the previous case study. This could also be intentional, as it helps keep the abductee from escaping. It should also be noted that the tripod configuration of a UFO's landing gear is nearly universal as well, which further denotes consistency among reports, and similarities in the physical characteristics of these craft.

Realizing his tractor had been rendered moot, Villas-Boas attempted to flee on foot, but he soon felt someone grabbing his arm from behind. He was able to thwart this initial arrest but was eventually overpowered once three more oddly dressed individuals joined the effort. These beings lifted him off the ground and carried him toward the ship, which was resting on three supports approximately two meters off the ground. A door opened from the bottom of the craft and a ramp rolled out. The visitors put Villas-Boas down and pushed him up the ramp and onto the ship. Once inside, the door closed and sealed behind them, to the extent that he could no longer see a seam where the metal door had been, as if it had merged into the wall entirely.

Villas-Boas and his abductors entered a small square room, which was illuminated by lights encircling the ceiling. He was then taken to a much larger oval-shaped room, with a metal column in the center that ran from floor to ceiling, growing wider as it moved out from the middle in both directions. There was also an oddly shaped table, which was surrounded by swivel chairs with no backs. He could see the table was firmly attached to the floor, but the chairs were fixed to an adjustable ring that allowed them to be moved around the room.

The visitors forced Villas-Boas to lie down on the table while they spoke to each other in an incomprehensible language, which he described as sounding like short barks and grunts. In addition to their odd vocalizations, Villas-Boas made note of their strange attire. He described them as form-fitting grey uniforms that covered every square inch of their bodies. These uniforms were also seamlessly joined to round helmets that obscured all features of their heads, apart from their two eyes, which appeared to be covered by some type of lens.

Because of what they were wearing, Villas-Boas was unable to get a good look at the skin color and craniofacial form of his captors. However, he did note that their helmets were much taller than what a modern human would wear, suggesting their heads were larger than our own. Beyond their outsized heads, these beings walked bipedally, had two arms, two legs, two eyes, bilateral symmetry, and the same general body configuration of a modern human.

Villas-Boas also reported that their uniforms connected through tight-fitting sleeves to 5-fingered gloves. This is again indicative of shared ancestry, considering pentadactyly, meaning five digits on each limb, is a characteristic of all tetrapods here on Earth, which dates to nearly 400 million years in the past. Pentadactyly is a homologous structure and shared derived characteristic inherited from the common ancestor of all tetrapods, which just happened to have limbs with this five-digit configuration.

This common skeletal pattern among earthly animals was something Darwin noted early in his discovery of the process of evolution. He was also one of the first to comment on the fact that this singular skeletal structure—shared so widely among extant and extinct creatures on this planet—is not the best arrangement for carrying out the diverse array of activities these limbs perform, for vastly different animals, that use them across entirely different environments. Rather, he pointed out that this commonality must be the result of shared common ancestry, and these homologous structures adapted to perform tasks specific to the animals that used them. Because the beings who abducted Villas-Boas also shared this and so many other traits characteristic of earthly vertebrates, it strongly suggests they also evolved on this planet.

In addition to the traveler's one-piece uniforms that attached seamlessly to their helmets and integrated shoes, Villas-Boas remembered seeing three hoses that connected their helmets to the rest of the suit. One of these hoses terminated in the middle of their backs near the spine, and the other two attached on either side of their bodies near the ribs. We can't know for certain why the beings who abducted Villas-Boas wore these suits. However, because he was aggressively abducted on a whim, and was not subjected to a decontamination procedure upon entering the craft—as was the case with Mike and Leo Dworshak in the previous case study—these suits may have provided a sterile environment for those inside, similar to the personal protective equipment (PPE) used by modern medical professionals.

Further indication of the potential PPE-function of these suits may come from the fact that Villas-Boas was stripped naked, and his entire body was washed with a viscous, clear, odorless liquid. This liquid may have been some type of antiseptic chemical agent, particularly considering what was about to transpire. Although this is a speculative interpretation of what they were wearing and why, it is consistent with other cases where pathogen mitigation was a stated concern, like in the Dworshak case study, and with the 16-year-old boy from New Zealand, who was taken through a "waterless shower" with 20 other people. This is also intuitive if we are indeed the same biological species, since disease transmission is more common among conspecifics as discussed previously.

After he was thoroughly washed, three "men" led Villas-Boas deeper into the ship. They took a couple quick blood samples then left him alone in a smaller room. Taking in his new surroundings, Villas-Boas described seeing a large bed, which was covered in a material like that of modern-day memory foam. Villas-Boas sat down on the bed to calm his nerves, though his attempt at relaxation was short-lived, as a smoky haze soon began to fill the space, which made him feel nauseous, to the extent that he vomited in a corner of the room.

After some time had passed, the door opened again. This time, the individuals who captured and transported him around the ship were nowhere to be seen. Instead, he was surprised to see a beautiful and very human-looking woman walk into the room. She had light blond hair, blue slanted eyes, a wide face with prominent cheekbones, thin lips, a very pointy chin, and, like him, she was entirely naked.

> I was flabbergasted, and not without good reason. The woman was stark naked, as naked as I was... Moreover, she was beautiful, though of a different type from the women I had known... her hair was fair, almost white.... Her eyes were large and blue, more elongated than round, being slanted outwards... her nose was straight, without being

pointed, nor turned up, nor too big. What was different was the con-
tour of her face, for the cheekbones were very high, making the face
very wide... the face narrowed very sharply, terminating in a pointed
chin. Her lips were very thin, hardly visible. Her ears were small and
appeared no different from those of the women I know... Her body
was much more beautiful than that of any woman I have ever known
before. It was slim, with high and well-separated breasts, thin waist
and a small stomach, wide hips and large thighs.[125]

Despite the awkwardness of the situation, and the misery he had
endured thus far, Villas-Boas found himself feeling very attracted to
this woman. As he gazed across the room at her, they locked eyes. She
then walked toward him and pressed her naked body tightly against his.

This woman came towards me silently, looking at me with the expression of someone wanting something, and she embraced me suddenly
and began to rub her head from side to side against my face. At the
same time I felt her body all glued to mine and also making movements. Her skin was white (like that of the blonde women here) and,
on the arms, was covered with freckles... I began to get excited... I
think that the liquid they had rubbed on my skin was the cause of
this. They must have done it purposely. All I know is that I became
uncontrollably excited, sexually, a thing that had never happened to
me before. I ended up by forgetting everything and I caught hold of
the woman....[126]

At the close of their presumed intertemporal intercourse session,
the other individuals with whom Villas-Boas had more hostile rela-
tions reentered the room and gestured to the woman to come with
them. She got up from the bed, turned toward Villas-Boas, rubbed
her abdomen, pointed at him with a smile, then pointed up toward
the sky. At first, he took this to mean she would someday return and
whisk him away to join her and his apparent offspring on her home
planet. Though as time passed and she didn't return, he realized she

was likely just looking to become pregnant, and he happened to be the one they selected for this purpose.

After the woman was escorted away by the others in uniform, Villas-Boas was given his clothes and was taken back to the same room with the table and movable chairs. Although he was incredibly anxious when he was first abducted, Villas-Boas suddenly felt much more relaxed. In this novel state of post-coital calm, he decided to engage in some petty larceny. While the uniformed men were gathered across the room, speaking in their unintelligible language, Villas-Boas attempted to steal a small glass box that looked like a clock, considering it had marking around the outside which corresponded with the same quadrant positions of three, six, nine and twelve on our own clocks. He thought this object could help prove to himself and others that he had indeed been captured and bred onboard an alien craft. However, one of the men caught him in the act, shoved him aside, and returned the clock to the table.

After getting busted for petit theft, Villas-Boas was led back through the ship to the door he entered earlier. The men signaled for him to descend the ramp, and once Villas-Boas was back on the ground, the craft began to rise into the air. The tripod landing gear retracted into the belly of the ship, and like the door, left no indication of where it had been while extended. The ship continued to climb higher until it was approximately 30-50 meters off the ground. Villas-Boas then heard a buzzing sound, as the lights surrounding the ship grew brighter, and the disc-shaped craft began to rotate at an incredible speed. After reaching a stable brightness and speed of rotation, the craft made an abrupt movement, listed slightly to one side, then shot off like a flash of lightning into the night sky.

Checking his own earthly timepiece, Villas-Boas noted that it was approximately 5:30 a.m., meaning 4½ hours had passed since he was initially abducted. Fortunately, Villas-Boas was not married at the time, as this type of encounter is sure to cause a marital rift. He didn't develop any sexually transmitted diseases either, though he did suffer from a number of medical conditions, which included fatigue, nausea, loss of appetite, headaches, weird bruises, lesions, pain throughout his body, a burning sensation in his eyes, and perhaps most notably, radiation poisoning.

Similar symptoms are common among contactees who stand close to a UFO, especially in instances where it hovers above them, powers up, and quickly speeds away. The same occurred in both of the previous two case studies, where Udo Wartena and the Dworshak boys reported extreme fatigue and weakness after having been in close proximity to the craft as it departed. However, despite some temporary burns and discomfort, it is rare for anyone to die from these injuries, and most abductees go on to live long lives following the incident.

Because of his numerous novel medical issues, Villas-Boas made an appointment to see Dr. Olavo T. Fontes, at the National School of Medicine in Rio de Janeiro, Brazil. After hearing the incredible account of what happened, Dr. Fontes convinced Villas-Boas to go public with his story, which he did a few months later, on February 22, 1958. A thorough investigation of this case was later carried out by Gordon Creighton and the Sociedade Brasileira de Estudos Sobre Discos Voadores, which, along with the medical report compiled by Dr. Fontes, were made public approximately eight years later.[127]

After going public with his account, Villas-Boas began to receive international attention, which kicked up considerably in January 1965, when *Flying Saucer Review* published a story about this incident in the United States. The Brazilian magazine *O Cruzeiro* also ran a feature article about Villas-Boas's encounter, though it received less attention in Brazil than it did abroad. This was seen as a blessing to Villas-Boas. As a respected lawyer who got married and had children that stayed in his own time, he was content to live out the rest of his life without the burden of being in the public eye.

While surely strange, this encounter would also be expected to garner high marks on J. Allen Hynek's *Probability Scale*,[128] which rates on a scale from one to ten how reliable and trustworthy the witnesses are. This is partly because Villas-Boas was a well-respected and successful attorney of sound mind and body, who vehemently stood behind his claim, and who could consistently recount the specifics of this encounter until his death in 1991.[129] [130] Additionally, the details Villas-Boas divulged are more reliable because he was able to retain conscious memories of the abduction, since his memories were never erased or replaced with screen memories prior to departing the craft, as is common in other abduction events.

Numerous aspects of Villas-Boas's account suggest these individuals were human, and likely humans from the not-too-distant future. Their temporal proximity is indicated by Villas-Boas's description of the woman that seduced him, who had only slightly more derived features, which are entirely consistent with traits delineating the hominin clade. Additionally, they both possessed the requisite anatomy for having sex with each other, and though Brazil has less stringent rules against bestiality, there are no indications that Villas-Boas copulated with another species.

It is patently possible to copulate with any variety of animals, though we are not usually attracted to ones different from ourselves, regardless of how much aphrodisiac, antiseptic, viscous, clear, odorless liquid is rubbed on our bodies. Additionally, beyond mere physical attraction, or the functional capacity for copulation using projecting phalluses and recessed vaginas which lifeforms who evolved on other planets may not have, the basic ability for two organisms to reproduce viable offspring has long been the gold standard used to determine whether they are the same species.

Simply stated, the biological species concept (BSC) asserts that if two separate organisms can mate, reproduce, and produce viable offspring—meaning their offspring are also able to reproduce—then they are considered the same species. The most common example involves the mating of a donkey and a horse, which results in a mule. However, mules are always infertile, which makes the horse and donkey two separate species using the BSC criteria. If there is truth to the plethora of reported instances of gamete, zygote, and fetus extraction, as well as sex, interbreeding, hybridization, and the production of viable offspring in any form, then we and these visitors are not just similar due to shared ancestry, but, by definition, we are the same species entirely.

An emphasis on gamete procurement is apparent in that abductees are most often healthy, under the age of 50, and reproductively viable. The importance of workable gametes can also be seen in an abduction where a man was rejected by "the aliens" because he had previously undergone a vasectomy.[131] This clearly was not the case with Antonio Villas-Boas, since he went on to sire offspring in later life, and according to Gordon Creighton, he was a handsome, brown-skinned man, who was "evidently a Caboclo," the term used to describe someone of Portuguese and Amerindian descent.[132] In fact, this aspect of Villas-Boas's genetics may have made him more attractive to these visitors, if they were seeking to add greater genetic variation to a stagnant future human gene pool.[133]

We cannot know why these travelers chose Villas-Boas, but all indications are it had something to do with reproduction. The fact that they took blood samples prior to the coital act may well have been to assess Villas-Boas's value as a sperm donor. Through a simple blood draw, his DNA could be analyzed to look for heritable defects, and a wealth of other information about his health and wellbeing could give insight into his worth as a baby daddy. As with modern sperm banks, age, intellect, health, and physical appearance are all taken into consideration when choosing a potential donor.

The plethora of reports of gamete, zygote, and fetus extraction, as well as those involving concurrent coitus, as seen with Villas-Boas and in subsequent case studies, suggests we and these visitors share the same *Homo sapiens sapiens* species designation. If we are indeed the same species, and we are able to produce viable offspring with our time-traveling human descendants, it raises the equally important question: Why? It is certainly in our nature to want to have sex, and we have a long history of getting it on with those both like and unlike ourselves. This was clear during colonization, missionization, military conquest, and in instances of interbreeding between modern humans and the Neanderthals prior to the latter's extinction. However, other factors beyond an insatiable appetite for sex might also be at play.

Cross-temporal reproductive tissue sampling, in vitro fertilization, and sexual intercourse, if true, could have immense implications for the genetic future of our evolutionary lineage. Efforts to manage reproduction and the future human gene pool could help explain the intense focus on gametes in abduction reports, particularly if past and current trends in population genetics persist into the future. Instead of thinking of this aspect of abductions in the context of what they may be doing to or for us, perhaps we should consider what we might be providing them, and how past genes may help mitigate genetic issues in the future.

Throughout hominin history, our ancestors inhabited only a small part of the vast expanse of dry land on this planet. Though beginning around 2 million years ago, when *Homo erectus* first migrated out of Africa, we began to occupy a larger portion of the Old World. Over time, as we continued to saturate these previously unpopulated parcels, voyaging into what would become the Americas around 20,000 to 30,000 years ago, humans came to inhabit nearly every landmass on planet Earth. Beginning around 1,000 years ago with Viking explorers, and more overtly around 500 years ago with European colonialism, a trend toward large-scale homogenization of the human gene pool was set in motion. Today, with the ability to hop on an airplane and make a baby with anyone anywhere in the world in under 30 hours, we continue to chip away at long-standing localized gene variants, as we trend toward becoming one massive interbreeding intercontinental population.

Large-scale homogenization of the human genome could present problems if this trend continues, as it is likely to do. Most evident is the degradation of genetic variation, which is vital to maintaining the adaptability and survivability of any organism, as per the laws of evolution. For example, decreased genetic variation in the human leukocyte antigen system (HLA) that encodes the major histocompatibility complex (MHC), which together form the backbone of our immune system, would make us more susceptible to disease. These critical components of our immune system have evolved to be one of the most variable parts of our genome, as this adaptability helps protect us from a vast array of deadly pathogens.

However, if past and current demographic and geographic trends persist, and we continue to move toward large-scale genetic homogenization, we may ultimately be forced to look elsewhere, or more aptly elsewhen, for novel gene variants. Because we cannot simply go to a different planet to sample gametes from other lifeforms—since extraterrestrial organisms wouldn't be expected to share the same molecular coding system—taking a dip into the gene pool of the past may be the only viable option for bolstering future human genetic variation, in an effort to stave off a state of global incest. It is also possible we may someday attempt to alter our own genome and that something goes horribly wrong in the process. Given our curious nature and the accelerating rate of technological change, we may eventually attempt to manipulate the human genome in some way, whether it be to eliminate diseases, to make designer babies, or for some other reason.

We have vastly expanded our ability to alter genes in recent times, and most notably since 2012, when the Nobel Prize-winning scientists Jennifer Doudna and Emmanuelle Charpentier published an article demonstrating how to harness the natural CRISPR-Cas9 system to be used as a tool to cut any DNA strand in a test tube.[134][135] Yet, because of off-target effects, where the CRISPR system binds to and edits the wrong gene sequence, along with the looming fear that even "somatic cell editing" could cause heritable effects if the gene editors travel to reproductive organs and inadvertently affect sperm and egg, we could be looking at widespread millennia-long effects, which would be incredibly difficult to contain and correct.

Recently, the world was shown just how quickly things can go wrong. He Jiankui, former researcher at the Southern University of Science and Technology, and current prisoner serving a three-year sentence for "illegal medical practices," was attempting to alter the CCR5 genes of two Chinese children. He was attempting to convey the same immunity to HIV that about 1 percent of Northern European-descended individuals have. However, Jiankui botched the procedure in these two children, who ended up with altered and heritable versions of the CCR5 gene, which are entirely new to the human genome.[136][137]

He Jiankui broke laws, forged documents, failed to perform adequate safety test measures, and misled the parents of these children about potential risks. He also accidentally endowed the children with versions of the CCR5 gene that are entirely new, and for at least one of them, that don't provide protection against HIV. These novel gene variants, which may not exist anywhere else in the global human genome, could have negative effects we don't yet comprehend.

Although this was the first known attempt at performing gene editing on humans, and the research was wrought with ineptness, fraud, and deception, it is a stark reminder of the dangers of "playing god." Yet we continue to tinker. Recently, a joint research team from China and the United States created and grew the world's first part-human-monkey embryo, which hybridized a human and a crab-eating macaque. Although it was only grown in a test tube for 20 days, this human-monkey chimera embryo blazed a new path, while raising concerns about legal and ethical issues in the future of gene editing.[138]

Although "designer babies" are still illegal in most countries, the prospect of prolonging life with lab-grown organs, or saving a sick child, may cause us to overlook potential risks associated with gametic and somatic cell editing. It is easy to admonish this research, and particularly considering how poorly our first attempt at human gene editing went. However, if someone's child is sick or dying, or someone is in desperate need of an organ that could be grown in a lab through the mechanism of gene editing, it becomes harder to criticize these practices. There are success stories as well. For instance, a family from Brooklyn, New York, recently raised millions of dollars to get experimental gene therapy for their child, which involved drilling bore holes into the boy's skull and injecting trillions of virus particles that carried the correct version of a gene he was missing.[139]

Our innate drive to survive, and instinctive desire to help our children at any cost, may provide enough of a benefit that we turn a blind eye to the risks of genome editing and gene therapy. And if we do decide the benefits outweigh the costs, but we happen to get something wrong, it could result in numerous irreversible effects, and potentially impact human reproduction in the future. Furthermore, if this were to occur, it could force us to seek wild-type genes from the only place they still exist: the human past.

Further future fertility issues may also arise due to the modern practice of in vitro fertilization and other fertility treatments. While these are beneficial for the couple attempting to become pregnant, the practice could have deleterious effects for the human population as a whole since we are helping those who have natural difficulties reproducing to reproduce. In an evolutionary context, this increases the frequency of what would otherwise be deleterious genes outside our culturally constructed environment, as natural selection would quickly act to remove any heritable trait that reduces reproductive fitness. However, with fertility interventions we are increasing the frequency of genes that wouldn't normally be present in a natural environment, which could affect human reproductive viability in the future.

Considered in association with dominant trends toward lower birthrates in most countries, dropping sperm counts in the Western World, and rapidly declining fertility rates for the whole of humanity, which Dr. Shanna Swan, a professor of environmental medicine and public health attributes to the recent flood of chemicals and plastics in our environment,[140] widespread reports of gamete extraction in abduction cases could potentially be our distant descendants' own attempt at self-preservation.

If something were to go awry with human genome editing and it negatively impacted our future fertility and fecundity, seeking unadulterated genes from past groups may be the best option for fixing mistakes and helping alleviate problems caused by our own inquisitiveness, botched attempts at combating disease, or our age-old desire to create the perfect human specimen. Of course, until we can ask why they do it, there is no way of knowing what purpose this gamete extraction serves, but given its ubiquity in abduction encounters, clearly there is something about our DNA that is of utmost importance to these visitors.

# Case Study 4

~

# 1961
# Betty and Barney Hill
# New Hampshire, USA

*One person looks friendly and he's looking at me, and he's smiling. His face is round,*
*I think of a red head Irishman... His eyes were slanted, but not like a Chinese.* [141]
*Oh, those eyes. They're in my brain.* [142]

– BARNEY HILL

One of the first highly publicized UFO abductions in the United States, which is also representative of the way these incidents typically unfold, took place in a rural area of New Hampshire in 1961. This incident involved Betty Hill, who was a 41-year-old social worker, and her husband Barney Hill, who was 39 years old at the time, worked for the US Postal Service, and sat on the board of their local civil rights commission. According to their testimony, on September 19, 1961, after taking a vacation to Montreal and Niagara Falls in Canada, the two were driving home to Portsmouth, New Hampshire, along US Route 3. A little after 10:00 p.m., approximately three miles south of Lancaster, NH, Barney saw something he initially thought was a shooting star—at least until this bright light started moving erratically in the night sky, as opposed to fading out like a meteor streaking across the horizon. [143]

Nearing North Woodstock, the odd light began to move even more erratically, so Barney stopped the car to get a better look through his binoculars. As he did, the object abruptly changed course and started heading toward them. [144] Alarmed, the Hills began driving again.

101

However, it rapidly caught up and descended from the sky in front of their car, which stalled as it approached this large glowing object that now blocked the road ahead. As seen in the previous case study, this also happened to Antonio Villas-Boas, where his tractor suddenly turned off as he attempted to flee a similar situation.

Once the light descended and stopped in front of the Hills' car, they could see it had a physical form, which Barney described as looking like a huge pancake. Peering through his binoculars again, Barney could see 8 to 11 humanoid figures looking back at him from inside the craft. Then, all but one of them moved out of view, and the individual who remained began speaking to Barney, telepathically, in English, telling him to "keep looking and that no harm would be done to you."[145]

Barney remembered hearing a loud buzzing sound that filled the inside of their vehicle, and which put the couple into a trance-like state of dulled perception. His next conscious memory was of hearing a series of beeps and feeling a sense of confusion. Betty and Barney became even more perplexed when they realized they were now near Ashland, NH, approximately 35 miles farther down Route 3 from Woodstock, where they had initially stopped. Even stranger, the couple noticed it was now two hours later than when they pulled over to look at the odd light in the sky. The two of them also had the sense that something extraordinary just happened, though they were unable to recall what took place over the previous two hours of lost time.[146]

Upon returning home, each of them took a long shower and attempted to make sense of this missing time, and how their car had moved such a long distance from where they first stopped. Barney also reported having a strong urge to examine his genitals, and Betty noticed that her dress was torn, her shoes were scuffed, and there was an unexplainable pink powder on her clothes. The next morning, they noticed small concentric circles on the trunk of their car that had not been there previously, and when they put a compass close to the circles it spun wildly, but returned to normal when moved away from the car.[147] Since a compass works by detecting and responding to magnetic fields, this occurrence, which is also seen in association with crop circles and other places where UFOs were reported to have been, it again indicates the importance of the electromagnetic force as an aspect of the antigravity propulsion system and potential spacetime manipulating abilities of these craft.

Taking the advice of her sister Janet, the next day Betty called the nearby Pease Air Force Base to report what happened to them the previous night. She ended up speaking with Major Paul W. Henderson, who told her "The UFO was also confirmed by our radar."[148] Soon after, Betty began having vivid dreams about the encounter, which tended to focus on the beings who abducted them. Seeking clarity and an end to the nightmares, the Hills contacted Dr. Benjamin Simon, a well-regarded psychiatrist, neurologist, and professional hypnotherapist in Boston, Massachusetts.

The Hills had their first visit with Dr. Simon on December 14, 1963, about two years and three months after their abduction.[149] Dr. Simon conducted separate sessions with Barney and Betty, and found both had similar accounts, with only slight differences in their recollection of events. Although he would not allow himself to "believe" in UFOs, Dr. Simon concluded that some traumatic event did indeed take place, and that the Hills were not fabricating the story.[150] However, he noted some minor distortions of whatever this event may have been, and postulated that Barney's abduction story may have been a fantasy created from Betty's dreams.[151] Nonetheless, through these hypnosis sessions, the Hills managed to achieve some sense of closure, and all involved saw them as productive.[152]

From her conscious, and later subconscious, memory, Betty described the beings as humanoid, standing approximately five and a half feet tall, with bald heads, large eyes, small ears, small noses, and greyish skin.[153] Compared to the humans Udo Wartena and the Dworshak boys saw, and the one Villas-Boas slept with, the traits Betty Hill described are indicative of what we might expect to see in the craniofacial morphology of our more distant human descendants. For instance, Leo Dworshak and Udo Wartena both described interacting with individuals who possessed technology far beyond our own but whose physiological form was entirely consistent with that of modern humans. The woman Villas-Boas had sex with was also described as human, but with a slightly higher forehead and larger eyes. However, the "humanoids" described by Betty and Barney Hill possessed a suite of characteristics most commonly associated with the archetypal "grey aliens," which likely represent a more evolved hominin grade.

In fact, the Betty and Barney Hill case represents one of the first formal descriptions of these so-called Greys, though encounters between past people and these presumably more distant future people are common. From the Dr. Edgar Mitchell Foundation FREE study mentioned previously, of the 708 individuals surveyed who claim to have encountered beings onboard a craft, those described as "human-looking" (48%) were the most reported form, followed closely by the "short greys" (45%) then the "tall greys" (33%). Again, based on enduring morphological trends throughout hominin history, the more derived characteristics of these big-headed, large-eyed, small-faced, grey-skinned beings suggests they are also human, just from a more distant point in our evolutionary future.

Through hypnotic regression, Betty was also able to recall some aspects of the craft the travelers arrived in, which she described as disc-shaped and metallic in appearance. Betty also remembered that while she was in a trance-like state, both her and Barney were taken inside, separated, and told they were going to be examined. Shortly thereafter, Betty recalled that a different "man" entered the room, who she referred to as "the examiner."

This man told Betty they were going to conduct a few tests to look for differences between her and them. He then examined her eyes, ears, mouth, throat, arms, legs, hands, and took some fingernail trimmings and skin scrapings from her leg.[154] Additionally, and as a further indication of the future importance of past genes and gametes to these travelers, Betty had a long needle inserted into her abdomen and was told they were checking to see if she was pregnant. Later, Barney reluctantly acknowledged that a semen sample had been taken from him during the abduction.

Betty noted that the examiner had a calm demeanor and spoke to her in English. However, she recalled that he did not have a complete mastery of the language, as it was broken English that was harder for her to understand compared to the other individuals aboard. As discussed previously in the Leo Dworshak and Udo Wartena case studies, this dichotomy in who does the talking suggests some sort of occupational specialization exists among the various individuals aboard.

In the case of Betty Hill, "the examiner" was likely brought along solely to perform biomedical examinations, while others on the ship executed the vital roles of pilot, engineer, cook, kidnapper, linguist, and cross-cultural ambassador. These latter positions would require a better mastery of the language spoken in a specific time and place to help ensure meaningful information exchange and a safer abduction and release of the test subjects. In this way, the phonological ineptness of the medical examiner could be mitigated by his linguistically literate colleagues, whose more interactive role would require they first attain some level of expertise in the language and culture of mid-20th century America.

In addition to the many common physical and technological traits shared among our ancestors, ourselves, and our presumed future human descendants, the ease with which the visitors can communicate with us, both telepathically and using conventional vocalizations, is a further testament to our shared ancestry. As mentioned previously, the Dr. Edgar Mitchell FREE study showed that communication took place in the native language of 75% of survey respondents.[155] The Villas-Boas abduction represents one of the rarer cases where no communication occurred, save for some simple hand gestures and the intertemporal language of love. This case may have been more about sexual experimentation or obtaining a direct deposit of DNA, as opposed to collecting or disseminating information, which would require a skosh of linguistic proficiency.

The relative ease with which communication takes place across cases is also remarkable considering we are not likely to still speak any of our contemporary languages in the distant future. This is indicated by the rapid rate of linguistic evolution, and because abductees often describe seeing strange symbols and writing on, in, and around these ships. Even so, if no modern languages are spoken once our descendants begin to visit the past, they may be able to look back through historic records and other forms of preservable media to learn the language of certain cultures at specific times, which is a luxury that may not be available to extraterrestrial visitors.

It would be convenient to choose only those case studies that fully conform to the ETM, or to dismiss parts of individual accounts that do not cleanly fit the model. However, this would not provide an accurate representation of what is going on. Rather, it is necessary to address all aspects of an encounter, to develop broader knowledge of the phenomenon, and to help assess which model best fits the description of events. Although a multitude of close encounters scream time travel, in some cases, the abductees are told that the visitors came from a different solar system, or in the case of Leo and Mike Dworshak, from an entirely different galaxy. It is exceedingly improbable that an extraterrestrial race could ever find us or travel here from a distant galaxy, considering the tremendous space between, though this proclamation should be considered, as should all others, regardless of how well or poorly they conform to a particular point of view.

This common pitfall of ufology, which applies to the investigation of both conventional and mysterious phenomena, was eloquently stated in a 1990 article by Michael D Swords. Swords was a professor of natural sciences at Western Michigan University, was editor of the *Journal of UFO Studies*, and was on the board of directors for the Center for UFO Studies (CUFOS). These positions, along with numerous insightful publications written about various other topics related to the phenomenon, have made him a vital contributor to our ever-expanding knowledge of UFOs. In his 1990 article titled: "UFOs as Time Travelers," Swords states,

> The range of UFO phenomena is interesting, to say the least. Even the archskeptics agreed to that. And these phenomena are so odd as

to demand extraordinary, deep and interdisciplinary research. Some types of reports differ so wildly from one another that they cry out for different explanatory schemes. And yet many UFO commentators keep getting caught in the trap of picking a single favorite idea and ferociously applying it to every case that crosses their path. And woe to those who see it otherwise.[156]

This is a valid critique of ufology, which applies to most areas of inquiry, and especially those with numerous unknowns. Academics are also guilty of dogma and relentlessly defending a specific point of view, and are also occasionally guilty of confirmation bias, which involves only looking for evidence that supports preconceived notions of the way things are. Like any study, it is important to be wary of both selection bias and confirmation bias while investigating abductee experiences in the context of the Extratempestrial Model. This is a part of why I include statements, and entire case studies, which do not fully conform to the ETM, including the Betty and Barney Hill abduction. In the same 1990 article, "UFOs as Time Travelers," which offers a critical approach to the Time-Travel Model, Swords states,

> I cannot accept the time hypothesis as a neat solution to the abduction phenomenon for this reason: I believe it would be quite difficult to argue that abductions really happen without including Betty and Barney Hill among them. And I believe it would be awkward to accept the Hills story and arbitrarily drop out any of the key details (for example the star map).[157]

A controversial component of the Betty and Barney Hill encounter involves a star map Betty claims she was shown while onboard the ship. The map was reportedly presented to her in three dimensions, similar to a holographic projection. It was approximately three feet wide by two feet tall, was composed of various sized dots that represented stars, and had lines drawn between and among these stars. According to Betty, one of the visitors asked her "Where are you on the map?" to which she replied, "I don't know."[158] This is a relatively strange question for both extraterrestrials and extratempestrials, considering most mid-20th century Earthlings were largely unaware of the location of specific stars in our galaxy.

In 1964, under post-hypnotic suggestion with Dr. Benjamin Simon, Betty was asked to draw what she could remember of the star map. She was meant to sketch it without paying attention to what she was drawing, with the hope that this flow state drawing procedure would allow her subconscious mind to bring out a more accurate depiction of the star map she recalled seeing. However, because she made two revisions to the map, erasing a couple sections as she drew, her conscious mind was in control for at least part of the time. In the end, the two-dimensional representation of the three-dimensional star map she reported seeing consisted of approximately 12 dots, connected by lines, and with a distinctive triangle shape toward the left side of the image. Because there was no concentration of stars to represent the galactic plane of the Milky Way, it was assumed that this was depicting stars in a localized region of space.

In 1968, after reading J.G. Fuller's book about the Hills' abduction titled *Interrupted Journey*,[159] an elementary school teacher and amateur astronomer named Marjorie Fish became interested in the star map aspect of Betty's account. Using beads, thread, and data on stellar distances published in the 1969 edition of the *Gliese Catalog of Nearby Stars*, Fish made a three-dimensional model, attempting to identify a group of stars that might match the drawing Betty made under hypnosis. Over the next five years, Fish examined numerous star clusters from different vantage points and concluded that the best match was the binary star system of Zeta Reticuli, in the southern constellation of Reticulum.

Fish went on to solicit feedback from professional astronomers about her conclusion, seeking peer reviewers to assess how well Betty's star map coincided with the Zeta Reticuli double-star system. Although there was occasional support, most disagreed with the assessment. This included Carl Sagan, who pointed out that the star map was really nothing more than a random alignment of stochastic points, and that without lines drawn between these stars to represent true distances among them, Betty Hill's star map bore little resemblance to the true position of stars in the Zeta Reticuli cluster.[160]

Betty's star map is also problematic because it was drawn from memory, under hypnosis, more than two years after the event. Furthermore, because there are 100 thousand million stars in the Milky Way galaxy alone, scanning for a specific pattern of stars is likely to result in finding that pattern somewhere, but due to chance alone. This is akin to data mining, or looking for patterns in large databases. Because there are so many stars, there is a high probability that even monkeys with typewriters putting random periods across a page will eventually, and often, create a similar pattern to a group of stars somewhere in the galaxy.

Unequivocal rejection of Marjorie Fish's interpretation of Betty Hill's star map came with the eventual release of new astronomical data that revised previous stellar distance estimates. More specifically, parallax observations made by the Hipparchus satellite in the early 1990s provided more accurate distance measurements between and among over 100,000 stars.[161] Some of these stars were those used in Fish's elucidation of Betty's map, which were now considered to be much farther away than previously thought. Furthermore, some of the stars Fish counted as being potentially habitable were no longer assumed to be such, once astronomical and astrobiological tools and technologies began to improve. Considering these developments, Marjorie Fish herself issued a public statement rejecting her earlier hypothesis that the group of stars drawn by Betty Hill represented the binary star system of Zeta Reticuli.[162]

Betty may have been shown a star map by people who, despite their similarity to us, were indeed from a distant star system. Though it is also possible that Betty was simply told this because at that time, much like today, we struggled with complex notions of time and time travel. Claiming space travel may have been the easier option, especially since it was already the dominant view of UFOs in the early 1960s.

In the same way we should not dismiss Betty's star map in examining the time-travel model, we should also recognize that everything about the ship, technology, language, the way the abduction and examination played out, and the hominin form of these visitors, is consistent with other abduction accounts, which, like the Hills' report, most commonly describe human or humanlike beings. As discussed earlier, we wouldn't expect humans, or anything remotely similar to a hominin, to evolve independently on a separate planet with different chemical, gravitational, solar, environmental, and ecological conditions. Furthermore, it is incredibly implausible that the same hominin form would evolve independently on multiple different planets at the same time.

Because there is so much consistency across reports regarding the size and shape of these craft, the form and function of the technology used, and the physical description of the visitors themselves, it seems safe to assume a common origin for most cases. By comparison, if these beings evolved on different planets in the various places people claim the visitors say they come from (i.e., Zeta Reticuli, The Pleiades, Nibiru, etc.), we would expect to see far more variation in their technology and morphological form, and we would not expect to see humans so often. Of course, because some variation is observable across cases, it is possible that a percentage of these beings originated elsewhere in the galaxy, universe, or multiverse. However, because most are described as human, or humans with more evolved features, they likely share the same spatial origination point here on Earth but are spread across different periods of the proximate and more distant future.

In the above section, Dr. Michael D. Swords highlights the importance of considering all available evidence in conducting UFO research, and he acknowledges the common problem of selection and confirmation bias, or "cherry picking" evidence in support of an idea, while ignoring what does not neatly fit the model. In his 1990 article, "UFOs as Time Travelers," Swords invokes the Betty Hill star map as support for the Extraterrestrial Hypothesis and evidence against the Extratempestrial Model, since Betty claims her captors told her they were not only from outer space, but from a very specific place in it. To expand on his most recently cited quote above,

If one accepts the star map, then the Zeta Reticuli argument is as good as any yet offered; but even if you don't accept the exact star designations, the map would indicate an extraterrestrial origin of the visitors.[163]

Swords states that if one accepts the reality of Betty Hill's star map then they must also accept the Extraterrestrial Hypothesis. However, this puts far too much weight behind one small part of one individual account, which was only brought about through hypnosis over two years after the abduction. Additionally, because she and Barney were among the first abductees who went public with their experience, this outer space recollection may have been a false memory, since a space-alien explanation was one of the only available interpretations of that time.

It is also tenuous to argue that "even if this particular star map is wrong, because Betty was told they were from outer space, they must have come from outer space." Because Zeta Reticuli is over 39 light years away, it is not a likely origination point for extraterrestrial visitors, but regardless of where these travelers claimed to have come from, the star map represents a single datapoint conjured from the muddled memory of just one individual. Furthermore, there are other abductees who claim to have encountered beings that looked the same and arrived in the same type of craft as what the Hills saw, but these abductees were told by their captors that they were humans from the future. So which accounts do we believe, and which do we awkwardly and arbitrarily drop from the narrative?

Dr. Swords argues that any consideration of the time-travel model is only valid if it also takes into consideration the Betty and Barney Hill account. While I agree, to state that this one small part of the Hills' experience makes the Zeta Reticuli theory as good as any, means dismissing all other available information in favor of this one small data point. In science, we never base the validity of a model on one piece of information, and regarding this case in particular, we should not judge the legitimacy of the time-travel theory solely on something as tenuous as a hypnosis-induced memory. Betty's recollection of being shown a star map should undoubtedly be considered in any holistic analysis of the Extratempestrial Model, but it cannot be invoked as the only evidence for or against it.

I have great respect for Dr. Swords, particularly after recently learning how thick one's skin must be to work in academia while also seriously researching UFOs. However, I find this argument to be somewhat simplistic, as it ignores the mass of evidence in support of the ETM. Evidence which Swords himself laid out so eloquently only five years earlier in a 1985 article published in the *MUFON UFO Journal* titled "Ufonauts: *Homo sapiens* of the Future?"

Naturally, I was delighted when a fellow scientist and friend of Dr. Swords sent me copies of the above two articles, especially after seeing how similar our arguments were, and particularly those related to long-term trends in hominin evolution. While outwardly critical of the time-travel hypothesis, Dr. Swords's 1985 article actually provides a lot of support for it. This includes an entire section on neoteny, and specifically, persistent trends toward increased paedomorphosis in hominin evolution.

As I argued extensively in my book, *Identified Flying Objects*, this shift toward the retention of childlike features could help explain much of the craniofacial and postcranial morphology of these visitors, which I dubbed *extratempestrials* and he referred to as *UFOnauts*. Upon reading these articles, I was surprised they were written as a criticism of the ETM, considering the evidence put forth in favor of it was stronger than the arguments against. This is apparent in the portion of the article subtitled, "What does the Neoteny Theory explain about the 'ufonauts,'" where Swords lists 13 arguments in support of the time-travel model, but only 2 arguments against it. Furthermore, neither of the two critiques are entirely valid.

1. How in the world do you travel in time?, and is it even imaginable in a rational universe?
2. This theory is essentially post hoc, and those few things which it might predict are things which are likely never to be tested.[164]

To the first point, although some critics have argued against the reality of backward time travel, most physicists agree there is nothing in the laws of physics that prohibits it. Additionally, given our long track record of accelerating cultural and technological progress, if there is nothing that disallows backward time travel, once we have the right materials, technology, knowledge, and a large enough energy source to power this type of craft, we are sure to build one.

A lot has also changed since 1985 regarding our knowledge of how time travel to the past might take place. For instance, a paper by Earman et al. (2009) titled "Do the Laws of Physics Forbid the Operation of Time Machines?" used a broad approach rooted in physics, history, and philosophy to examine whether backward time travel is in fact *impossible*. This review paper scrutinized the vast amount of literature concerning time-travel research, with a specific focus on more critical studies claiming that travel to the past is prohibited.

These included more skeptical approaches like Stephen Hawking's Chronology Protection Conjecture, which is the idea that the laws of physics prevent time travel for macroscopic objects as a result of perceived causality violations.[165] These researchers also considered other disparaging studies of time machines under classical general relativity, semi-classical quantum gravity, quantum field theory on curved spacetime, and Euclidean quantum gravity.[166] The results of this research, as well as an earlier investigation by Earman (1995),[167] demonstrated that these anti-time travel studies, including Hawking's Chronology Protection Conjecture, do not preclude time travel to the past.

> Our verdict on the question of our title (*Do the Laws of Physics Forbid the Operation of Time Machines?*) is that no result of sufficient generality to underwrite a confident 'yes' has been proven.[168]

Swords's second point is also not supported. The ETM is not a post hoc theory based on fallacious assumptions. Rather, it is supported by tangible trends observable throughout long periods of the hominin past, which involves only one assumption: that humans will continue to exist in the future. However, the testability of the model does not hinge on this assumption, considering the extermination of humanity would also allow the model to be tested, and falsified, even if there is no one left to know.

As mentioned in chapter three, the most critical component of a scientific hypothesis is that it must be testable and falsifiable, and though it may seem counterintuitive, the current proposed time-travel model does adhere to this requirement. Without making any assumptions about the future of our species, if we continue to exist, whether it is on this planet or elsewhere, we will eventually know whether we were in fact the ones traveling back through time. However, it is also possible that we will not have to wait that long. For if we are destined to eventually become the visitors observed now and in the past, we would expect to learn of this imminent inevitability long before the creation of any actual time machine, at whatever point in the future our intertemporal or interdimensional descendants wish to inform us of this ensuing reality.

# Case Study 5

◦‿◦

# 1973
# Charles Hickson & Calvin Parker
# Mississippi, USA

*They gave a thorough, I mean a thorough, examination of me,*
*just like any doctor would.[169]*

- CALVIN PARKER JR.

L ike most authors of books, articles, and other written works that
are difficult to change once they go to print, shortly after publishing
*Identified Flying Objects*, I began to think of numerous things I wished
I had included in it. This tends to be the case with most creative pursuits, where final publication gives way to consternation about what was
erroneously added to, or omitted from, a music album, 3D model, or a
work of art, for example. Despite thinking about this time-travel theory
for most of my life, acquiring a PhD in a field that would allow me to
dive deeper into the science behind it, and after spending seven years
researching and writing the book, some seemingly obvious omissions
emerged.

In addition to overlooking intertemporal disease transmission, as
discussed in the Dworshak and Villas-Boas case studies, an important
aspect of the phenomenon I did not give proper attention to is the role
that artificial intelligence (AI) is likely to play in the human future. AI is
simply the capability of a machine to imitate intelligent human behaviors, and it is rapidly becoming an integral aspect of our modern lives.
For instance, AI is currently used in surveillance and security, virtual

assistants or "chatbots," warehousing and supply chain logistics, weather forecasting, sports analytics, robotics, self-driving cars, and in numerous other established and budding industries.[170] [171] With machine learning and an adept human skillset, there are many ways AI can contribute to our advancement as a species. As such, we may expect the results of continued research and development in artificial intelligence and robotics to be seen in association with UFOs, if these are indeed our future human descendants coming back through time to visit and study their own past.

One aspect of artificial intelligence I did mention in my first book is that the safety, uncertainty, and logistical difficulties involved with developing and testing time-travel machinery may require AI, as this could be a difficult and dangerous pursuit early in the process. For instance, how do we gauge just how much of which parameters are required to safely send someone or something to the intended time period? How do we measure the efficacy of this temporal displacement, particularly if the device malfunctions and does not return to its original position in spacetime? It is better to lose a preprogrammed droid with machine learning capabilities than a human with family and friends. With this in mind, early tests may require that we first have a firm grasp on how to send, then return back to its original time of departure, an AI automaton. This way, the results of a roundtrip voyage could be thoroughly analyzed, long in advance of any attempt at sending humans back through time.

Other tasks performed in the past may also be better suited for intelligent machines, such as those related to reconnaissance, data collection, or to minimize potential risks to future human researchers. There are indications of artificial intelligence being used in UFO reports for things like scouting, navigation, during biomedical exams, and in various other capacities. However, there are few instances where this technology could be of greater use than in the actual abduction process itself, considering how dangerous it would be to kidnap easily agitated past humans who are unaware of what is happening, who is taking them, and what their intentions are. A sturdy droid tasked with carrying out the initial abduction might be an asset.

This technology would also be of use to our more proximate descendants if they had not yet developed mind control and the ability to make people fall asleep for easier capture, like what we commonly see with the more paedomorphic greys, whose technology and physical form suggests they come from a more distant point in the future. The role of kidnapping panicked people, sedating them, and bringing them onto the ship may be best carried out by intelligent self-directed machines, most notably when the target is sizable, awake, and terrified of what is happening to them. The 1973 abduction of Charles Hickson and Calvin Parker stands out as a potential example of this exact situation.

At the time of their encounter, Calvin Parker was 19 years old, and Charles Hickson was 42. The two men worked together at Walker's Shipyard and shared the same hometown of Gautier, Mississippi. At around nine in the evening on the night of October 11, 1973, while fishing on the Pascagoula River in the southern US state of Mississippi, the men suddenly heard a buzzing sound behind them. As they turned around to see what it was, they were shocked to see a large, glowing, egg-shaped object hovering about a meter off the ground, and only about 10-15 meters away. They described it as having a dome on the top and blue lights shining down from the front of the craft.

A door opened on the underside of the ship and three strange "beings" emerged from it. Although they appeared to have what resembled legs, they were not walking. Instead, these entities hovered and began floating across the surface of the river toward the two men. Later that night, in a recorded interview conducted by Sheriff Fred Diamond and Captain Glen Ryder, which took place around eleven o'clock at night at the local sheriff's office, Hickson and Parker provided more detail about these odd entities.

In the recording, the men described these things as standing approximately five feet tall, with bullet-shaped heads, no necks, a small slit for a mouth, and a few conical triangle-shaped objects sticking out from where their ears would have been, which Hickson compared to antennas. Parker and Hickson also stated that they had grey, wrinkly, elephant-like skin, round feet, no eyes, and claw-like hands.[172] According to a 2002 interview with Charles Hickson,

> All of a sudden, these three things began coming out of that door. They looked like they had elephant skin. Wrinkled. Real wrinkled. And triangle shaped ears that had to be some sort of antennas. These things were robots. They seemed to come right out of that beam of light. They never touched the ground. They moved right out there beside me and Calvin.[173]

In addition to Charles Hickson referring to these entities as robots, in a 2019 interview with *Sun Herald* reporter Karen Nelson, Calvin Parker says something similar, calling them "mechanical things," while also noting that there was a "female" onboard who never stepped out of the craft.

> So, we stood up, turned around and that's when the bright light happened, that's where they came out of the craft and they come and picked us up and took us back aboard. Took us aboard their craft, the mechanical things, three of 'em did. Now the one I call the female, she never came out of the craft, they sent what I call the soldiers or the ugly ones, they come out and got us.[174]

During a later hypnosis session, Charles Hickson also recalled seeing "people" on the ship.

> There were people on that spaceship—living beings in another compartment. They never came in there where we were. And I'm telling you, they looked almost like us.[175]

The "woman" described by Parker and the "people" described by Hickson denote a human presence on the ship, though the two men never interacted with these other humans, at least while they were awake and aware of what was happening. Considering the vast number of abductee reports in which human or humanlike individuals are observed, it is extremely rare for there to be no formal interaction between the abductors and abductees. This suggests that if there is a division of labor for those aboard UFOs, as discussed in the Dworshak and Hill case studies, we may need to include autonomous abduction robots to the list of specialized roles.

In the Parker and Hickson case, the ugly mechanical robots were apparently tasked with carrying out the initial abduction, but they appear to have been involved with other procedures as well, or at least those requiring close contact with the agitated abductees while they were in a conscious state. Furthermore, because these "mechanical things" communicated with one another while capturing Parker and Hickson, this encounter may represent an instance of artificial intelligence being used to perform a specific task, which is arguably a more dangerous part of the process.

**Hickson:** They just glided up there to me. Then one of 'em made a little buzzin' noise, and two of 'em never made no noise.

**Sheriff:** What kind of noise?

**Hickson:** Just ZZZZZZ zzzZzZZZ.

**Sheriff:** It sound like a machine?

**Hickson:** Yeah, like that. It might have been contactin' the others. See, I don't know. By then I was so damn scared I didn't know anything. And two of 'em just floated around behind me and lifted me off the ground.[176]

A second use of artificial intelligence, or at least highly sophisticated machinery, was witnessed by Charles Hickson when he was brought onto the ship and into a brightly lit room. There, Hickson described seeing an eye-like device about the size of a football, which scanned his entire body while he was held in front of it by the levitating golem. This scanning equipment may also be considered AI, in the sense that it is a machine imitating intelligent human behavior. As a further testament to the marked consistency across abduction accounts, an eye-like scanning device has been described in other reports, such as the abduction of Garry Wood and Colin Wright that took place near Edinburgh, Scotland, in 1992, where Wright described being examined by a similar contraption:

> An angular device rose from the floor. It was long and thin, like a rod with a small triangular head; two glowing red lights were set into one of the sides…. The entire machine moved up and down continuously and the appendage swung from left to right; although there was no pain, Colin thought it might be scanning him.[177]

Both Parker and Hickson saw humans on the ship, though formal contact may have been deemed unnecessary since the two men could be captured and returned by abduction droids and because the scanning procedure carried out was far less invasive than the standard biomedical examination. However, because Hickson and Parker were both given an injection that temporarily paralyzed and sedated them, it is possible that more intrusive procedures took place once they were asleep. The shot may also have been a fallback safety procedure to help ensure the two men wouldn't be a threat if they happened to escape while onboard the ship. While rare, this occasionally occurs during abductions, which includes the case study examined in the following chapter.

Hickson and Parker's paralysis only wore off once they were placed back outside and some additional time had passed. In fact, Calvin Parker recalls finding himself standing on the shore looking back toward the river with his arms stretched out as if he were still being carried. He remained unable to move his arms for a few minutes, and he heard Charles cry out that he couldn't move his legs.

> We was in there and then they took us back out and set us down there, I was standing there facing the river with my arms stretched out, and I couldn't move 'em. I mean, it took a minute just to get 'em freed up and that's when I heard Charlie calling me in the back and

then they kind of limbered up.  He was down on the ground he said he lost control of his legs, and I didn't lose control cuz I never had no control.[178]

The relatively primitive means with which Parker and Hickson were abducted suggests these people, if extratempestrials, were from a more proximate point in our future. Of course, the robotic artificial intelligence used indicates they are still far more advanced than us, but the means with which these fishermen were kidnapped, incapacitated, scanned, and returned to shore suggests these travelers were less advanced than other groups who can pause time and make people fall and stay asleep at will. Had the travelers who captured Parker and Hickson possessed this technology, or had mind-control capabilities, there may have been no need for levitating robots and scanning footballs.

If the shot given to these men was not a sedative, or an aspect of the visitor's security protocol, it may have been to implant a tracking device, especially considering how often foreign objects resembling modern tracking devices are found in the bodies of abductees. This is also indicated by something Charles Hickson stated in an October 2002 interview with *Clarion Ledger* columnist Billy Watkins, where he is quoted as saying, "I think they know where I am at all times. Too many strange things have happened."[179]

Whether it was to incapacitate them, track them, or for some other purpose, these men were clearly injected with something. Furthermore, because Hickson and Parker both had the same mark on their bodies, this aspect of their abduction lends more credence to the overall account. To this end, Calvin Parker's recent book, *Pascagoula – The Story Continues: New Evidence & New Witnesses*, presents what is referred to as a smoking gun "puncture wound" document. This document demonstrates that Parker and Hickson were injected with something, which helps explain the unusual marks on their bodies, while bolstering the reality of the event.[180]

After regaining some control of their bodies, the two men stumbled toward each other on the banks of the Pascagoula River. Feeling comforted by each other's company, Parker and Hickson turned back toward the craft, which was slowly rising above the ground. Once it reached a height above the power lines, it abruptly "disappeared," instantly vanishing from sight. According to Parker, "then the lights just disappeared, the bright light disappeared... it picked straight up, went up a little ways, and then just disappeared like lightning, I mean, it was gone."[181]

A common occurrence across close encounters can be seen when UFOs abruptly appear or disappear, while maintaining the same position in the sky. This is crucial to consider in the context of the Extratempestrial Model, because if an object suddenly pops into or out of our three observable dimensions of space, there is a good chance it just changed its position in the only other known dimension: time. This regularly reported occurrence, while seemingly bizarre from the standpoint of our conventional notion of linear time, is in fact what we would expect of a time machine entering or exiting a specific point in spacetime.

As shown in *Identified Flying Objects*, this phenomenon is so common that a simple content analysis focused on the words *appear* and *disappear*, across vetted reports filed by the National UFO Reporting Center (NUFORC) from the year 2014 returned over 290 descriptions.[182] [183] Some reported instances of this phenomenon were associated with people using the word *appear* to describe something suddenly seen, regardless of whether it appeared to have appeared out of nowhere. To account for this potential source of bias, these 290 reports were examined individually to assess the intended meaning behind the usage of these words (*appear* and *disappear*). Even after this corrective procedure, 229 reports remained, where people described seeing a light or an actual craft that abruptly appeared or disappeared directly in front of them.

A UFO's seemingly psychic propensity to appear or disappear in a percipient's presence, despite its perinormal façade, is exactly what one would expect to see as a time machine ventures through the fourth dimension. Understanding the sudden materialization and dematerialization of these craft in the context of their movement through time also makes the Extratempestrial Model more acceptable, in that it helps account for this strange behavior, which Jacques Vallée saw as an important prerequisite for any theory put forth to explain the UFO phenomenon. In his 1975 book *The Invisible College*, Vallée writes:

No theory of UFOs can be deemed acceptable if it does not account for the reported 'psychic effects' produced by these objects. By 'psychic effects' I refer to the spacetime distortions experienced by percipients of craft-like devices which appear or 'fade away' on the spot, in ways that are reminiscent of descriptions of 'materializations' in the spiritualistic literature.

The instantaneous appearance or disappearance of lights and physical objects may be a latent liminal consequence of our extratempestrial descendants traveling through the fourth dimension, as they pop in and out of the temporal reference frame of the befuddled bystanders who happen to be in the right place at the right time to observe it. Or in the case of Charles Hickson and Calvin Parker, and Garry Wood and Colin Wright, the wrong place at the wrong time. In addition to the shape and physical properties of UFOs, their high electromagnetic fields, and the way they are often seen to spin faster while the lights around them change color before disappearing, the sudden appearance and disappearance of these craft is exactly what one would expect of a device capable of moving into and out of different regions of block time.

The abduction of Charles Hickson and Calvin Parker is unique in the sense that it was carried out almost entirely by artificial intelligence and advanced machinery. Importantly, robots can't build themselves, or at least not without initial assistance by human hands and minds. As such, it is safe to assume that the robots involved in the catch and release of these men were designed and built by the human society associated with the people Parker and Hickson saw onboard the ship. We are currently being warned of the dangers of artificial intelligence by some of the brightest minds of our time,[184] and perhaps a robot uprising will take place at some point in the future. However, because these mechanical "soldiers or the ugly ones" were sent out by the people in the ship, if these were our future human descendants, we apparently still have some time before humanity must bow down at the feet of our android overlords.

# Case Study 6

~

# 1975
# Travis Walton
# Arizona, USA

*They were a little under five feet in height. They had a basic humanoid form: two legs, two arms, hands with five digits each, and a head with the normal human arrangement of features. Their bald heads were disproportionately large for their puny bodies. They had bulging, oversized craniums, a small jaw structure, and an underdeveloped appearance to their features that was almost infantile.*[185]

– Travis Walton

The Travis Walton saga began on November 5, 1975, in the Apache-Sitgreaves National Forest near the town of Heber, Arizona. Walton was 22 years old at the time and was working on a government contract doing tree-thinning on a 1,200-acre area of national forest near Turkey Springs. He was working on a six-man crew under the supervision of Mike Rogers, who had been doing contract work for the United States Forest Service over the previous nine years.

After finishing work for the day, the men piled into a pickup truck to head down the hill when they suddenly caught glimpse of a large glowing object that looked like a flattened disk, which was hovering in the air about 100 feet from the truck.[186] Initially, it was reported to be about 8 feet high and 20 feet wide, though in a 2017 HuffPost interview, Walton stated that it was about 40 feet in diameter.[187] Others in the truck described it as very smooth, with a yellowish-white light that glowed brightly all around its outer edge.

Because Travis Walton had a lifelong fascination with UFOs, he got out of the truck and started walking across a clearing to get a better look at it. As he approached, the UFO began to rock back and forth slightly. Then, an extremely bright blue light shot out of the bottom of the craft. It struck Walton, sent him flying back through the air, and knocked him unconscious. According to Kenneth Peterson, one of Walton's co-workers who watched from the truck, "I saw a bluish light come from the machine and Travis went flying—like he'd touched a live wire!"[188] Another of Walton's coworkers, Dwayne Smith, stated, "It sure looked like he got hit by lightning or something! I heard a zap—like as if he touched a live wire!"[189] Walton also remembers a blast of energy hitting him and a numbing shock that coursed through his body right before he lost consciousness.[190]

It is likely that Walton was struck by a strong electrostatic discharge (ESD) when he approached the object. Because UAPs move through the atmosphere at incredible speed, it is logical to assume they pick up static electricity in the process. This aspect of UFO flight was explicitly stated in one of the Dworshak encounters, when the boys asked if they could touch the ship. In her book, *Montana UFOs and Extraterrestrials*, Joan Bird notes that before Mike and Leo Dworshak were permitted to touch the craft, one of the visitors told his crewmates to first make sure it was well-grounded, as the ship may have picked up some electricity during its travels. Bird also cites another case from the 1950s, where a man named Howard Menger was warned about the dangers of electromagnetic fields around these craft.[191] This further denotes the high energy and static electric characteristics of these machines, as well as the potential dangers associated with getting too close to them before they have been properly discharged.

Another indication that electricity played a part in what happened to Travis Walton can be seen in how the light was described by those who witnessed it from the safety of the pickup truck. Specifically, his coworkers stated that it was a tremendously bright, bluish light, which sounds a lot like a corona discharge emitted from high-voltage systems like Tesla coils. Furthermore, upon regaining consciousness, Walton expressed that he felt immense pain, like he had been badly burned all over, even inside his body, where he described "feeling as though someone had whacked him with a baseball bat."[192]

Walton is now convinced that this bolt from the ship was a static electric discharge. He is also confident it was accidental and that they were not trying to hurt him as he approached the aircraft. This is also indicated by the fact that the visitors took Walton onto the vessel to perform emergency medical procedures once they saw he had been injured by the static discharge. So, rather than an intended abduction, Walton sees this encounter as more of a spur-of-the-moment "ambulance call."[193]

Regardless of their intent, Walton's fellow crewmembers were understandably terrified when they saw their coworker shoot through the air after being struck by a lightning bolt ejected from the bottom of a large metal ship. Panicked, the remaining six men fled down the hill in the pickup truck. After regaining their composure, realizing they might have overreacted to the situation, and recognizing that Walton may need help, they turned the truck around and headed back up the hill. However, upon returning to the location where Walton was knocked unconscious, they found no trace of him—or the mysterious disc-shaped craft that started the ordeal.

After searching the woods and calling out for him repeatedly, the crewmen decided to head into town to get help from the local police. There they met Deputy Ellison, and later, Sheriff Marlin Gillespie. The officers took note of the fact that these men were distressed and obviously traumatized by what they had seen. They agreed to help look for Travis Walton, and together, the officers and remaining crewmembers went back up the hill again. By this time, it was now dark, so after briefly searching the area with flashlights, they decided it might be better to look for Walton in the morning.

After realizing that they weren't going to find him that night, around one thirty in the morning, two of Walton's coworkers, Coplan and Rogers, went to inform his mother, Mary Kellett, of her son's disappearance. Surprisingly, his mother was entirely calm about the situation, stating, "well, that's the way these things happen." Because Travis Walton and his brother had long shared a fascination with UFOs, it didn't come as much of a surprise that her son had been taken by one. This overly relaxed response might seem strange to most, though I have a hunch that if I suddenly went missing in the presence of a UFO, my family might have a similar reaction to the situation.

Over the next few days, Walton's coworkers, the police, and others continued to search the area where he was last seen, but they found no indication of where he might have gone. Additionally, once the press got word of what had happened, the entire town of Snowflake exploded in a frenzy of reporters, ufologists, and countless others who were fascinated by the strange circumstances of Travis Walton's disappearance.

Understandably, Walton remembers very little about the early stages of his abduction/ambulance call since the presumed electrostatic discharge knocked him unconscious. His first mindful memory was of waking up in what he presumed to be a hospital bed. This assumption seemed logical because he was in tremendous pain, feeling as though he had been burned inside and out, and because his shirt and jacket were pushed up around his shoulders and there was a large, curved device around his abdomen. As his eyes began to focus on objects in the room, he could see three forms moving around him, which he assumed were nurses and doctors tending to him. As the blurry figures started to come into focus, however, it soon became clear that he was not in a hospital.

For most abductees, the outsized and intense eyes of the visitors are often the first thing they notice and what they remember most about the experience. Walton also recalls feeling captivated but terrified by the eyes of his captors, describing them as having large luminous pupils about the size of a quarter, which were so big that part of the pupil was hidden by their eyelids. He also recalls that very little of the white part of the eye, or sclera, was showing, due to how large their pupils and irises were.

It is remarkable how impactful the visitor's ocular characteristics are for abductees. However, this response becomes easier to understand after looking into the eyes of someone who just had their pupils dilated at the eye doctor. Even with our relatively small modern human eyes, administering tropicamide, which induces mydriasis, meaning a widening or dilation of the pupils, gives people an uncanny and somewhat forbidding appearance. Interestingly, a recent study demonstrated a correlation between baseline pupil size and intelligence, which was determined using several measures of cognitive ability.[194] If this relationship exists now, we might expect to see even larger pupils in the eyes of our more intellectually evolved descendants.

In addition to relative pupil size, future human eyes are likely to grow larger as a result of the ontogenetic, allometric, and pliotropic relationships between the eye and brain, assuming our brains continue to expand, change shape, and increase in complexity as they have for the last six million years. Encephalization exists as one of the most dominant trends in hominin evolution, and despite a small diachronic decrease that occurred in association with reduced body size over the previous 30,000 years, our brains have grown larger at an accelerating rate, and most notably over the last 800,000 years. Additionally, a 2014 study published in the journal *Frontiers in Neuroanatomy* showed that a brain size of about 3500 cm³, which is nearly three times larger than our current cranial capacity, is the size at which the human brain reaches its maximum processing capacity.[195]

Our brains have already grown to be three times larger than our great ape cousins. According to a 2021 study published in the journal *Cell*, this is largely attributable to the ZEB2 gene switching on later in humans relative to Chimps and Gorillas, which allows our cells to divide more before maturing.[196] If optimal brain size is another three times larger than what humans have already achieved over the previous six million years, then we may still have a way to go. Furthermore, because the rate at which our brains expanded and changed shape has been accelerating in more recent human evolution, it could happen sooner than we think.

Although the eye rests predominantly within the confines of the orbital walls, it does not directly influence orbital size in humans.[197] [198] [199] Rather, research examining ocular ontogeny indicates that the eye generally keeps pace with the brain throughout growth and development.[200] [201] [202] [203] In fact, as mentioned above, because the eye and brain are so intricately linked, they are thought to be the product of pleiotropic gene control,[204] [205] meaning the same gene or set of genes is responsible for guiding the development of both the eye and brain in humans.[206]

Genetic and spatial integration between the brain and eye also makes sense because the optic vesicles, which mark the earliest stages of eye development, grow directly out of the forebrain during early fetal ontogeny.[207] Further evidence of this pleiotropic relationship is indicated by the common pattern of postnatal ontogeny in the eye and brain, where both features grow the fastest during early life, then cease growth at approximately the same time during late adolescence. So, if the human brain continues to expand, reorganize, and change shape, as it has throughout the long history of hominin evolution, we might also expect our eyes to grow larger in the ensuing human future.

In addition to their enormous haunting eyes, Walton states that the beings he encountered had smooth, pale skin, so void of color that it had a chalky appearance. This lack of pigmentation is so conspicuous it became the namesake of these "grey" aliens, and like eye size, loosing melanin in the skin is consistent with another dominant trend in hominin evolution: self-domestication. We humans have been domesticating ourselves for approximately 20,000 years, and the effects of this process have been accelerating since agriculture became our primary subsistence strategy beginning around 12,000 years ago.

This trend is important to consider in the context of these visitors because the process of domestication has been shown to result in depigmentation over time. Originally demonstrated in foxes, the underlying mechanism driving this loss of pigment is a retardation in the proliferation and migration of melanoblasts from the ectoderm germ layer of the neural crest. This results in fewer melanoblasts, the embryonic precursors to melanocytes, which form melanin in the skin and give it a darker color.[208] [209] [210] [211] [212] This tendency toward depigmentation in domesticated species like *Homo sapiens* could help explain the exceptionally white/grey skin color of what are presumed to be our more distant future human descendants.

Beyond their large eyes and chalky skin, Walton reported that these individuals had no eyelashes, eyebrows, or any hair at all on their big bulbous heads. He also described their heads as appearing too large for their bodies, giving them an infantile or childlike appearance. This comparison with modern human infants, which is common across contact reports, is also important to consider in the context of the Extratempestrial Model. This is because neoteny, or paedomorphosis, which means the retention of juvenile features into adulthood, is another dominant trend in hominin evolution. Furthermore, if this enduring trend persists, it may help explain why these visitors are so commonly described as having accentuated childlike traits.

As mentioned in the Betty and Barney Hill case study, Dr. Michael D. Swords discussed this aspect of evolutionary biology in a thoughtful analysis of the time-travel theory. Though critical of the idea, in his article "UFOnauts: *Homo sapiens* of the Future?" Swords summarizes how neoteny and other aspects of human physiology and behavior could indicate a future origin for these visitors.

What does the Neoteny Theory explain about the 'ufonauts'?
1. Their facial features.
2. Their general build proportions.
3. Their lack of hair and pigmentation.
4. Their sex organ diminution; and unisex look.
5. Their head-to-pelvis anomaly (artificial birthing).
6. Their lack of normal speech.
7. Their abduction behaviors.
8. Their need not to interfere in obvious ways with their past.
9. Their need to create a sophisticated campaign of unreality (in order to ensure non-interference).
10. Their ability to breathe our (and their) atmosphere.
11. Their non-need to go great spatial distances (only to go temporal distances, which may involve no spatial involvement).
12. Their general interest in us (their ancestors).
13. Their possible association with - 'old-style' (non-neotenous) Homo sapiens in the same craft.

When a board member for the Scientific Coalition for UAP studies and a friend of Dr. Swords sent me his articles in January 2020, I was fascinated to see how similar our arguments were regarding the morphology and behavior of these visitors. It is also important to note his last point in the above section, regarding associations between "old-style" *Homo sapiens* and more neotenous humans seen working together on the same ships. This is commonly reported in contact cases where highly paedomorphic humans are observed in association with completely ordinary looking modern humans on the same craft, which, as we will see shortly, was also the case with Travis Walton's encounter.

As indicated by the quote that begins this chapter, the visitors Walton initially encountered had a quintessential human form. They walked bipedally and had two arms, two hands with five digits on each, heads with the normal human arrangement of features but with larger eyes, a larger and rounder neurocranium, tiny ears, little rounded noses, narrow mouths with thin lips, and small faces that terminated in a pointy chin. As mentioned previously, this suite of characteristics is exactly what we would expect to see in our distant descendants if enduring trends in hominin evolution continue into the deep future.

Our shared evolutionary heritage was apparently lost on Travis Walton when he awoke in this strange environment with oddly shaped humans, to the extent that he became hysterical and picked up a weapon to fight them off. Since these individuals were much smaller and more childlike by comparison, and because they lacked abduction droids or "soldiers" like those used in the Pascagoula case study, the three visitors tending to Walton abruptly fled the room. Incidentally, they retreated just as Walton readied himself to lunge at them in attack, which may indicate they were reading his thoughts and could sense his intent, as is common across abduction reports.

Walton also attempted to flee by darting out the open door and into a narrow hallway that curved sharply to the right, indicating he was in a circular structure. While racing down the corridor, frantically looking for an exit, he saw an open door inside the curved hallway to his right, which took him into the center of the craft and what appeared to be the navigation room. This is indicated by a chair in the center of the room that had several buttons and screens around it, and when Walton touched these buttons, it made the ship move.[213]

Further indication that this space was used for piloting the ship is apparent in how it changed as Walton walked toward the chair near the center of the circular room. As he approached the chair from behind, Walton could see the walls and ceiling begin to disappear, and the stars outside slowly came into view. As he stepped back away from the chair, the stars faded, and the walls and ceiling became visible once again. Other abductees have also reported seeing this advanced technology in action. For instance, twin sisters Audrey and Debbie Hewins were abducted numerous times since they were young girls by entities they referred to as the "Bald Men." According to Debbie, "I remember one time being on a spaceship and standing there on the spaceship and the floor and the walls disappeared. And I was staring at the Earth."[214] In addition to the wand that could freeze time from the Dworshak case study, this on-demand windshield in the form of disappearing floors, walls, and ceilings is toward the top of my list of astonishing and coveted ET technologies.

Up to this point, Travis Walton had only interacted with the three grey-skinned individuals in the room where he woke up, but while checking out the control center of the ship, Walton heard a sound behind him, and as he spun around to see what it was, standing in the open doorway was an entirely normal looking human man. The man was about six feet two inches tall, weighed around 200 pounds, and had a very muscular physique. He was also wearing a tight-fitting, bright-blue jumpsuit made of a soft material.[215] Seeking comfort in the man's more familiar anthropomorphic features, Walton ran up to him and frantically began asking questions about where they were and what was going on, but the man never spoke to Walton.

Considering the different occupational roles apparent among those onboard UFOs, there is a good chance this man did not speak English. It is also likely that he was never meant to be a part of the encounter but became instrumental once Walton escaped and the visitors realized they needed someone closer to his size, and who looked more like him, so they could calm Walton down and make him leave the control room before he crashed the ship. The latter scenario seems to have been the case as well, since the man firmly grabbed Walton's arm and led him out of the room, through a series of hallways, and into a small space that looked like an airlock.

The man then took Walton down a steep ramp and out of the craft, where he welcomed some breaths of fresh air. Looking back at the ship they just exited, Walton could see it was approximately 60 feet in diameter, which was much larger than the one he initially encountered in the forest. He could also see that he was in a large, half-cylinder-shaped room, similar to an airplane hangar, which suggests he was at some sort of established base, wherever—or whenever—that may be. Walton could also see three or four other shiny oval-shaped UAPs, each about 40 feet in diameter, which looked more like the ship he saw in the Apache-Sitgreaves National Forest on November 5, 1975.[216]

The muscular man continued to lead Travis Walton through another hallway and into an entirely white room with a table and chairs. There, Walton was surprised to see two more men and one woman, who were all very similar to the one who came and got him from the navigation room of the ship moments earlier. Walton noted that the striking similarity among these people seemed almost familial, as if they were related. He also noticed that each of them had very gender-specific features, great skin, and striking good looks.

These people also ignored Travis Walton's many questions and instead took him by the arms and placed him on the table. Together, the three men gently pushed Walton down while the woman placed a small mask over his face, which he likened to an oxygen mask. However, rather than having hoses and tubes, this mask simply had a small black sphere about the size of a walnut on the outside. The black ball on the mask must have contained a sleeping agent as well, since Walton felt weak and quickly lost consciousness once it was placed over his face. This was the last thing Travis Walton remembered before waking up on the side of the road near Heber, Arizona, five days after he and his fellow tree-thinners first witnessed the UFO at Turkey Springs.

Walton eventually made it into town and called his brother-in-law Grant to come get him. Because the clock in Grant's pickup showed it was just after midnight, and because he only remembered being conscious for a couple hours, Walton assumed he'd only been gone for the duration of that evening. However, on the way back to Snowflake, from Heber, Arizona, Walton's brother Duane told him to feel his face so he would notice how much his beard had grown. Confused, Walton explained he had just shaved that morning, at which point his brother informed him that he had been missing for five days.

Given the severity of his injuries, Travis Walton may have been unconscious and in critical condition for the first few days of his encounter and only aware of what was happening for a small part of the overall experience. Because he was missing for five consecutive days, and because he shaved before leaving for work on November 5, but he exhibited five days' worth of facial hair growth when he was found, this indicates that Travis Walton was in fact with these visitors for that amount of time. Though as we will see in the ensuing chronicle of Corporal Armando Valdés, and in another case study examined later, differences often exist in the way time passes between abductees and those who stay behind.

# Case Study 7

~

# 1977
# Corporal Armando Valdés
# Pampa Lluscuma, Chile

*You don't know who we are or where we come from but we will be back soon.*[217]

— ARMANDO VALDÉS ET AL.

A brief but fascinating UFO encounter occurred late one night at the foothills of the Andes mountains in the northern Chilean desert. The details of this event would also seem to suggest that physical time travel occurred in close proximity to an otherwise stationary craft. In this case, a six-man Chilean army patrol was stationed at the secret outpost of Pampa Lluscuma near Putre, which is approximately 85 miles inland from Arica, a coastal city at the northern tip of Chile. At around four in the morning, on April 25, 1977, the soldiers witnessed two bright purple lights descend from the sky.

One of the men, Private Rosales, ran back to alert his commanding officer, Corporal Armando Valdés, about the unusual illuminations they just witnessed. Around that time, one of the lights moved down near the foothills of the Andean mountains, while the other came toward their base, landing only about 450 meters from where the men were standing. The soldiers described it as a bright violet light emanating from a craft, which illuminated the entire area. They could see red lights visible on each end of the object, and the entire thing was shrouded in a mysterious oscillating glow. The men also noted that the craft emitted no sound; instead, an eerie and absolute silence permeated the area.

137

Valdés ordered his men to put out their fires and stand with weapons at the ready. He then started walking toward the mysterious object alone. Now closer, Valdés said a quick prayer and ordered the light to leave, as if it were a soldier under his command. Because it was not, and it didn't leave, Valdés next demanded that the object identify itself. When this tactic also failed, he began walking toward the object again, but as he drew nearer, Corporal Valdés suddenly disappeared from sight. Because the bright violet light had been illuminating the entire area, his men could plainly see that he did not simply disappear into the darkness, but instead, he vanished entirely. This caused confusion and consternation among the six soldiers who were watching intently as Valdés marched toward the peculiar craft.

According to his men, about 15 minutes after Cpl. Valdés disappeared, he abruptly reappeared. However, he looked entirely different from the last time they saw him. In fact, in a matter of only 15 minutes, Valdés went from being a strong, imposing military officer, to appearing frail, weak, and extremely unsteady on his feet. Then, in an almost trance-like state, as if channeling the visitors inside the craft, he said, "you don't know who we are or where we come from, but we will be back soon." Valdés then lost consciousness, fell to the ground, and didn't wake up again until seven in the morning. When he came to a few hours after passing out near the craft, Cpl. Valdés was aware that something had happened, but he was unsure what had transpired, since the last thing he remembered was walking toward the strange object earlier that morning.

This is where the story takes an interesting turn. As Valdés looked down to check his watch, rather than showing April 25, which was the actual date, it instead read April 30, five days in the future. This suggests that Corporal Armando Valdés was near or perhaps on this ship for five days, even though, from the standpoint of his men, only 15 minutes had passed between the time he disappeared and then reappeared in a haggard state. Similar to the previous Travis Walton abduction, the passage of these missing five days was corroborated by excess beard growth on Valdés's face, which, according to his men, was cleanly shaven prior to the incident.[218]

Missing time is extremely common across UFO reports. This was also the case for Corporal Armando Valdés, whose last memory was of walking toward the object shortly after four in the morning. Later, once word of the encounter got out, Valdés began to assert that he was not abducted or taken into any form of aircraft. Instead, despite stating earlier that he had no memories of what transpired, Valdés claimed he was able to see his men and hear them talking the entire time he was gone. However, this assertion is not supported by his wristwatch, a device whose sole purpose is to measure the passage of time.

It is possible that Valdés was abducted and his memory of the encounter was wiped clean prior to his return, which is extremely common across abductions. Although, it is also possible that when he approached this craft, and entered a radius in which the spacetime metric was modified for the visitors' own purposes, Valdés experienced their speed of time, and no longer the one he had previously shared with his men just moments prior.[219] This would also help explain why Valdés appeared to have disappeared, given that if he entered a space in which time moves at a much different speed, he would no longer share a mutual "now" with his men. In the same way you can't see someone standing in front of you who had been there yesterday, or who will be there tomorrow, Valdés's men could no longer see him as part of their four-dimensional reality, as he was still in that same place, but suddenly at a different time.

Experiencing some form of spacetime distortion in and around UAPs is exceedingly common, and additional examples will be presented in other case studies as well. The ubiquity with which spacetime is warped in the area around these craft is also indicated by a recent GQ magazine interview with Lue Elizondo, who headed the Advanced Aerospace Threat Identification Program (AATIP), an unclassified but unpublicized organization set up by the US government to study UFOs. While discussing how frequently pilots see and interact with UAPs in the air, he mentions that it is also common for them to experience alterations in the passage of time while in close proximity to these machines.

And then you might get somebody who gets really close and says, 'You know, Lue, it's really bizarre. It felt like I was there for only five minutes, but when I looked at my watch 30 minutes went by, but I only used five minutes' worth of fuel. How is that possible?' Well, there's a reason for that, we believe, and it probably has to do with warping of space time. And the closer you get to one of these vehicles, the more you may begin to experience space time relative to the vehicle and the environment.

...Current hypothesis is that it creates a bubble around it and that bubble is insulating itself from the space-time that all of us experience. And so, therefore, the way it experiences space-time within the bubble is fundamentally different from outside the bubble.[220]

A similar and slightly more extreme example of how these craft can alter spacetime is apparent in the recent testimony of former CIA director R. James Woolsey. In an interview with the *New York Post*, Woolsey described an encounter in which his friend's plane was "paused at 40,000 feet." He goes on to state that his friend, who he respects and who he considers a reliable source, had his aircraft completely stop, and "not continue operating as a normal aircraft."[221] This is yet another indication of the incredible ability of UFOs to alter the fabric of reality around them.

Valdés's claim that he could see and hear his men, as well as the fact that he was very weak upon returning to the soldiers' frame of reference, may indicate that he and his watch were living at a faster rate inside a warped region of spacetime near the craft. However, if time were passing at a much faster rate in the vicinity of this UAP, one would think Valdés should have seen and heard his men moving and talking extremely slowly, relative to the speed at which time was passing for him within this altered spacetime bubble. In the same way we struggle to swat flies who live much faster, or how we may seem to move like flies to a sleepy three-toed sloth, changing the rate at which time passes for Valdés should have altered the way he perceived the speed of life for those farther from the craft.

The visitors' apparent ability to manipulate spacetime, and the resulting divergence in the rate with which time passes in their reference frame relative to our own, may also explain how they can accelerate and decelerate at tremendous speed without dying. These incredible maneuvers would surely generate massive g-forces. However, if these visitors are in fact altering the speed of time in and around their UFOs, then what we see as a 75-g acceleration may feel like a slow 1-g acceleration to them inside the ship. Rather than thinking of these seemingly impossible accelerations and decelerations as a real-time phenomenon, and questioning how any biological entity aboard could withstand the insane g-forces generated, the Valdés experience leads one to wonder if it is only an illusion, resulting from the divergent way in which we see them and they see us in different temporal reference frames.

If Valdés did experience the passage of five days over the course of 15 minutes, it may help explain his physical condition once he reappeared. Not eating or drinking for 120 hours would naturally make someone very weak, and while people can die within three days of not having any water, death from dehydration typically takes closer to 10 days, depending on factors like age, activity level, and overall health.[222] Valdés's extreme weakness and fatigue also could have been exacerbated by standing too close to the operative object, since similar symptoms are common across such accounts.

This occurred in a few of the above case studies, where extreme fatigue was reported by both Leo Dworshak and Udo Wartena, and something similar to radiation poisoning affected Villas-Boas after he stood in close proximity to a rapidly spinning UFO just before it shot off into the night sky. Like in the Villas-Boas case, these symptoms seem to be more severe in instances where the craft was energized while preparing to take off, which is a process that is sure to release a tremendous amount of energy. Yet, negative health effects can occur from being close to these objects during normal operation as well.

In the same interview with GQ magazine, Lue Elizondo was asked about a novel UAP office, which has been proposed to help investigate UFOs. The interviewer notes that this new agency "would be required to report on health-related effects for individuals who have experienced UAPs." When asked, "what kind of things might happen if you were near one?" Elizondo replied,

A lot. Let me give you a notional... I've got to be careful, I can't speak too specifically, but one might imagine that you get a report from a pilot who says, 'Lue, it's really weird. I was flying and I got close to this thing and I came back home and it was like I got a sunburn. I was red for four days.' Well, that's a sign of radiation. That's not a sunburn; it's a radiation burn. Then [a pilot] might say, if [they] had got a little closer, 'Lue, I'm at the hospital. I've got symptoms that are indicative of microwave damage, meaning internal injuries, and even in my brain there's some morphology there.'[223]

Since spacetime seems to be distorted close to these craft, Corporal Armando Valdés may have experienced an alteration in the passage of time as he approached the UFO, albeit a rather extreme one, considering five days passed for him. However, as mentioned above, it is also possible that Valdés was physically abducted and kept in the ship for five days, but he was returned to a time closer to when he initially disappeared. As we will see in a later case study, in instances where other people observe the abduction, and display concern about the abductee's wellbeing, they can be returned to a time near to when they were taken, even if they spent multiple days, or as much as a week, with the visitors.

In this scenario, Valdés could have been abducted when he disappeared, spent approximately five days on the ship where he likely underwent biomedical exams and other standard procedures, had his memory of these events wiped, and been returned to a time that was only 15 minutes after his disappearance, as perceived by the six men who remained near the outpost. Since the visitors are apparently able to manipulate spacetime, and could use this ability to travel through time, returning Valdés to the same place, but only 15 minutes after he was initially taken, would be the polite thing to do, especially since these six witnesses were understandably disturbed by the unusual nature of his disappearance.

Regardless of whether Valdés was taken into the craft for five days, or simply subjected to a different reference frame where time passed faster than near his men, some form of spacetime distortion or physical time travel was evidently involved. Because Valdés was only gone for 15 minutes, but he had aged by five days, and the calendar on his watch read five days in the future, all indications are that this UFO, like so many others, is capable of time travel. Furthermore, if this was a capability of the UFO Valdés and his men encountered in the northern Chilean desert, one must wonder if this craft–despite being seen coming down from the sky–had not come from the stars above but had instead come from a different time in a more advanced human future.

Valdés doesn't remember seeing living beings during his encounter, which makes it harder to assess the hominin status of any individuals who may have been aboard. However, the message spoken through Valdés suggests that there were intelligent beings inside the craft. Additionally, because the message was given to Valdés in his native language of Spanish, and seemingly spoken through him using telepathy, extratempestrials may have been involved, especially considering how commonly this form of communication occurs across contact accounts.

Possibly due to the unwanted media attention that came with this encounter, Valdés later attempted to explain away much of what transpired that night in 1977. As part of his self-imposed debunking campaign, Valdés also began to disagree with certain details provided by his men, who, notably, retained actual conscious memories of how these events unfolded. Despite some discrepancies, in a September 2003 interview with *Terra.cl*, Valdés did acknowledge, "that the matter of the beard and the wristwatch was true."[224] Still, it wasn't long before Valdés began contradicting himself about the details of the encounter again, including the strange way his wristwatch seemed to have leapt forward in time.

Researcher and journalist Patricio Abusleme Hoffman investigated this close encounter for his 2010 book, *La Noche de los Centinelas*, and got the opportunity to interview Valdés about the event, which had now taken place some 30 years earlier. In the interview, Valdés controverted some previous assertions, including the matter of the wristwatch, which he had just claimed was true about seven years earlier. However, while speaking with Hoffman, Valdés stated that his watch had been broken for 10 to 15 days before the events of that night in April 1977.

Upon reading Valdés's statement about the wristwatch in Hoffman's book, some immediate red flags were raised. For instance, it is hard to believe that anyone would continue wearing a non-functioning watch for nearly two weeks, or that they would give such a broad range of time (10-15 days) for when it had stopped working prior to the UFO encounter. Wearing a broken watch for two weeks is also suspect for Valdés specifically, given that he was the commanding officer of a six-man platoon.

As a corporal in charge of a small military unit, Armando Valdés was required to document events as they happened, so that a record of where and when things occurred could be archived. Additionally, having just been in town prior to going out to this remote area of the Chilean desert, one would think Valdés might have purchased a new wristwatch, or had his repaired, if he knew it had not been working for some time, and particularly since a functioning timepiece was an important part of his job.

However, the main reason why this "broken watch" argument doesn't add up is because if Armando Valdés's wristwatch were broken, and it had been broken for 10 to 15 days before this contact event that took place on April 25, 1977, then it should have read the date as 10-15 days prior—not five days to the future of when the close encounter occurred. Because Valdés's watch read April 30, as opposed to April 25, or some earlier date between April 10, and April 15, when he claims the watch stopped telling time, this defective watch excuse doesn't hold water.

The fact that Valdés changed his account of events could be seen as detracting from the fidelity of this occurrence. However, hesitancy would be expected of someone who was given orders from higher up the chain of command to downplay the event. Flip-flopping behavior is extremely common in cases involving military personnel, and in this instance, the order to cease discussion of the event came from the highest office in Chile, as then president and commander in chief, Augusto Pinochet, prohibited further interviews with the soldiers once word got out about it.[225] Additionally, we must consider the stigma and common stereotype that people who see UFOs must be crazy. In Armando Valdés's position as corporal in the Chilean army, he would be required to maintain an air of mental stability to retain legitimacy in that role, so it is no surprise he attempted to modulate the narrative after this encounter.

Perhaps the most crucial thing to consider regarding the reality of what transpired that night in the Chilean desert is that six other military men were also witnesses to the event. Furthermore, each of these men remembered the course of events better than Valdés, and because their accounts were all compatible and independently corroborated, the case retains a high level of credibility, despite Valdés's later vacillations.

Putting aside minor incongruities in the story, if the beard-growth and five-day-fast watch aspects of the account are true, as Valdés himself claimed they were throughout most of his post-contact life, then something remarkable took place in the Chilean desert on that night in 1977. Furthermore, because Valdés was missing for five days but was returned only 15 minutes later, or, alternatively, he experienced an altered rate in the passage of time while in the vicinity of this UFO, the case remains worthy of consideration in the context of the Extratempestrial Model. More specifically, this encounter indicates that these craft possess the ability to warp spacetime, which could potentially allow the ship and its occupants to move forward and backward through time in ways we are only beginning to understand.

# Case Study 8

~

# 1977
# Terry Lovelace
# Arkansas, USA

*They look like, no, fuck no, these are human beings? But no, these can't be living human beings, they're different. Oh God, they're not like us. One moved its head and turned toward us, and its eye blinked, oh, fuck no!*[226]

— TERRY LOVELACE

Alien abductions are most often portrayed as a horrific occurrence, and some undoubtedly are. Yet, a majority of contactees actually have either a positive or neutral experience. Furthermore, if the visitors' appearance is similar to that of modern humans, the abductee tends to remember the event in a more positive light. According to the Dr. Edgar Mitchell FREE study, out of 1,534 individuals who claimed to have had a physical close encounter, only 5% stated that the interaction was negative, while 66% described their experience as positive, and 29% as neutral. Additionally, if these encounters persisted, survey respondents started to view them more positively and yearned for further contact in the future.[227]

The results of this global survey of nearly 4,000 abductees and contactees revealed that most enjoyed, or were ambivalent about, their experience. A small percentage of abductees are traumatized by these events though, and they continue to carry feelings of fear and uncertainty about when it might happen again, along with many questions about what transpired, why, and who was responsible for these perturbing occurrences. One abductee who has been plagued by nightmares of these types of encounters since he was a young boy is Terry Lovelace, a 65-year-old attorney and former assistant attorney general.

Many of Lovelace's bad dreams centered on frightening "monkey men" who would appear in his bedroom late at night, pleading with him to come away with them. For Lovelace, these encounters began at the age of eight, and memories of them have haunted his dreams and waking life ever since. The intense disdain he felt for these little monkey creatures can be seen in a poem he once wrote for a high school literature class.

We must take from you blood and other things we do need, many entities one day will be born of your seed.' I swear by all that is holy and all that is right, the next time you come to take me at night, when four little monkeys crouched near to my bed, with my revolver I'll shoot all four of them dead.[228]

In later life, while under hypnosis, Lovelace would discover that these "monkey men" were not monkeys at all. Rather, they were "little grey people" who wore monkey masks when they came to his bedroom late at night to abduct him.

They look like little monkeys, there were four of them and they all wore masks. I can see them now and their masks are off. These aren't monkeys at all, these are little grey people! They took me, they took me to play when I was little.[229]

Based on numerous other encounters like this, it is possible the little grey people, rather than wearing physical masks, may have replaced their true form with implanted screen memories of monkeys, in a failed attempt to make these encounters less traumatic for Lovelace when he was a child. A further indication of the visitors' ability to manipulate our minds and memories may exist in how they are able to make abductees fall asleep and stay asleep without administering any drugs. While a sedative was injected into Parker and Hickson in the Pascagoula abduction, with cases involving these "more evolved" hominins with grey skin and rounder crania, they appear to be able to communicate with us telepathically and are capable of controlling our minds, memories, and sleep.

For instance, one night when he was young, Lovelace remembered seeing a UFO outside his bedroom window, but rather than feeling frightened by this strange machine hovering near his house, he simply lay back down in bed and fell asleep. Typically, becoming aware of a large metallic craft hanging in the air right outside your bedroom window would elicit feelings of fear and anxiety. However, in many abductions, people note the oddity of a bright light or a ship, but they remain outwardly ambivalent about it, and they often just ignore it and fall asleep, or more likely, they are put to sleep.

This phenomenon is known as "alien apathy," and it commonly occurs in association with "alien amnesia," which is when abductees are initially unable to remember all or part of the ensuing encounter. This pattern of apathy and induced sleep was a common occurrence throughout Terry Lovelace's childhood. It also occurred prior to one of the most impactful abductions of his life, which took place as an adult, the night he and a fellow army buddy named Toby were camping in a relatively remote area of Arkansas, near Devil's Den State Park.

One night during the trip, while they were lying in the grass looking up at the stars, the two men noticed an enormous, five-story-tall, triangular megastructure moving toward them. Although they were keenly aware of it, and both considered it highly unusual, they just lay there and watched, before calmly drifting off to sleep. A similar instance of alien apathy can be seen in the Antonio Villas-Boas case study, where he and his brother lost interest in the strange bright light outside their bedroom window the night before Antonio was abducted.

In addition to the incident at Devil's Den, alien apathy and alien amnesia happened often throughout Terry Lovelace's life. These commonly occurred in association with "missing time" events as well, which is an aspect of alien amnesia where an abductee is aware that something impactful had happened, since some time had passed since their last conscious memory, but they are unaware of what took place in those lost moments. These missing memory scenarios are exceedingly common across abduction reports and include the Betty and Barney Hill encounter, which was one of the first and most widely reported instances of missing time. The Travis Walton and Armando Valdés cases are also interesting to consider in this context because both men felt as though they were gone for only a short time, but for each, five days had passed, and seemingly in two very different ways.

Patterns across cases seem to suggest that abductees' memories are most often erased or replaced with screen memories in cases where they were disturbed by the experience. For instance, Mike and Leo Dworshak, Udo Wartena, and Villas-Boas were never subjected to this practice, as they were allowed to retain conscious memories of the entire interaction, and each had a relatively or intensely pleasant experience with the visitors they encountered. However, Barney and Betty Hill, Calvin Parker, Charles Hickson, Travis Walton, Armando Valdés, and Terry Lovelace were all extremely frightened by their experience, and they came away from the encounter with alien amnesia, missing time, and screen memories. Or in the case of Parker and Hickson, they retained conscious memories of being taken and returned, but had little knowledge of what happened to them while on the ship.

This relationship between alien amnesia and the valence of the interaction as either positive or negative can be seen in subsequent case studies as well. Furthermore, this pattern suggests that the visitors modify our memories out of respect for us, in an attempt to mitigate mental distress brought about by the encounter, as opposed to clearing our minds to keep us from remembering things about them. In essence, it would seem they do it more for us, and less for them.

Like Terry Lovelace, many other abductees report multiple instances of close contact throughout their lives. A slight majority also discover a type of tracking device implanted in their bodies. According to Marden and Stoner (2012), 53% of the 40 contactees sampled for their study reported having felt an implant in their bodies after contact.[230] Interestingly, this number was almost identical in the Dr. Edgar Mitchell FREE study, where 52% of the 1,302 individuals who had close contact believed a permanent foreign object was placed in their bodies.[231] Although it is impossible to know the exact purpose of these implants, most of these devices possess a form consistent with the function of tracking the individual.

Implanting a tracking device also makes sense if the visitors need to be able to find their research subjects for subsequent examination as part of a longitudinal study, much like how we tag various other animal species for our own long-term studies. This also seems to have been the case for Terry Lovelace, since he was taken multiple times throughout his life, and because there was a small metal device with two wires sticking out of it embedded almost four centimeters deep in his right thigh just above the knee. Lovelace also believes this device may have been inserted for the purpose of tracking him throughout his life.

> My experiences with UFOs stretch back to my early childhood. Why was I singled out for these 4-5 experiences throughout the span of a lifetime, I think it's because I was tagged like an animal on the Serengeti plains of Africa. I was captured, hopefully anesthetized, and metal devices were implanted in my legs.'[232]

Whitley Strieber, whose experiences with the visitors will be discussed later in this text, also carries a device that was implanted in his ear. Strieber's apparatus is interesting because it occasionally sends out a detectable signal, which is again indicative of their function as a tracking device or transmitter of some sort. Strieber's implant is also noteworthy because he claims it was put in his ear "by two people, they were not aliens." These people pushed it through his skin, and oddly, there was no scar where it was inserted.[233] An unusual absence of scaring also exists with Terry Lovelace's leg implant. This baffled doctors, who said there definitely should have been a scar on his leg if something that big was in there.

The same way we use transmitters to locate other animals, tracking devices implanted in abductees could help the visitors conduct longitudinal research on specific individuals, especially considering how often and how far humans move relative to other species. This technology would allow multiple instances of contact throughout an abductee's life, and information about their specific location could help guide when and where the best time might be to apprehend them. The frequency with which the same people are taken on multiple occasions is also consistent with what we would expect to see if our future human descendants were engaged in intertemporal research.

Having the means to pick up the same individual at different times in their life could facilitate a plethora of longitudinal studies. As discussed in the Leo Dworshak case study, if our descendants were aided by the technological tool of time travel, lifetime longitudinal research could be carried out by the same scientists, throughout an abductee's lifetime, but over the course of only a few days or weeks in the timeframe of these intertemporal investigators. Using a time machine, these travelers could pick up the same research subject and collect data from them at various points throughout their life. However, while the subject moves from being a small child to an aged adult throughout the course of the study, they see the researchers age by only a day, or possibly a few days or weeks depending on how long the study takes.

One can imagine picking up an eight-year-old child for their first abduction. Then, after tucking them back into bed and having a quick coffee break, jumping forward in time to nab them again as a 23-year-old adult. Later that day, they snatch them again at age 38. After lunch, the researchers hunt them down using an implanted tracking device and bring them back onboard at age 53. Then, as their extended workday draws to an end, they visit the study subject one last time in old age, as the abductee struggles to understand what has been happening throughout their lives and why these visitors look exactly the same as when they were first taken as a young child. *Pa'u Hana.*

Both Leo Dworshak and Terry Lovelace noted this phenomenon independently, where they had multiple interactions with the same people over the course of decades, but the visitors never appeared to grow older. Regarding Terry Lovelace's experience specifically, his most recent interaction occurred in 2017, soon after he returned home from a public appearance at a UFO conference in Houston, Texas. One night, he was surprised to see a large-eyed, small-faced woman sitting in his living room. While she was there speaking with him telepathically, it dawned on Lovelace that this was the same person he'd seen and interacted with on numerous occasions throughout his life, almost as if she were his personal ambassador, or some sort of intertemporal caseworker. Furthermore, although Lovelace was now a much older adult, she looked as if she hadn't aged at all.

> Seated directly across from me is what I first mistook to be a small Asian woman…. She wore oversized sunglasses that hid her large almond eyes and part of her face… This was the same being I encountered a long time ago…. The voice I heard in my head came as plainly as spoken words. She spoke with perfect English grammar with no discernible accent. She responded to my thoughts immediately, 'yes I am that woman.' I stared at her and recognized her face. I recognized her voice too. I was amazed that she hadn't aged since I last saw her in 1987. Her body shape and facial structure were identical to the woman I met in 1987.[234]

Another example of an abductee having a lifelong interaction with the same person who didn't seem to age can be seen in the case of Jerry Wills. In an interview with Mark Snider, on the show *Ohio Exopolitics*, Wills described meeting the same "man" he remembered from childhood. Like Lovelace, Dworshak, and others, Wills noted that this man, named Zo, hadn't aged since their first meeting when he was a young child.

**Interviewer:** Did Zo look like he had aged at all? It had been like 20 years since you had seen him, did he look identical?'

**Wills:** I wouldn't say identical, but pretty close. Imagine if you don't see a friend for 2-3 years, there's a little difference there, but there's nothing like ohh, you're getting some grey going on there, there wasn't anything like that.

**Interviewer:** Yeah, I've heard that more than once from contactees.[235]

Cases like these suggest the visitors possess the ability to move through time, and they are able to pop in and out at different points throughout an abductee's lifetime. Although, there could be other reasons why the visitors do not appear to age, or age more slowly, which may be related to changes in our life history cycle, health, or rate of senescence in the human future. Considering this ageless phenomenon in the context of the other dominant models, if they are extraterrestrials, they may have evolved an entirely different ontological cycle, or if they are ultraterrestrials they might always manifest in the same physical form that is outside the realm of temporal change, which would also apply if they are visiting us in a computer simulation. However, if they are extratempestrals, it is fascinating to consider how we may continue to slow the rate of senescence and prolong our life history cycle in the future, and someday conduct lifelong longitudinal research on the same subject using the bioethnographic tool of time travel.

In his book *Incident at Devils Den*, Lovelace refers to this perpetually present woman as Betty, mostly because of the large wig she wore to hide her big round head, which reminded him of Betty Rubble from the Flintstones. Lovelace also believes Betty's role was to take care of him while onboard the ship when he was a child, since she gave him and the other abducted children toys to play with during these encounters. However, because Lovelace remembers Betty as a constant presence throughout his life, and since he was allowed to remember her, while most of his other memories were suppressed or replaced with screen memories, Betty's position likely extends well beyond the role of childcare.

As mentioned above, Betty's status seems more consistent with that of a personal guide, chaperone, concierge, psychologist, or caseworker. This would also make sense in the context of longitudinal scientific research, since modern studies like these involve special protections for children as research subjects. Minimizing physical and psychological harm to each individual would be easier if there were an omnipresent sympathetic maternal figure to mentor abductees and contactees throughout a lifetime of odd and often alarming encounters.

Occupational specialization is apparent across contact cases, and it may exist as part of a much larger collaborative operation. For instance, during one of Terry Lovelace's 4-5 abductions, he was taken aboard a large triangular craft where he recalled seeing numerous specialized human groups exhibiting diverse physical characteristics, who were carrying out different but coordinated tasks. This included one group that would line up abducted people, strip them naked, and take them into rooms that stretched as far as he could see.

While we can't know what was happening inside these rooms from this part of Lovelace's account, based on countless other abductee reports, the people who were stripped naked were most likely subjected to a biomedical examination, which also involved sperm and egg extractions. Evidence of the latter, as well as the results of this ubiquitous practice of taking gametes from people during UFO abductions, can be seen in the fact that Terry Lovelace and his friend Toby were also subjected to this practice of sperm withdrawal—and from what Lovelace saw lining the walls of this massive triangular craft.

> There was a crowd of people too… Fifty or sixty. A lot of people… some of the human beings were crew members. They just ignored us…. They marched us past a long wall of aquariums…. They are big fish tanks…. A hundred or more aquariums… they cover a whole wall. There is pink water inside and some are bigger. They look like, no, fuck no, these are human beings!? But no, these can't be living human beings, they're different. Ohh God, they're not like us. One moved its head and turned toward us, his eyes blinked, ohh fuck no! [236]

What Terry Lovelace reveals in this section of the book, if true, is exceedingly informative. He claims to have directly observed gestating fetuses, on a large trilateral ship, where humans at various stages of evolutionary development were working alongside fully modern humans. These ranged from tall, almost insect-like humanoids to the more conventional "grey aliens," and included other groups with bigger eyes and heads who looked more like his chaperone Betty Rubble, while there were also entirely average-looking modern humans who were working alongside these other groups, onboard what appears to be a massive floating fertility facility.

The reproductive focus of this levitating trilateral structure is indicated by the expansive rows of incubation chambers lining the walls of the ship, the sperm extractions Lovelace and his friend Toby endured, and his observation of other abductees being stripped naked, which may have been for the same purpose, considering how common gamete withdrawals are in abduction accounts. In the context of the Extratempestrial Model, widespread sperm, egg, and fetus extraction could again signify the significance of past human DNA to our distant descendants. Furthermore, as discussed in the Villas-Boas case study, it may signal future problems with reproduction.

In addition to past and current trends related to reduced fertility and fecundity in both men and women, humans have long suffered from difficult childbirths, which anthropologists jocularly refer to as the "big-head-small-hole problem." Because humans have large brains, but still need to escape the womb, our ancestors developed some evolutionary tradeoffs that have allowed encephalization to continue relatively unabated. These include a fontanelle at the top of the skull, an extra suture in the frontal bone of the neonatal neurocranium called a metopic suture, we give birth to altricial, or underdeveloped young, which means our offspring are born in an underdeveloped state and thus have smaller brains at birth relative to other mammals. More recently, we have also began doing cesarean sections, which has changed our relationship with the big-head-small-hole problem as it existed among our encephalized ancestors.

These biological and technological adaptations, which allow us to exit early, modify the shape of our skulls as we pass through the birth canal, and use surgery to deliver our children, means we have continued to grow bigger and more intelligent brains throughout hominin evolution. However, if our neurocrania keep expanding, in part due to long-term paedomorphic trends and an optimal brain size that lies near 3500 cm$^3$, external gestation like that observed by Terry Lovelace onboard this large triangular craft may become a necessity at some point in the human future.

As mentioned in the Betty and Barney Hill case study, paedomorphism, meaning the retention of juvenilized traits into adulthood, is a dominant trend in hominin evolution. Childlike traits are also a commonly described characteristic of the visitors observed during close encounters. For instance, Travis Walton described his captors as looking like "oversized fetuses," and the large round heads, big eyes, and small faces of the people Terry Lovelace saw reminded him of children as well. In fact, when placed back in his tent after having just been abducted with his friend Toby near Devil's Den State Park in 1977, Lovelace turned to Toby and said, "My god these are children, maybe a dozen or more kids about the same height. What the hell would children be doing here underneath this giant thing in the middle of the night?"[237]

Considered in conjunction with naked abductees and pervasive gamete extractions, past problems with childbirth, current trends toward reduced fertility and fecundity, and the fact that they contained blinking paedomorphic humans that were not that different from ourselves, the rows of pink aquariums Lovelace saw lining an entire wall of this triangular ship were likely external gestation incubators. Such devices may represent a cultural connection between our past and future as well, since doctors and researchers are already working on artificial uteruses, which as the name implies, are devices that facilitate extracorporeal pregnancy and gestation. It is quite possible that what Lovelace saw onboard this craft represents the future result of fecundity technology that is currently in development.

Terry Lovelace's description of the wall of incubating humans suggests something interesting and important is taking place. Also, because other abductees have independently observed and described seeing the same thing upon entering large triangular craft, including the aforementioned abductee Jerry Wills, there is reason to take this seriously. As a biological anthropologist, I find these accounts fascinating, particularly when considered in the context of the Extratempestrial Model. The visitors' apparent emphasis on fertility and gestation also raises numerous questions. For instance, what is the purpose of this widespread sperm and egg extraction? Why are our gametes seemingly being used to grow hybrid or cross-temporal babies? Does something happen in the human future that may require these practices?

As with most things related to fertility and reproduction, there is some debate about exogenesis (or ectogenesis) as a means of gestating human fetuses. Some critics feel it would disconnect us from the natural birthing process and the innate bond that forms between parent and child during birth. While this may be true to some extent, there are also reasons why ectogenesis could be a good thing for the future of humanity. For instance, beyond helping us overcome maternal and infant mortality issues resulting from the big-head-small-hole problem, exogenesis could help stave off a global population collapse, while also contributing to a more permanent state of ethnic and gender equality.

As discussed in the Villas-Boas case study, and examined further in *Identified Flying Objects*, sampling gametes from past human populations might be the only way of obtaining and interjecting novel gene variants into a stagnant future human gene pool to mitigate problems resulting from increased genetic homozygosity, as we trend toward becoming one enormous interbreeding and incestuous population on the island of Earth. In addition to this tendency toward extensive genetic homogenization, there is a potentially more serious trend happening now, which could have dire consequences for our sociocultural, medical, political, and economic future: global population implosion.

According to estimates and projections by the U.S. Census Bureau and the United Nations Population Division, fertility levels for the world as a whole fell by more than 40 percent between the early 1950s and the end of the century—a drop equivalent to over two births per woman per lifetime.[238]

Most people think of population growth and projected overpopulation numbers as a bad thing. This common Neo-Malthusian view looks at the last 200 years of accelerating population growth and perceived overpopulation and blames it for things like famine, poverty, limited economic development, instability, conflict, and environmental degradation. However, when you have some people dying of starvation, while others are dying from obesity, diabetes, and heart disease resulting from opulence and overconsumption, the issue is not scarcity, it is inequality.

There are numerous reasons why a growing or stable population can be a net positive. For example, resources aren't yet more scarce or expensive, largely because our technology continues to evolve. We have also been able to find new resources and more efficient ways of using them. A larger population means more consumers, but it also means a continuous supply of young people who are net producers, and while many countries transition to consumer-based economies, more people means more demand for goods and services. Even though it may seem counterintuitive, a rapid and sustained population decline could actually be more problematic, and currently, that is exactly what is happening.

For some time now, most countries have been trending toward population decline. Considered in association with reduced male and female fertility, and decreased sperm counts among males in the Western world, this trend is not only predicted to continue, but projections about the impact it could have on the global economy, and society as a whole, are stark. In fact, Elon Musk, cofounder of PayPal and founder, CEO, and chief engineer of SpaceX, recently stated that population collapse is "potentially the greatest risk to the future of civilization."[239]

According to a *Lancet* article by Vollset et al. (2020), the global total fertility rate (TFR) is forecast to drop to 1.66 in the year 2100. This means we will be well below the replacement rate of 2.1, resulting in marked population decline and a rapidly changing population structure. Their model also predicts that the global population will peak at 9.73 billion people in 2064, decline to 8.79 billion people in 2100, and because societies will tend toward a TFR lower than 1.5, once this decline begins, it is likely to continue inexorably.[240]

What is perhaps most troubling about these predictions is how this population decline will affect future human demographic structure. According to the article, the number of people under the age of five will drop from 681 million in 2017 to 401 million in 2100. Meanwhile, the number of people over age 80 will rise from 141 million in 2017 to 866 million in 2100. This could result in tremendous social, political, and economic change, as well as rampant labor shortages, which we are currently experiencing throughout the developed world.

Despite some potentially dire results stemming from an inverted demographic structure, there are positives as well. For instance, much of this trend toward population decline is the result of increased gender equality and more opportunities for women to attain educational and occupational goals, while also gaining more control over reproduction and family planning throughout much of the world. Circling back, exogenesis and external gestation may be a part of how we mitigate some of these future demographic problems, while continuing to expand gender and ethnic equality in occupational, economic, and political spheres.

External gestation and other fertility innovations and interventions, while consternation causing for some, could help ameliorate numerous future human fecundity, demographic, health, and social equality issues. For instance, ectogenesis could help us get around the big-head-small-hole problem; reduce maternal and infant mortality rates; minimize the high cost of and other challenges associated with cesarean sections; lessen the exorbitant cost of fertility consultation and medication while bolstering the odds of successful in vitro fertilization; reduce gender inequality resulting from women being the only ones currently able to bear offspring; and mitigate issues stemming from population decline, a shifting age structure, supply-demand imbalances in the labor market, and not having enough young workers to meet the needs of an aging population.

Taken together, these biocultural trends could help explain the walls of gestating fetuses that Lovelace, Jerry Wills, and others have reported seeing aboard these large triangular craft. It may also help explain why a multitude of more modern-looking humans were observed working as part of the crew, if current and future humans from different time periods are being bred and given different roles in these intertemporally integrated societies. Additionally, if large-scale fertility programs exist in the future, it could help explain why Travis Walton experienced something so similar toward the end of his abduction. Specifically, in addition to the more paedomorphic humans he initially encountered when he woke up on the UAP, Walton interacted with entirely modern-looking humans who worked alongside the others, which he described as appearing similar to one another, almost as if they shared a family connection.[241]

In the same way we currently breed prized steers, horses, dogs, orchids, and countless other species of plants and animals, these hybridization programs could be nothing more than adept human breeding programs. Our distant descendants might be using exogenesis and advanced genetic engineering technology to create lines of vivacious individuals to help alleviate problems stemming from difficult childbirths, trends toward global genetic homogenization, congenital diseases, reduced fecundity, inexorable population decline, and broad-based socio-cultural changes in the human future.

In addition to seeing multiple different human groups all working together on the same ship, there are other consistencies between Travis Walton and Terry Lovelace's accounts. For instance, both men recall being taken into a huge room that looked like an airplane hangar, where silvery saucer-shaped vehicles of various sizes were parked. As referenced in a few places above, numerous correlates also exist between the narratives of Terry Lovelace and Jerry Wills, who both describe being taken to and shown a large base on the dark side of the Moon. In fact, considering the vast consistencies among their individual reports, it's possible that each of these three men, Walton, Wills, and Lovelace, visited this same base around the same time.

Terry Lovelace was in the military at the time of his 1977 Devil's Den encounter. As such, it should be no surprise that his account also includes instances of intimidation, coercion, and a forced hypnosis session, where information was aggressively extracted from him by the

US Air Force's Office of Special Investigations (OSI), which reports directly to the Secretary of the Air Force. According to Lovelace, the OSI mandated that he undergo hypnosis in an attempt to reveal to the higher ups what he saw and what he had potentially photographed. It is important to note that Lovelace was adamant that these OSI officers already knew everything he was telling them and that they were far more focused on making sure he didn't have photographic evidence of anything he might have seen.

Because the OSI seemed to have already known about the triangular ship and the moon base, because Betty Rubble told Lovelace that we have been in contact with the visitors since 1947 and have been working closely with them for the last three decades, and because Lovelace observed entirely modern-looking humans wearing tan military flight suits with insignias of rank shown on their shoulders while he was on the triangular ship and at this moon base, there is reason to believe we have indeed been in close contact with the visitors for some time. Certain high-ranking members of the US government have also expressed that some factions of the military are knowledgeable about what is going on. For instance, in 1994, TV host Larry King aired a prerecorded interview with former senator and presidential candidate Barry Goldwater, who stated,

> I think the government *does* know. I can't back that up, but I think that at Wright-Patterson field, if you could get into certain places, you'd find out what the Air Force and the government knows about UFOs... I called Curtis LeMay and I said, 'General, I know we have a room at Wright-Patterson where you put all this secret stuff. Could I go in there?' I've never heard him get mad, but he got madder than hell at me, cussed me out, and said, 'Don't ever ask me that question again![242]

I am a very skeptical person, and I will be the first to admit that a lot of this ET collaboration, breeding program, moon base, military coverup stuff sounds a little crazy. However, after researching the UFO phenomenon for over a decade, none of what Lovelace describes seems overly outlandish, especially when viewed in the context of the Extratempestrial Model, where people from the future interact with people from their own past. Additionally, I've always found it odd that we haven't officially been back to the moon since the last US mission departed the lunar surface in December 1972,[243] even though the technology we've developed since that time would make it much easier now.

We are constantly sending out probes to take pictures of the surface of other planets and their moons, but we never see recent high-quality pictures of the entire backside of our own moon. There is this colossal ball of rock sitting up there in the sky, reflecting light down upon us most nights of the month, but we generally ignore the fact that we can only ever see one side of it. Along with Antarctica, and pretty much anywhere in the deep oceans of Earth, the backside of the moon would be an ideal place for future humans or extraterrestrials to hide a base, particularly if they have been working closely with people from our time for so long.

Terry Lovelace's experience is entirely consistent with other reports describing paedomorphic humans, aircraft, UFO hangars, exams, extractions, moon bases, lifelong chaperones, implants, and other interactions with these advanced beings and their technology. In fact, because Lovelace saw so many people being stripped naked and taken into examination rooms in an almost factory-like setting, many share the same experience from the same time. In this context, it is interesting to think that Lovelace may have watched an abduction unfold which is currently being recounted by one of these same people from their own vantage point.

Much about what Lovelace describes in his fascinating book, *Incident at Devils Den*, is also consistent with the Extratempestrial Model. This includes his lifelong experiences seeing the same woman who didn't age; the sperm extractions and artificial wombs; the modern human military personnel and plain-clothed humans he saw working alongside those with larger foreheads, bigger eyes, and telepathic abilities on large triangular ships and at a base on the dark side of the moon; the forced hypnosis by his superior officers and coercion by the US Air Force Office of Special Investigations who he was sure already knew everything he was telling them; and the large triangular craft characteristic of a floating fertility facility. Separately and together, his observations and experiences are in line with what we would expect to see in the context of cross-temporal contact.

Lovelace's account of seeing different forms of humans working together in various places at different times gives me hope that we are approaching a time when knowledge of these collaborative efforts becomes conventionally understood. In fact, this day of divulgence might not be too far off. For if we have been in contact with these visitors since 1947, and we have been working together for the last three decades, as Lovelace's chaperone Betty Rubble once told him, then existing barriers to intertemporal interaction may have already begun to be broken down, and we could be poised to learn the true nature of these long-standing relationships in the near, rather than distant, human future.

# Case Study 9

~

# 1979
# Lynda Jones
# Manchester, UK

*I remember at the point when we had turned to run away from the object, I saw several people running toward the object. These people looked like men, dressed in long dark coats and wearing trilby hats holding what looked like satchels. There was also a strange mist that surrounded them and when they got close to the object, they simply disappeared.*[244]

— LYNDA JONES

Another abduction case from the 1970s, with numerous parallels to others, is that of Lynda Jones, a 36-year-old homemaker from Didsbury, Manchester, in the UK. One evening during the summer, Jones was at home chatting with an old friend who had stopped over while her husband, Trevor, was on shift at a local factory from 2 to 10 p.m. Remembering her friend had ridden a bike with no headlamp, Jones suggested he begin to make his way home before it got dark, and she offered to show him a shortcut that would take them through some nearby fields.

Jones and her two children, aged 5 and 15, set out with her friend and arrived at the River Mersey around 7:30 p.m. After bidding farewell, Jones and her children began the return trip home. Because her husband would not be back for another two and a half hours, they took their time and occasionally stopped to admire wildflowers along the way, as Jones was rather passionate about flowers.

While admiring some wildflowers along the path, Lynda Jones's oldest child suddenly shouted out "Mum, the moon is coming toward us."[245] As she turned to see what all the commotion was about, Jones saw a strange object moving swiftly across the sky and over the Didsbury golf course on the other side of the river. Jones described it as looking like a large Frisbee, which was spinning along its axis while tilted at a slight angle.[246]

The strange object slowly and silently passed overhead, then dropped down in front of Lynda and her children on the other side of a flood embankment. Jones felt an overwhelming urge to investigate. At first, she walked toward the object, but as her excitement mounted, she began running up the flood embankment to get a better look. There she could see the large craft about 25 meters in front of her.

Now able to see it better, Jones described the object as having an oblong shape like a rugby ball. It was approximately 18 meters across, glowed a bright orange color, and had a detached bright white light on top. Jones also recalls that the object was spinning, and peculiarly, it disappeared and reappeared in front of them, as if it were fading in and out of existence.

She also remembered being astonished by an absolute silence that fell over the entire area. This complete calm that suddenly washed over Jones and her children in the presence of the UFO was remarkable and memorable. It was made more manifest by the fact that just across the River Mersey from where they were standing was the M60 Manchester Outer Ring Road, a busy highway circumscribing the city of Manchester. An all-encompassing quiet that occurs in the presence of these craft is an exceedingly common characteristic of close encounters, and it could potentially teach us much about these machines and how they are able to operate in our presence while often going unnoticed.

As discussed in the Corporal Armando Valdés case study, one explanation for the sweeping calm often observed by contactees and abductees is that these vehicles are capable of warping spacetime in their proximate vicinity. The differential rate of time's passage near these ships creates the sense that time inside this bubble has slowed or ceased entirely relative to the outside world, since no movement means no sound. This may also help explain why the ship Lynda Jones observed appeared to fade in and out of existence while it engineered the timescape around them.

During a keynote lecture at the 2021 Anomalous Aerospace Phenomena Conference, sponsored by the Scientific Coalition for UAP studies,[247] noted American engineer Dr. Harold (Hal) Puthoff drew on his 2010 paper "Advanced Space Propulsion Based on Vacuum (Spacetime Metric) Engineering,"[248] as well as a book by Paul Hill, former chief scientist at NASA Langley Research Center, titled *Unconventional Flying Objects*.[249] During his presentation, Dr. Puthoff contended that the utter silence and missing time experienced by so many contactees and abductees may be related to spacetime metric engineering, which he considers an important part of the functional capabilities of these craft.

> Basically, if you are able to change the temporal aspect of your surrounding space you can either speed it up or slow it down. The reports that often come forth, people say, 'well there I was, I was close to a craft and suddenly all the sounds of nature, the birds, the wind, you know I didn't hear anything.' Well if time has been slowed down in that area, and has gone into infrasonics so that you wouldn't hear it, that's one of the elements that you would expect to experience…
>
> So then you also have obviously both kinds of things where you would interpret it as missing time, because suddenly if time got slowed down, so maybe you might be, let's say, in the craft's vicinity slowed down for five minutes, meanwhile, outside several hours have gone by, then when you emerge you say 'ohh my gosh, I've got missing time.' It might not be that you actually missed any subjective time, it's just one of the consequences (of spacetime metric engineering).[250]

The visitors' ability to engineer the spacetime metric could also help explain other observed aspects of these craft and their flight characteristics, including how a roughly 30-ton ship can withstand estimated accelerations ranging from 100 gs to 1000s of gs, and travel through our atmosphere at upwards of 9,000 miles per hour with no sonic booms, air disturbances, or evidence of excessive heat, while also displaying "transmedium" capabilities, as they seamlessly move from air to water, and back again.[251] [252] Spacetime metric engineering may also help explain the bright light so often seen emanating from these ships, as well as why people who get close to them report suffering from sunburn-like injuries indicative of radiation damage, which would happen if the electromagnetic spectrum is blueshifted in association with this spacetime metric engineering. Dr. Puthoff also addressed these issues in his 2021 presentation.

> Under the conditions with which the spacetime metric has been engineered, to produce the kinds of effects you might expect to see with a UAP, you get blueshift, which means, first of all, some of that infrared is going to be upshifted into the visible part of the spectrum, so you expect craft to be quite bright, which is one of the things that is in fact reported....
>
> With this blueshift there is a prediction of nearfield exposure injuries. For example, the visible can be blueshifted up into the UV and you get sunburn injuries, often reported by people who claim to have encountered a powered up craft at relatively close range. Or if you're too close it can even, some of that visible spectrum, which ordinarily isn't harmful, can be shifted up into the soft x-ray region and you get radiation injury.[253]

Regarding the visitors' apparent ability to change the speed of time in the vicinity of these craft, it is interesting to note the juxtaposition between the Lynda Jones and Armando Valdés case studies. As Dr. Puthoff mentioned in the first quote, "if you are able to change the temporal aspect of your surrounding space you can either *speed it up or slow it down*." Both options appear to have played out separately in the Jones and Valdés encounters. For example, it is apparent from Lynda Jones's report that time was slowed down around them, as sound shifted into the infrasonic range and she experienced a couple hours of missing time. However, the opposite seems to have been the case with Armando Valdés, where he aged by five days during the 15-minute period that he was gone from his men, indicating that time moved much faster in proximity to that craft.

Once Valdés crossed into the proximate radius of the ship, which seemingly changed the temporal aspects of that surrounding space, and apparently by speeding up time relative to the outside reference frame of his platoon, he disappeared entirely. When he reemerged from this spacetime bubble, Valdés was five days older than the men with whom he had just shared temporal mutuality. By contrast, with Lynda Jones, and in other contact cases, rather than speeding up time, it appears to have slowed down within the confines of this warped spacetime bubble, which, as Dr. Puthoff notes, may help explain her missing time and why everything around them seemed to stop.

A slightly more extreme example of the differential passage of time in and around UFOs can be seen in the experience of a neatly dressed engineering executive, which Jacques Vallée recounts in his book *The Invisible* College. In July, 1961, while he was still a university student, the man was walking through the countryside with four other individuals while conducting archaeological field work when he suddenly became separated from the others. As he walked alone through the forest, the man came across a disc-shaped craft on the ground, which brought him inside via a translucent elevator. He was transported to a more remote area and was placed in front of a large computer-like "teaching machine" that was five feet tall and twenty feet long. The engineer spent three hours with this machine, which played recordings that fed information directly into his brain. He was then taken back to within a couple feet of the exact spot where he was last seen by the archaeologists, but he would soon learn that 18 days had passed since he became separated from the group, which to him, was just three hours earlier.

The engineering student's concerned father who worked in government amassed several military and police search parties to look for him over the course of those 18 days. And when they finally found him in the same place where he was last seen, the man's clothes were still clean, he did not need a shave, and the same flower he wore in the buttonhole of his shirt was not wilted in the least. While time often passes differently for those on or near a UFO, this undoubtedly classifies as one of the most extreme examples of divergent time. It is also interesting to note that following this intensive 3-hour information acquisition session, the man initially required a massive amount of sleep, but soon after the pattern shifted, and he found that he only needed a few hours of sleep each night. Back at university, he also discovered that new information now came easy to him and everything he was taught entered his mind with perfect clarity.

An aspect of the Leo Dworshak account also corroborates this notion that the visitors are capable of manipulating spacetime, and it sheds light on how they can operate these brightly lit machines without being detected. In his book, *UFOs Are with Us - Take My Word*, Dworshak recounts a conversation that took place during one of his last visits with the travelers, who by this point he had interacted with throughout much of his life. While standing outside the ship where they were speaking, Dworshak noticed how incredibly bright the lights on the craft were, and he asked, "does this light show up for any great distance?" The visitors replied, "yes." When Dworshak asked if they were worried about people noticing it, they replied,

> You have been cleared to enter our area, and as you have noticed, there was no movement around you when you were coming over to our ship. We have stopped all movement for three miles around us. There is no way that anything can move within that area. No person can approach the ship unless we allow them entrance. It will be some time, well in the future, before people will be able to understand and do much, if any, of what we are capable of doing now. This new understanding will make a tremendous change on your planet Earth.[254]

I have often wondered how these massive, brightly glowing objects can move into an area and abduct people without being seen, which occasionally occurs in heavily populated places, like suburban Manchester, for example. A potential answer to this question may lie in their ability to alter spacetime in and around these craft, speeding up, slowing down, or stopping time in its vicinity. This spacetime cloaking mechanism would allow the visitors to abduct people and go about their business without widespread knowledge of their presence.

If the visitors Lynda Jones encountered possessed the same technology that allowed them to construct a cloaked, spacetime bubble where time stopped for all but them, and no one else was allowed to enter this bubble, their activities wouldn't be detected by anyone in the outside world, regardless of how many people were in the area at that time. This could also help explain how Calvin Parker and Charles Hickson were abducted in a relatively populated area near the Pascagoula River without anyone noticing.

Possessing an ability to change the rate at which time passes indicates these visitors have mastered physics and engineering. Furthermore, if these beings have developed technology that allows them to alter the fabric of spacetime, it is reasonable to assume they can also travel through it at will. This may represent yet another indication that the intelligent beings piloting these craft are indeed our distant human descendants, who have discovered how to manipulate spacetime on both a large and small scale. Controlling time's passage in and around these ships while also using them to travel forward and backward through global spacetime.

Like Leo Dworshak, Lynda Jones and her children were permitted to move in the vicinity of the UFO that passed overhead and came to rest nearby. However, this craft appears to have stopped time in a much smaller area around them, compared to the three-mile radius described by Leo Dworshak's lifelong friends. Because the field Jones and her daughters were walking through was already void of people, this provided the visitors a clear space in which to slow time without disrupting the speed of life in the broader environs.

From her report, Lynda Jones also may have been under some form of hypnotic control within this warped spacetime bubble, considering her first response was to leave her children and walk, then run, toward the ship. While ostensibly the wrong thing to do when approached by a large unknown object with your children nearby, this may represent yet another example of UFO apathy. A similar situation occurred in the previous case study, where Terry Lovelace felt an inexplicable desire to go camping, in a very specific place on the outskirts of Devil's Den State Park, despite not owning any camping gear and never having felt an affinity for camping at any point prior. Additionally, once there, both Lovelace and his friend Toby nonchalantly acknowledged an enormous black triangular ship passing overhead before calmly nodding off to sleep in a state of misplaced tranquility.

It was only when her daughter shouted out "Mum, come back," that Lynda Jones snapped out of this trance and stopped running toward the ship. Once her UFO apathy subsided, Jones quickly transitioned to a state of fear, while also experiencing a strong feeling of déjà vu. Putting all this aside, Jones grabbed her children and ran swiftly down the embankment away from the ship, but she quickly realized that it was now moving alongside them. While running, Jones made a strange but revealing observation. The short grass they were running through had suddenly grown tall beneath their feet, rising almost six feet in height, while it was also being pushed down by a strong force from above.

This is an interesting aspect of the Jones encounter, and it again speaks to the differential passage of time in and around these craft. It is also important to note that for sounds to go into the infrasonic range and for everything nearby to have grown quiet, time must have initially slowed down for Lynda Jones. However, because the grass was now growing rapidly around them, the previous effect was reversed, and time had now sped up in the vicinity of this ship.

Something similar was also observed in the Travis Walton case, where vegetation close to where he was abducted had grown much faster than the flora farther from the site. In a 2015 *Huffpost* interview with writer and producer Lee Speigel, Travis Walton described more recent research into his abduction case, which included details about an advanced rate of growth in the trees surrounding the area where he was taken.

About 15 years later, it was discovered that the trees nearest to where [the UFO] hovered had been producing wood fiber at 36 times the rate it had in the 85 years before that, Walton says. More recently, a complete core sampling revealed that this thickened growth was only on the side of the trees towards, or in the direction that the craft had been.[255]

Lynda Jones initially claimed that once she and her children fled the ship they never stopped running until they were safe inside their house, but there are some indications that this was not the case. For instance, upon returning home, Jones noticed that the skin around her eyes was red and scaling. She also noticed that her husband was already home from work, and that it was now 10:50 p.m. This meant she lost almost two hours since she began walking home sometime before 9:00 p.m. As discussed above, this missing time could have been a result of the differential rate at which time passes near these objects. Although, as more details about the encounter eventually came to light, they indicate that Lynda Jones may have spent some time onboard the ship.

In an effort to discover the true nature of her experience, and to gain deeper insight into what might have happened during these missing moments, Lynda Jones, like so many other abductees, decided to undergo a series of hypnotic regression sessions. Each of these sittings were video recorded, though Jones found them to be too disturbing to watch. Despite her reluctance to look at them, the videos were useful for piecing together the details of what happened to Lynda Jones and her children near the River Mersey on the night of the encounter.

As indicated by the quote that begins this chapter, something Jones remembered during one of the hypnosis sessions was seeing people at the site of the abduction. However, these were not simply bystanders who happened to be in the area at that time. In addition to the men in fedoras described in her first quote, Jones observed other people who were relatively short and dressed in one-piece jumpsuits. Additionally, much like what Travis Walton and Terry Lovelace reported, Lynda Jones noted that the human men she and her children saw all looked nearly identical to one another.

Although Jones didn't initially retain conscious memories of being abducted, she must have encountered these men around the time of her capture. While accessing her repressed memories under hypnosis, Jones remembered feeling a floating sensation, then finding herself standing in a room surrounded by six people. She noted that these individuals also looked human, but rather than wearing the pervasive one-piece jumpsuits, they donned dark suits that resembled motorcycle garb. Like so many other abduction accounts, Jones stated that these people "looked Oriental, they had slanted eyes, dark hair and a yellow / olive complexion."[256] Additionally, much like Terry Lovelace's lifelong interaction with the woman he would call Betty in later life, Lynda Jones had the sense that she already knew one of the men in the room.

Like most abductions, Jones was then placed on a table and examined. After learning this, she began to wonder if the examination might be related to a number of medical issues she had shortly after the UFO encounter, including some strange things involving her menstrual cycle and reproductive system. After the abduction, but before learning these details through hypnosis, Jones visited the doctor and was shocked to learn she had suffered a miscarriage, though she had no memory of being pregnant. Confused by this, Jones saw a specialist and was informed that her fallopian tubes had scar tissue on them, which was caused by an ectopic pregnancy. This was particularly surprising because tubal pregnancies are extremely painful, and occasionally fatal, but in addition to having no memory of a recent pregnancy, she couldn't recall feeling any pelvic or abdominal pain.

After learning about her pregnancy, miscarriage, and fallopian tube scar tissue, a flood of memories began to pour in about strange things that had happened throughout her life. Jones also came to realize that the missing time she experienced that summer's evening was not the first time it had happened, as she began to recall numerous instances of missing time prior to this most recent UFO encounter. One of the earliest incidents occurred when Jones was just a small girl and went missing for a few hours while playing in a field near her home. She couldn't recall seeing anything odd during this time, nor does she remember having ever left the field, but she had disappeared for some time while her family frantically searched the area.

Another odd and inexplicable event occurred in 1972, when Lynda Jones and her husband Trevor went out for a drink at the Swan public house in Knutsford, a market town in Cheshire, UK. While en route to this libation destination around 9:00 p.m., the couple stopped at a traffic light, when all of a sudden their car began spinning. The next thing they remembered was driving away from the stoplight, turning a corner, and finding the pub was in complete darkness, as it was now 2:30 a.m.[257] While the amount of missing time people experience can vary widely, this occasion was a longer duration than most, since nearly five and a half hours had been wiped from their memories.

Something similar happened again in 1988, while Trevor and Lynda were driving home after visiting some friends in Nottingham. As they made their way through the countryside, the car headlights began to fade, making it hard for Trevor to see. As he pulled off the road to stop, the couple looked up and saw a large, bright, circular craft rising above their car. It had apparently been there for some time, but they only remembered seeing it once it ascended in front of them. This memory of seeing the craft rise into the night sky most likely followed the abduction, since it would be easier to wipe their memory of the craft approaching, and the abduction occurring, when the two were on board, while it seems harder to erase a memory of the visitors as they leave the scene once the couple is back in their car. Like their Swan hotel and pub experience, the couple returned home to find that the trip back from Nottingham took three hours longer than it should have.

Lynda Jones also recalls seeing a man in a fedora who would occasionally appear or disappear in front of her. On one such occasion, Jones saw the man in her back garden. Alarmed, she called the police, but when they made their way into her backyard the man suddenly disappeared, right in front of the police officer. Another odd incident occurred when she was instructed to visit the hospital for a specific test, but she later discovered there was no record of her visit, the treatment, or the doctor who administered it.

Like so many other abductees, Jones also believes she had a tracking device implanted in her. This makes sense when considering the specific nature of her encounters, since knowing her location at any given time would be critical to the visitors if they were in fact impregnating her and monitoring the gestating fetus for eventual extraction. Another indication that Lynda Jones might have been fitted with a tracking device may be seen in how her name would mysteriously disappear from an identification tag she was required to wear while working as a beauty consultant in 1987. By this time, Jones was keenly aware of and more interested in the odd occurrences in her life. As such, she hired an investigator to analyze her name tag, who determined it was adversely affected by radio waves, though it is unclear how radio waves would cause her name to be erased from the badge.

Looking across accounts, it is fascinating how each abductee has a different relationship with their memories regarding what they are able or unable to remember. Prior to her 1979 abduction, Lynda Jones remained largely blind to the reality of what was happening throughout her life. By comparison, Terry Lovelace was at least partly aware of his encounters, as he had vague memories of circus monkeys beginning at a young age. However, it wasn't until the USAF OSI forced him to undergo hypnosis that the true nature of these events emerged. Although Lovelace was not entirely privy to the details of what was happening to him, his knowledge of the monkey men, and general awareness of these encounters, suggests his mind was more resistant to whatever method the visitors used in their efforts to mask conscious memories of these interactions.

As mentioned previously, the decision to erase an abductee's memory appears to be related to how traumatic the experience was for them. In this way, the manifest function of these memory wipes and implanted screen memories is likely to reduce post-traumatic stress resulting from being kidnapped, probed, and prodded by these seemingly alien beings, as a benevolent act aimed at mitigating the negative effects of an otherwise upsetting occurrence. This is also indicated by the fact that screen memories are most often things that seem like they would be calming to us, like owls, circus monkeys, and Disney characters, for example. Although, the circus monkey screen memoires Terry Lovelace was given appear to have elicited the opposite effect.

There are many odd aspects of abduction encounters, though after reading enough of them, they start to become normalized, despite deviating wildly from our everyday experiences. It is also important to acknowledge the confusion and stress these events elicit among a certain percentage of abductees, and there is always the issue of ethics and human rights. While human rights are not universal and shift through time, they do seem to be evolving. For instance, it was relatively recently that people felt they had the right to breed, sell, enslave, and kill entire human groups deemed different from themselves. With the issue of abduction, and the mental and physical stress it often causes, we must wonder if the ends justify the means, especially when it involves things like impregnating people against their will and removing gestating fetuses from them.

This is particularly troubling considering the high rate of recurrence where these intrusive acts are perpetrated against abducted women. In addition to the Lynda Jones case study, in a well-documented and well-publicized case, Clayton and Donna Lee, a husband and wife from Houston, Texas, report having been abducted several times throughout their lives. On one particular occasion, Donna Lee recalls having a gestating fetus removed from her uterus by beings she described as "tall, slender, blonde," and who "looked human but not human, not quite human; they didn't really use their voices to talk."[258]

Numerous women, including one in a subsequent case study, have also described situations in which they were abducted, impregnated, and placed back in bed with a clouded memory, only to be abducted again later to have the developing fetus removed from their bodies. Still others have reported being given a small child to hold and told it was a baby they helped create, which includes a man who was told telepathically that he was the father of two "baby aliens" he could see floating in an incubator.[259] These intrusive procedures don't just rob women of developing embryos and fetuses, and occasionally leave scars on their reproductive organs, such as in the case of Lynda Jones, but they can leave lasting psychological scars as well. In addition to the horrors of being abducted, undressed, examined, and enduring unsolicited touching, tissue sampling, and gamete extraction, being given a baby and told it's yours, but never being able to see it again, would unquestionably cause intense stress and anxiety.

These acts are also paradoxical, considering the frequency with which love and empathy are expressed by these visitors. Because they espouse such harmonious sentiments, while also kidnapping, impregnating, and occasionally raping people, it suggests that whatever purpose these abductions serve, they must be incredibly imperative to the visitors. Furthermore, if they are someday shown to be our distant descendants, one can only hope that the occasionally traumatic events perpetrated upon people in their past contribute in some meaningful way to the greater good of our omnipresent species.

# Case Study 10

# 1980
# The Rendlesham Forest Incident Suffolk, UK

*I've never believed that it was extraterrestrial. I still don't. We believe it's, based on the evidence, it's an interdimensional-type craft, and it's clearly us from the future.*[260]

– JIM PENNISTON

The Rendlesham Forest incident is a well-known case. In fact, it is often referred to as "Britain's Roswell." However, other than the fact that both involved US military personnel, and both were widely publicized, these two events have relatively little in common. The Rendlesham Forest incident does share many common features with other contact cases though, and there is potentially much we can learn from it, including certain aspects of the human future. This is especially true if we can admit as evidence the testimony of Sergeant Jim Penniston (ret.), who had the closest encounter of anyone involved in the incident.

Since the end of World War II, and more so following the Cuban Missile Crisis of October 1962, tensions ran high between the United States and the Soviet Union, although toward the end of the détente period in the late 1970s, the friction between these two nations began to subside, for a while. Throughout much of this Cold War period, and up until 1993, the United States Air Force was permitted to lease and operate the joint Royal Air Force / US Air Force bases, Woodbridge and Bentwaters, located near the historic towns of Ipswich and Woodbridge in Suffolk, England. Because these bases were much closer to the Soviet

Union than the United States, they provided a tactical advantage for the USAF during this period of pronounced pomposity.

The Rendlesham Forest lies between these two military installations, and at approximately 0300 hours, a bright white light was seen emanating from an area of the forest just outside the east gate of RAF Woodbridge.[261] Fearing the integrity of the base had been compromised, two patrolmen alerted their commanding officers about the strange light and asked the on-duty flight chief, Woodbridge base Staff Sergeant Jim Penniston, for permission to investigate. Penniston granted permission and joined Staff Sergeant Bud Stefens and Airman First Class John Burroughs in the initial investigation of the unusual light observed near the base.

Their first thought was an aircraft must have crashed, but Staff Sergeant Stefens insisted that was not the case, since he had seen the light slowly descend through the trees and into the forest without an ensuing explosion.[262] Stefens's ground observation was also corroborated by radar images from both RAF Bentwaters and RAF Watton in Norfolk, which showed an object appear shortly after midnight on December 27, perform high-speed and high-altitude aerial maneuvers, then disappear into the Rendlesham Forest near the Bentwaters base in Suffolk.[263]

These aerial maneuvers were also observed at close range by an Air Force pilot who was sent to investigate. According to Mal Scurrah, one of the radar operators working that night,

> We didn't have the faintest idea what it was. We checked through the air traffic agencies. There should have been nothing in that area at the time. The only thing we could do was send a jet aircraft in to find out what it was. They got to within about a quarter of a mile and the pilot suddenly started reporting that they could see a very bright light in the sky in front of them. It was stationary on the screen and then, in seconds, it moved off at a fantastic rate of speed. Within the space of five minutes, it was reaching 90,000 feet and higher and we lost it off the top end of the radar scope. There's nothing we have in this day that can perform those kinds of maneuvers; the pilots wouldn't be able to take it.[264]

Colonel Charles Halt, deputy commander at the Bentwaters base, also saw UFOs at Rendlesham Forest in late December 1980. He submitted an official memo describing these UAP events to the Ministry of Defense (MOD) on January 13, 1981. In a more recent interview with the British Broadcasting Company (BBC), he offered "new evidence" confirming these early radar indicators of a strange, fast-moving object, which descended into the Rendlesham Forest on the night in question.

> I have confirmation that (Bentwaters radar operators) saw the object go across their 60-mile (96 km) scope in two or three seconds, thousands of miles an hour, he came back across their scope again, stopped near the water tower, they watched it and observed it go into the forest where we were. At Wattisham, they picked up what they called a 'bogie' and lost it near Rendlesham Forest. Whatever was there was clearly under intelligent control.[265]

Shaken by what he'd seen, Staff Sergeant Bud Stefens opted to stay at the base while Penniston, Burroughs, and Airman First Class Edward Cabansag, who was working security alongside S.Sgt. Penniston that night, ventured into Rendlesham Forest to investigate.[266] According to one source, as these three men entered the woods they could see a saucer-shaped craft with diminutive but large-headed beings, who were levitating above the ground in a beam of light, while scurrying about busily as if they were making repairs to their ship.[267]

According to the official report filed by Col. Charles Halt, the object had a metallic exterior and was more triangular in shape; it was approximately 2-3 meters across and 2 meters tall, and it had flashing red lights toward the top, with blue lights at the bottom. He also stated that it hovered or rested on three legs just above the ground. As the patrolmen approached the craft, it maneuvered through the trees away from them and disappeared. Concomitantly, the animals on a nearby farm suddenly went into a panicked frenzy.

As Cabansag, Burroughs, and Penniston approached the object, they began to experience problems with their radios, which is common in contact cases, and may be related to the electromagnetic properties of these craft. Penniston ordered Cabansag to stay back so he could act as a relay with the base, but as Burroughs and Penniston got closer to the object, their transmissions deteriorated further, and eventually, all radio contact was lost. As stated in Col. Charles Halt's report, Burroughs and Penniston also noted that the forest animals around them were acting erratically.[268]

At approximately 50 meters, Penniston was able to see a metallic object resting on three legs. A later sketch of what he remembered seeing looked something like a hybrid between a triangle and a disc-shaped UFO. Penniston could also see a shaft of light emanated downward from a hole in the bottom of the ship, and as he approached to within 20 meters, he noticed that the air seemed to be charged with static electricity, which is again suggestive of a strong electromagnetic field around these objects. Penniston may have been fortunate that this vehicle was grounded as well, or he could have been struck by a high-voltage static electric discharge like that which hit Travis Walton when he approached a UFO in the Apache-Sitgreaves National Forest in 1975.

As Penniston moved even closer to the craft, he noticed the forest, which had just been bustling with the sound of frantic animals, was now completely quiet. At this distance, somewhere within 20 meters, Penniston appears to have entered the same type of spacetime warp bubble experienced by Lynda Jones in the previous case study, which may relate to the visitors' ability to engineer the spacetime metric, as proposed by Dr. Hal Puthoff and Paul Hill, which results in a speeding up or slowing down of time in proximity to these craft.[269] At this distance, S.Sgt. Jim Penniston also felt a physical change, which he referred to as a "sphere of influence."

My movements were labored up to that point. I was feeling like I was walking through a pool of water. I was struggling to get close to it. And when I got within 10 feet of it, all of that dissipated. And there was like a, I call it a sphere of influence around it, around the immediate craft itself.[270]

Now within 10 feet, Penniston could make out more details of the craft, which he described as being about three meters wide, two meters high, and largely triangular in shape. He also stated that it had a shiny, black, and almost glasslike surface, with no visible means of propulsion, no rivets or seams, and with the same red and blue lights described in Col. Halt's report to the MOD.[271] Feeling intrepid, Penniston decided to touch the ship, which he described as very smooth and rather warm, despite the chilly late-December temperature. Penniston also noted a series of symbols on the exterior of the craft, which felt rough on the otherwise smooth surface.

One of the most intriguing parts of Penniston's account is that when he touched these symbols he remembers being engulfed in a brilliant white light and experiencing complete sensory deprivation. Penniston also experienced about 45 minutes of missing time while in contact with the ship, at least relative to the reference frame of those outside this sphere of influence. After the sensory deprivation subsided and his sight returned, Penniston could see he was still standing next to the object, which was now glowing a vibrant white color. It then lifted about a meter off the ground, maneuvered through the trees, climbed slowly upward, and once it was above the canopy, it darted off at a tremendous speed and disappeared from sight.

Shortly after this encounter, Penniston began seeing a series of ones and zeros in his mind, which he believed were telepathically communicated to him when he was engulfed in bright white light while touching the hiero-glyphic-like symbols on the outside of the craft. Penniston also felt a strong urge to write this series of ones and zeros down, so he transcribed them in a notebook where he had been documenting other aspects of the encounter.

That first night I kept seeing these ones and zeros, ones, and zeros. I decided, I said, 'well, I can actually see these so well, I think I can write that down.' I could write the 1, 0, 0, 0, 1, and the thing was, when I started it, I started feeling better. And the more I wrote, the better I felt. So, I took those pages and left them in the notebook and never looked at it again, until 30-some years later. And that was by accident.[272]

Having allayed his compulsive desire to notate these numerals, Penniston set the notepad aside and the digits began to fade from memory. Like many contactees who wish to learn more about missing time associated with a UFO encounter, on September 10, 1994, Jim Penniston visited a professional hypnotherapist for a regressive hypnotherapy session. This meeting was videorecorded and later made it into the public domain. While under hypnosis, Penniston revealed fascinating details about the origin and intent of the visitors he encountered in Rendlesham Forest nearly a decade and a half prior.

During the session, Penniston spoke of being interrogated by two agents from the US Air Force Office of Special Investigations (AFOSI) and one agent from the British military, who asked if there were any beings present when he encountered the metallic craft. Penniston responded that there were "visitors" present, and notably, that they were time travelers from the future. He reiterated that they were not extraterrestrials, but were humans, coming back through time to collect genetic material to help alleviate problems they were having with reproduction in the future.[273]

> **Penniston:**   They (the visitors) are asking me if I see binary code? I see the binary code. They are time travelers.... They are us.[274]

After Penniston divulged that the visitors were future humans and not extraterrestrials, the hypnotherapist asked what they need from us. Penniston stated that he wasn't sure, but that it had something to do with chromosomes that they take from us. However, rather than using us as some sort of breeding stock, as was suggested by the hypnotherapist, Penniston stated that they are taking gametes, and sometimes fetuses, to help with reproductive problems in the human future.

> **Interviewer:** Do they ever take fetuses?
> **Penniston:**   If it is tasked, they do. There are different ships for tasking. The government agents know about this.... That's why they want to contain the situation.[275]

This statement is particularly noteworthy because of its relevance to the other case studies, and most notably, the previous two. For instance, Lynda Jones reports having gametes and a developing fetus extracted from her person. Jones also stated that her reproductive services were very important to the visitors, beginning early in life, and to a greater extent once she reached reproductive maturity. Terry Lovelace's account is also notable in this context, since he claims to have seen developing fetuses floating in a pinkish liquid, inside exogenesis chambers, onboard a massive triangular craft. In conjunction with Penniston's above statement, this triangular ship may be an example of one that was specifically designed and built for a specific task, which in this case, appears to be related to reproductive tasks.

Similar to Terry Lovelace's experience, while Jim Penniston was being interrogated by agents from the US Air Force Office of Special Investigations, he started to realize that the interrogators already knew about everything he was telling them, and rather than seeking information, they were simply trying to "contain the situation." Their attempt at damage control also involved intentionally confusing the details of each man's account, which was done to dimmish the credibility of their testimonies and to cast doubt on the reality of the event. This imposed misapprehension is revealed in Penniston's hypnotherapy session.

> **Interviewer:** They see you as (requiring) damage control?
>
> **Penniston:** (Yes), they see me and John Burroughs and they're worried about Col Halt. They know all about us.
>
> **Interviewer:** What are the intelligence agents (NSA Agents) going to do with you?
>
> **Penniston:** They tell me when I was at the East Gate with John, they have five different stories to tell. It's important to scramble dates (which confuses and undermines consistency of eyewitness testimonies so there's no credibility with the public and media).[276]

In addition to revealing information about the staged coverup, the origin of these visitors as future humans, and their intent to collect gametes and genetic material from past peoples, Penniston provided an interesting and subtle detail about how these craft may physically travel back through time.

**Interviewer:** Does the government believe what you are saying about them coming from the future?

**Penniston:** Oh yes...This time they (time travelers) were having problems, but they got their machine off. They have to be in space to travel. *They need speed to travel.* (emphasis added)

**Interviewer:** How far into the past can they go?

**Penniston:** These ships can go forty or fifty thousand years. They can't go back much further. They might not get back.[277]

This statement corroborates a previously proposed concept related to how high-speed travel, while light cones are oriented toward the past, may allow our time-traveling descendants to venture deeper into that past. Light cones can be understood as having the same properties as light, meaning they travel at the speed of light, they propagate like light, and their trajectory can be warped and curved in the same way as light. When light cones approach an extremely large, dense, or highly energetic mass, their path becomes curved, and they can tilt (or tip over) while still maintaining their conical shape. Remarkably, as light cones tip over in association with a warpage of proximate spacetime, world lines within them can deviate from a strictly past-to-future linear trajectory. This means that anyone or anything traveling along a world line that lies within the margins of a tilted light cone in their localized region of spacetime, would now be permitted to travel into the global past via a closed timelike curve (CTC).

Albert Einstein's 1905 paper, "On the Electrodynamics of Moving Bodies," demonstrated that space and time are relative to the observer.[278] Then, ten years later, he showed how gravity and the curvature of spacetime can elicit these same time dilation effects.[279] [280] [281] As part of his 1915 General Theory of Relativity, Einstein published 10 nonlinear partial differential equations, known as the Einstein Field Equations. Many solutions to these field equations followed, and a number of them allow for the formation of closed timelike curves. According to mathematician and astrophysicist William B. Bonnor,

> In general relativity a timelike curve in spacetime represents a possible path of a physical object or an observer. Normally such a curve will run from past to future, but in some spacetimes, timelike curves can intersect themselves, giving a loop, or a closed timelike curve (CTC).[282]

These are crucial for understanding how we may someday achieve backward time travel since CTCs create loops that connect different points in time, which could allow someone from the future to visit the past. According to the astrophysicists Francisco Lobo and Paulo Crawford:

> A closed timelike curve (CTC) allows time travel, in the sense that an observer which travels on a trajectory in spacetime along this curve, returns to an event which coincides with the departure. The arrow of time leads forward, as measured locally by the observer, but globally he/she may return to an event in the past.[283]

Additionally, according to Leo C. Stein, NASA Einstein fellow in the Department of Astronomy at Cornell University,

> A closed timelike curve (CTC) is a trajectory that's perfectly normal everywhere, always sticking to the rules of moving in a timelike direction, always going (locally) forward in time, and yet ends up back where (and when) it starts…. The existence of a CTC in some spacetime would mean that a time machine is possible, just by going along that trajectory, and without violating any laws of physics.[284]

In *Identified Flying Objects,* I proposed that high-speed motion, and the time dilation effects resulting from it, may allow future human time travelers to move faster and farther back through time, if they're moving at very high speed while light cones in their localized reference frame are oriented toward the past. This could allow a time traveler to voyage deeper into the past and well beyond the place and time from which they left, essentially causing a closed timelike curve (CTC) to become an open timelike curve (OTC).

> Through the mechanism of time dilation—resulting from high-speed motion and/or increased gravitation—it may be possible to speed the rate at which a time machine moves backward through time, potentially allowing it to go even farther into the past at an even faster rate. Einstein's theory of special relativity demonstrated how high-speed motion, relative to those in a rest frame, allows for time travel to the future.
>
> But, if a time machine moves at a high rate of speed while light cones are oriented toward the past—as measured locally by the observer—this would be expected to move the craft even deeper into that past, and perhaps far beyond the origins of both themselves and their time machine.
>
> In other words, if a rapidly rotating disc with the right mass-energy-rotation parameters were to facilitate backward time travel, then sustained high-speed motion while spinning, and while light cones are tilted toward the past, may allow it to go even deeper into the future of that past.[285]

There are numerous indications that UFOs are not only capable of very high speed and almost instantaneous accelerations, but also that they possess the ability to manipulate spacetime. Considering the observable characteristics of UFOs, what was conveyed to Jim Penniston through binary code, and what makes sense in the context of both special and general relativity, it is reasonable to assume that these visitors are future humans, and at least some of the UFOs they pilot are time machines, which Penniston also believes as a result of his very close encounter.[286]

The upper limit of 40,000 – 50,000 years for how far back in time these visitors can go also seems logical. Physical constraints related to the speed limit of light, the advanced materials and engineering needed to construct these machines, and the incredible energy required to send one of these ships speeding through space for a sustained period of time may limit how far back into the past they can travel. However, as technology, material science, and engineering continue to evolve beyond the time from which these specific visitors came, humans from an even farther point in the more distant future may develop the ability to penetrate even deeper into our collective past, well beyond what the visitors Penniston encountered could accomplish at that time.

Jim Penniston's revelation that the visitors are returning to the past to get DNA and "chromosomes" to help with reproductive problems also corroborates previously stated assertions concerning our fecundity future. As discussed in the Antonio Villas-Boas and Terry Lovelace case studies, changing demographic and fertility trends, latent consequences of genetic engineering (CRISPR), fertility interventions, and an increase in the speed and scale of international travel and the potential for genetic homogenization could be problematic for the human reproductive future.

In addition to the information about why the visitors were here, Penniston was told from what specific future time they had come, and as indicated in a quote above, this revelation occurred quite by accident. On October 2, 2010, while casually discussing the hieroglyphic symbols he'd sketched in his notebook with investigative journalist Linda Moulton Howe on the film set of a TV documentary series, she asked Penniston about the ones and zeros he had written down in that same notebook 30 years earlier, and alerted him to the fact that the code could potentially be deciphered.[287] Interested in what the message might say, Penniston submitted the long string of digits to professional binary code expert, Joe Luciano.

Binary numbers get a value based on their relative position in the series. Luciano used sets of eight bits, or one byte, to map the 256 binary digits Penniston recorded with the help of an ASCII chart.[288] [289] The results of this deciphering process revealed both text and GPS coordinates, which supported Penniston's claim that these visitors were time travelers, while also providing some information about the specific time in the future from which they came. Below is what was deciphered from the 16 pages of binary code Penniston recorded in his notebook following the encounter in Rendlesham Forest in late December 1980.

Exploration *of* Humanity 666 8100
52.0942532N 13.131269W
Continuous for Planetary ADVAN*???*
*Fourth* Coordinate Continu*ot UQS CbPR* BEFORE
*16.*763177N   89.117768W
34.800272N   111.843567W
29.977836N   31.131649E
14.701505S   75.167043W
36.256845N   117.100632E
37.110195N   25.372281E
Eyes of Your Ey*es*
Origin 52.0942532N   13.131269W
Origin Year 8100 [290] [291]
* Italics indicates possible transmission errors or characters that were interpreted by the binary code expert in areas of possible transmission errors.

The deciphered binary code indicates these visitors hail from about 6,000 or 8,000 years in the future, if interpreted using our current dating system or simply years from present, respectively. This information about their temporal origins may also help support the previously proposed notion of both physiological and technological *temporal ancestry*. Although Penniston never saw these visitors, one report described diminutive humans with large round heads who appeared to be hurriedly moving around the craft as if they were attempting to fix something.

Based on accelerating craniofacial trends throughout the hominin past, this description of the observed individuals is consistent with what we might expect to see in the physiological form of people 6,000–8,000 years in the future. They would still look entirely human, but with accentuated traits consistent with the most pervasive trends in hominin evolution, encephalization, and facial retraction. If we can extrapolate further, the tall and short "greys," and perhaps the small percentage described as insect or reptile-looking, may hail from a deeper point in our evolutionary future, considering their more divergent craniofacial, technological, and telepathic traits. These outlying humans would have had more time to evolve their technology and physical form, to the extent that they may be capable of traveling from a future time beyond the 50,000-year limit foisted upon Penniston's extratempestrials.

With many aspects of the Extratempestrial Model, it is helpful to conceptualize how our ancestors may view us, if we were the ones traveling into the past. For instance, depending on the ancestry (formerly "race") of the modern humans going back through time, our forebears may notice slight differences in skin color, eye color, eye shape, head shape, height, weight, etc., and these distinctions would be more pronounced if they visited a geographic group with different ancestry than their own. For instance, if a modern human from east Asia traveled back in time to examine a group living in Sub-Saharan Africa 7,000 years ago, their technology and physiology may seem otherworldly, even though 7,000 years isn't a very long time, representing only 0.1% of hominin evolution. Though because our current technology is far more advanced, and because Sub-Saharan Africans never interacted with people from east Asia back then, these modern humans would seem alien to the people of that time, as geographic racial differences compound variation resulting from evolutionary change.

To extend the metaphor deeper into the past, if modern humans boarded a spinning disc and traveled 500,000 years into the past to abduct our *Homo heidelbergensis* ancestors, they would describe us as having a large bulbous cranium and high forehead, large projecting eyes, slender bodies, a small nose and mouth, and a pointy chin; in essence, all the same traits we attribute to the visitors in our own time. Additionally, depending on the sex, age, and ancestry of the individuals who ventured back from our present, these Middle Pleistocene abductees may also describe us as having more slanted eyes, a different skin color, very little body hair, and potentially, completely bald heads. However, this far back in the distant past, slight geographic racial disparities among modern humans would be less significant relative to the vast evolutionary differences that exist between us and them. In other words, even if an east Asian, Native American, Sub-Saharan African, and Western European were all aboard the same ship that traveled 500,000 years into the past, we might all look about the same to them.

As we descend upon these *Homo heidelbergensis* hominins, they would also see us coming down from the sky, which may cause them to falsely conclude that we came from the stars, as opposed to our rightful origin in time. In the same way our ancient ancestors would struggle to recognize modern humans, and the intricate instrumentation we currently possess, it is easier to appreciate how we would be limited in our ability to comprehend the morphology and technology of future humans visiting their own past. However, by examining the long-term biological and cultural trends that have gotten us to where we are today, while seriously considering what might be fleeting glimpses of our own future across contact cases, the broader composite mosaic of human time may begin to come into view.

# Case Study 11

⌒

# 1985
# Whitley Strieber
# New York, USA

*Across the depression to my left there was a small individual whom I could see only out of the corner of my eye. This person was wearing a gray-tan body suit and sitting on the ground.... There were two dark eyeholes and a round mouth hole. I had the impression of a face mask.... While the presence of others remains vague in my mind, the individual to my left made a clear impression. I do not know why, but I had the distinct feeling that this was a woman, and so I shall refer to her in the feminine.*[292]

– WHITLEY STRIEBER

*The alien in the visions of Whitley and countless other abductee accounts is often described as insectoid in form. These haunting figures are frequently compared with an immense praying mantis or a human-sized insect. They communicate with humans telepathically. The immense almond-shaped eyes are compared with those of bugs. And the visionaries repeat again and again their intuited sense that what they saw was us coming back from the future.*[293]

– JEFFREY J. KRIPAL

In addition to Betty and Barney Hill, Whitley Strieber was one of the first abductees to publicly reveal the details of his encounter. This brave decision proved to be instrumental in helping countless others who endured similar incidents but who felt sequestered by their societal circumstances. Partly because Strieber is an adept storyteller and a kind empathetic soul, millions of people who lacked knowledge of the abduction phenomenon suddenly became acutely aware of this odd actuality in 1987 when he published *Communion, A True Story*.[294] Soon after the book came out, Strieber and his wife Anne received tens of thousands of letters from other abductees and contactees, which are now part of the Archives of the Impossible collection conserved at the Woodson Research Center at Rice University in Houston, Texas.

These letters also helped Strieber, as they bolstered the veracity of his own experience and demonstrated just how common these incidents are. As mentioned at the beginning of this book, the cover of *Communion* was instrumental in sparking my interest in the phenomenon, when I happened to look up and see it on the living room shelf around the age of eight. The long, strange trip that followed came full circle about a year after publishing *Identified Flying Objects*, when Whitley invited me to be a guest on his podcast, *Dreamland*, which aired March 13, 2020.[295] It was an honor to speak with Whitley about myriad topics related to the UFO phenomenon, human evolution, time travel, consciousness, near-death experiences, and past lives. This conversation also gave me the opportunity to ask him something I had wondered about for some time, which involved the cranial shape of the being depicted on the cover of his book.

In many ways it resembles the classic "grey" alien, with large eyes and diminutive facial features. However, the individual on his book's cover had an unusually short and narrow neurocranium. This perplexed me because in nearly every other depiction of these beings they have overly large, round, and occasionally elongated heads. During our conversation, Whitley stated that the visitors who took him did in fact have big, round skulls, beyond what is depicted on his book's cover. I was happy to hear this since it had always seemed strange that this one individual had a different neurocranial shape than what is ubiquitously described. In addition to their typical craniofacial form, Strieber's description of the visitors' physiology, craft, tools, technology, wardrobe, and what they did to him during the encounter is quite consistent with other abduction reports.

Whitley Strieber was an accomplished writer even before *Communion* was published. He had authored numerous books, including the popular horror novels *The Wolfen* (1978) and *The Hunger* (1981), which were both made into feature films. *Communion* was different though, for in it he describes the true story of an abduction that took place at his cabin in upstate New York on the night of December 26, 1985. Like so many other abductees, this would prove to be just one of many encounters throughout this life.

The incident that occurred in late December was predated by an unusual event that happened a couple months earlier, on October 4 of the same year. That night, Whitley, his wife Anne, and their teenage son were staying at their cabin in upstate New York, along with two close friends they invited up for the weekend. They ate at a local restaurant, then arrived at the cabin around nine at night. Sometime around midnight, Strieber recalls waking up and seeing a bright blue light, which wasn't coming from the neighbor's house, a car on the road, or any other source he could identify. It suddenly occurred to him that the chimney must be on fire, and while this caused great panic, oddly, he fell into a deep sleep. The next thing he remembers is waking to see that the entire house was now engulfed in a bright light that extended deep into the fog. Assuming the chimney fire had spread to the roof, he leapt out of bed and ran to tell the others, but at that point the light suddenly disappeared.

At the time, Strieber didn't think anything strange had happened, though he did have a sense that something was wrong, and his behavior and mental state began to change. He also became acutely anxious about intruders in the cabin. Each night he would arm the security system and check in closets and under beds, worried that someone or something may be inside. Not long after, the cause of his consternation became clear.

It was a cold and cloudy night on December 26, 1985, and there was a fair amount of snow on the ground. After activating the burglar alarm and checking the house for intruders, Strieber went to bed around ten o'clock and was asleep by eleven. Later that night, he was startled awake by a peculiar whooshing and swirling noise, similar to the sound Terry Lovelace remembered hearing each time a UFO approached. Strieber also had the sense that there were people racing around his bedroom, which was strange considering the security alarm panel next to the bed showed the system was fully functional and that it had not been triggered.

Despite the strange sounds, and now having actual intruders in his house, rather than investigating, in an epic instance of UFO apathy, Strieber just lay back down and went to sleep. This counterintuitive behavior is incredibly common across abductee reports. In Strieber's case and numerous others like it, this behavior suggests the visitors possess the ability to consciously control our minds and emotions, which is likely done to make the abduction safer and easier for them.

Those who are not put to sleep or kept asleep remotely are occasionally made to lose consciousness with an anesthetic mask, like that placed over the face of Travis Walton prior to his return. In other cases, they may receive an injection to induce a state of temporary paralysis, such as in the case of Calvin Parker and Charles Hickson. As stated previously, these seemingly more primitive approaches to incapacitating us might be the best option available to our more proximate descendants, who have not yet evolved the technological, physiological, or mental ability to alter our conscious state of mind from a distance. For Whitley Strieber, both methods appear to have been employed, as he found himself repeatedly falling asleep and waking up, but even while consciously aware of what was happening, he remained unable to move any part of his body other than his eyes.

Waking up in bed after this initial instance of UFO apathy, Strieber was again confused by the sights and sounds around him. As he sat there, Strieber remembered feeling wide awake and in full possession of his faculties, so his memory of the early stages of the encounter are quite clear. Things grew increasingly perplexing when he noticed a human-looking, childlike figure lurking behind his bedroom door. Although small, standing only about three and a half feet tall, it had an air of someone ready for battle. It was wearing a smooth rounded helmet and a chest plate etched with concentric circles, which stretched from below the chin to its waist area. Below that was a similar semi-rectangular plate that ran from its lower waist to just above the knees. Strieber likened its attire to some sort of armored vest.

Perhaps sensing it had been spotted, the figure skulking behind the door suddenly rushed into the room as Strieber sat motionless in bed. The next thing he remembered was waking up naked, paralyzed, and feeling like he was being taken out of his bedroom. Although he could tell he was moving, Strieber did not feel like he was being carried. In fact, he had no physical sensation at all, almost as if he were being levitated and transported in some sort of bubble, en route to the next destination.

Strieber next remembers waking up to find he was sitting in a depression in the woods, though curiously, there was no snow in the roughly 4-foot-diameter area where he sat, even though there was about eight inches of snow on the ground when he went to bed. The lack of snow in his immediate vicinity may again imply the existence of a spacetime bubble around UFOs, and in association with the ever-present beam of light used to effortlessly levitate and transport abductees through windows, walls, and up into the ship itself. Because Strieber felt no sense of warmth or cold, no physical sensation of being touched, and was able to be transported through solid matter, these iconic light beams, much like the craft themselves, may also manipulate spacetime in some capacity.

While sitting in this snowless depression in the woods, off to his left, Strieber could see a small person wearing a greyish tan bodysuit, which is an extremely common type of attire described in these accounts. As stated in the quote that begins the chapter, this individual was also wearing a face mask, with two dark holes for the eyes and a round hole for the mouth. Although he was unsure why, Strieber had the impression that this person was female, and she left a very clear impression on him. He saw her again on board the ship that was hovering above them in the woods, and he recognized her voice and general presence at various other times throughout the ordeal.

Because of her continual presence, as well as Strieber's sense of familiarity with her, this may represent yet another instance where a specific individual acts as a chaperone or emissary, overseeing these interactions as they unfold, and occasionally, throughout the abductee's lifetime. Additionally, after reviewing numerous other encounters where this role appears to exist for the visitors, a pattern emerges. Specifically, it seems the person who fills this ambassador position is most often the opposite gender than the abductee they foster. This cross-gender relationship existed for Terry Lovelace and his chaperone, Betty Rubble; for Audrey and Debbie Hewins, who were purloined throughout their lives by "the Bald Men;" and in the multiple-abduction case of former United Sates Marine veteran, Terrell Copeland, who states,

> I was in a room, and I saw a woman who did not have complete human features. She had the typical black eyes that you hear about. She had an elongated skull. And that startled me. And the next memory I have is me standing on my balcony waving at this cylinder-shaped ship.[296]

In addition to the female to Strieber's left, off to the right he could see a figure wearing dark-blue coveralls. This individual was scurrying around busily, while quickly performing various tasks. Strieber then got the sense that he was moving again, but this time, instead of being carried out into the forest from his cabin, he was now rising up into the air. He could see the trees passing in front of his face as the entire forest grew smaller below. Now well above the trees, Strieber entered the ship that was hovering overhead, and once inside, the floor closed beneath his feet.

This was the first of many rooms Whitley Strieber was taken to, and considering how different each of these spaces were from one another, he may have been on several different ships or bases throughout the time of his encounter. For instance, Strieber described the first room he entered as circular, and very messy. Based on the space configuration of some other UAPs discussed previously, this may have been the center area of a smaller disc-shaped vehicle, possibly used for transporting people to and from abduction sites.

This differs from the large, circular examination rooms commonly seen at the center of bigger UFOs. These also differ from the smaller and more rectangular examination rooms, which appear to be toward the outside rim of some medium-sized ships, like the one Travis Walton woke up in before he escaped and fled to the control room. After messing with the ship's control system and being led out of the ship in a draconian fashion, Walton could see that it was about 60 feet in diameter, which is larger than the first UFO he saw in the woods, but still much smaller than the ones described as being the size of a football field, which is about 300 feet across by comparison.

Considering how messy it was, with clothes strewn about the floor, Strieber got the sense that the small circular room he first entered also functioned as a living space. Like most other abductees, Strieber noted that the room was brightly lit, but there was no observable light source. Instead, the light seemed to emanate directly from the walls and ceiling. Like the one-piece coveralls and Lycra suits so often seen being worn by the visitors, this form of ambient lighting is described in almost every abduction case, which suggests a common origin of these craft, and perhaps a similar period from which they come, if they are indeed from a future time.

While being transferred from one place to another, Strieber recalls feeling like a prisoner in his own brain. This might have been an aspect of the manifest mind-control faculties of the visitors, a side effect of paralysis drugs given to him, or a mental byproduct of the ontological shock he was experiencing in that moment. He compared this bewildered cerebral state to feeling like "an ape out of which we evolved long ago." I find this comparison especially relevant, considering that if modern humans are an earlier and more primitive grade of hominins, which exist in the distant past of our more derived descendants, then Strieber's assessment is not only a metaphor, but the reality of the situation.

Strieber's mental condition had been deteriorating throughout the ordeal, but it reached a tipping point when the visitors showed him a box with a small needle inside and informed him that they would be inserting it into his brain. As a natural response to the situation, he began to scream. At that point, all the work going on around him ground to a halt, and his female chaperone from earlier, in an auditory voice, said "what can we do to help you stop screaming?" Somewhat comically, Strieber replied, "you could let me smell you." While this spur-of-the-moment response may seem odd, as someone who vividly remembers past and future smells, I completely empathize with the request. Strieber's wish to smell the visitors proved to be quite valuable as well, since their scent helped him to eventually remember and come to grips with what had happened.

> The odor was distinct, and gave me exactly what I needed, an anchor in reality. It remained the most convincing aspect of the whole memory, because that odor was completely indistinguishable from a real one. It did not seem in any way a dream experience or a hallucination. I remembered it as an actual smell.[297]

Strieber describes being on a table in what appeared to be an examination room. Like other abduction accounts, around the outside were several rows of benches set at different levels, much like the tiered operating theaters used in modern medical training sessions. In this room, Strieber could see a variety of different individuals. In fact, the marked variation he observed among these visitors is one of the most intriguing aspects of his account.

While lying on the table in the center of the examination theater, Strieber describes seeing four distinct "types." As described earlier in the Betty and Barney Hill case study, and with the abduction of Terry Lovelace, each individual seemed to have a specific occupational role, or at least certain tasks they were best suited to perform. For instance, the first type Strieber described were "small robotlike beings," who he also saw in his bedroom during the earliest stages of his capture.

As discussed in the Parker and Hickson case study, sending abduction droids during first contact may be preferable if the abductee is not already asleep or able to be kept asleep throughout the abduction process. Additionally, because Calvin Parker and Charles Hickson were adult males, and because Strieber kept a shotgun by his bed, safety protocols may have required that robots be used to carry out the initial capture, in addition to the stockier humans in armored vests seen in the Strieber abduction.

This also makes sense in the context of the Extratempestrial Model, considering that enduring trends in human evolution have generally caused us to become more gracile and childlike in our physiology, which would make abducting larger past humans a more challenging task. This trend accelerated beginning around 12,000 years ago with the advent of agriculture, since which time we have seen a global reduction in cranial and postcranial size and robusticity, as well as a shift toward craniofacial feminization that occurred in association with human self-domestication.[298] [299] [300] [301] [302] If this tendency toward reduced body size, paedomorphosis, and self-domestication continues, we would expect our descendants to become even smaller and more childlike throughout the human future.

In addition to the robotlike individuals, Strieber also observed humanlike beings in dark-blue overalls, who joined the robotic one during his bedroom capture. Throughout the entire abduction ordeal these stocky beings were always present, and they appeared to be responsible for monitoring him and moving him from place to place. This gave the impression that they were something akin to soldiers, or the muscle behind the operation.

> I was aware that I had seen four different types of figures. The first was the small robotlike being that had led the way into my bedroom. He was followed by a large group of short, stocky ones in the dark-blue coveralls. These had wide faces, appearing either dark gray or dark blue in that light, with glittering deep-set eyes, pug noses, and broad, somewhat human mouths.... Throughout the whole experience, the stocky ones were always present. They were apparently responsible for moving and controlling me, and I had the distinct impression that they were a sort of 'good army.' Why good I do not know.

In addition to the abduction droids and stocky sentries, Strieber observed two other types of beings, whose humanness was harder to embrace but which was still palpable. The first of these were slightly taller than the others, standing approximately five feet tall, with slender bodies, massive and mesmerizing black slanted eyes, and small "almost vestigial" noses and mouths. Although Strieber struggled to see the humanness in this type of visitor, the form he described is consistent with what we would expect to see in our craniofacial form in the more distant human future, considering prominent long-term trends in our cerebral, ocular, cranial, facial, and postcranial anatomy over the last 6 million years of hominin evolution.

The last of the individuals Strieber observed were seen huddled together on the benches along the outer edge of the examination room. He described these beings as slightly smaller than five feet, with similarly shaped large round heads, but with smaller eyes, particularly compared to the more pronounced wrap-around eyes of the almost "bug-like" individual in the center of the room, who appeared to be heading the whole operation.

> I can sort of see that it had a bald, rather largish head for someone that size.... Its eyes are slanted, more than an Oriental's eyes. And they're quite—There's a piercing glare, almost. There's a real fierce look to the whole face. I'm not sure, but at some point I almost thought it looks like a bug. But not—you know, more like a person than a bug... but there were bug-like qualities to it.[303]

The above description of this more conspicuous bug-like individual was given during a hypnosis session conducted on March 1, 1986, by Dr. Donald Klein, a psychiatrist at the New York State Psychiatric Institute. In the session, Strieber also revealed that this more bug-like leader touched him on the forehead, which triggered a series of visual images that played so fast he was unable to think in between them. This method of communicating information, as well as Strieber's description of the beings observed, is consistent with other abduction accounts.

Whitley Strieber also noted some similarities between the beings he saw and what had been depicted in other contact cases. One of these was the 1957 abduction of Antonio Villas-Boas discussed previously, where he described the individual he slept with as female, with blond hair, blue slanted eyes, a wide face, thin lips, and a very pointy chin.[304] Strieber drew comparisons between this woman and the one he encountered, while also acknowledging her clandestine humanlike qualities, stating that the female observed by Villas-Boas "sounds very much like a cross between the individual I saw so clearly as the eidetic image, and a human being."[305]

Another correlate also exists between the Strieber and Villas-Boas case studies, in that both recall having intense sexual experiences with the female visitors they encountered. In his 2016 book *The Super Natural*, coauthored with Jeffrey J. Kripal, Strieber describes how about six weeks after his initial abduction, he began having conflicting feelings, as his fear gave way to desire, and he felt a deep yearning to see and feel his "bug-like" female chaperone once again, walking deep into the woods behind their cabin begging for her return.

> I wanted to be once again naked in those sweet arms, genuinely helpless and being penetrated in my soul if not my body. The supposed rape, which had so challenged both my sense of propriety and my sense of self, now returned on the wings of desire.[306]

Whitley Strieber would not have to wait long before his wish was granted and his deep burning desire was quelled, as he was about to have one of the most intense experiences of his life.

> The next experience I will describe is one that I have, in the past, only alluded to. It was the most intense experience in a lifetime of intense experiences, a sexual experience so beyond anything I had ever known that I am left to this day to wonder at the powers hidden in the body.... I woke up abruptly. To my surprise, I found myself in our guest room, not upstairs with Anne. A second later, I realized that I was aflame with desire. I wanted Anne, but she wasn't there. Instead, I was lying naked on my back and sexually excited. Sitting on top of

me was the woman from the cover of the book.... A fire went through me like no fire I have ever known before or since. When she shifted slightly, I arched my back, I screamed out my guts, abandoned to the pleasure of it, scalded by it, consumed by it.[307]

It is important to note that Strieber was and would always remain deeply committed to his wife Anne, and he would soon after share the details of this sexual encounter with her. He states that she not only "took it in stride," but he was left wondering if she "did not somehow share the experience."[308] We should also note that if he truly did share this intense sexual experience with this alien woman in waking life, despite her bug-like craniofacial form, her sex organs, like those of the woman Villas-Boas encountered, must have been similar enough to our own that such an act could occur.

The accounts of both men, and countless female abductees, should also be considered in the context of what appears to be a fine line between rape and willing participation, which Strieber felt in both contexts, as indicated by his short quote above. However, in the end, as with numerous others who have experienced similar things, there is often some sense of acceptance, and occasionally satisfaction and a felling of pride following these intensely intimate experiences. In his characteristic charismatic style, Strieber conveys the nuances of these physical and emotional complexities in the most succinct and poetic way.

It was a transformative nakedness. Lying there like that, I experienced total surrender and profound sexual satisfaction. I did not know that such absolute surrender could exist, let alone that it would open every secret door to pleasure in my body. And yet, as disturbing as it was, it was also gratifying. It seemed *needed*. I found myself glad to have been chosen for something that, although violent and exploitative, had about it a fiery holiness that I will never forget.[309]

Multiple other eyewitness accounts also emphasize the divergent yet entirely human attributes of the visitors, regardless of how bug-like they may outwardly appear. Like Whitely Strieber, many also note that some degree of variation exists among them, which they occasionally equate to what is observable among modern ancestral groups, using terms like "the Nordics," or "Orientals," for example. As described in the Rendlesham Forest case study, this physiological phenomenon could be interpreted as the persistence of geographic races into the future, if all those aboard were from the same period. Or, these slight morphological discrepancies could reflect the results of their ostensive breeding program, where distant future humans, mixed with modern humans, produce variants that look like a cross between bug-like aliens and a human being, which Strieber alluded to in referencing the Villas-Boas case.

It is also possible that these physiological and cognitive differences are the result of existing intertemporal variation, which may imply collaboration among researchers from different periods. In this context, ambassadors of different times would possess phenotypic characteristics representative of the specific era from which they came. This *temporal ancestry* aspect of time travel would add further variation to that which presently exists among geographically distinct modern human groups, as intertemporal interaction acts to broaden the range of physical variation observable among hominin groups that lies within reach of a time machine. This could have been the case with Whitley Strieber's abduction as well, where travelers from different times collaborated to execute a mutually beneficial objective.

This could also help explain why the taller being, with large mesmeric eyes and an almost vestigial nose and mouth, appeared to be the leader. If this individual hailed from a much more distant time in the human future, when our consciousness and technology have expanded beyond that of the other entities Strieber observed on the ship, we would expect them to have a more derived morphological form, an adept ability to communicate images and emotions telepathically, but also, as the most evolved hominin, that they would be in charge of the whole operation.

This temporal ancestry, genetic engineering, hybridization aspect of UFO encounters may help explain reported variation in the height, weight, skin color, craniofacial form, eye size, technology, telepathic ability, and other aspects of the visitors' behavior and morphology. Time travel from different periods may also help account for why about 5% of abductees report seeing more insect or reptile-like creatures.[310] During my nearly three-hour conversation with Whitley Strieber on his *Dreamland* podcast, we spent some time discussing this temporal ancestry aspect of the theory, including the bug-like beings occasionally described.[311]

As the conversation evolved, an idea emerged that I hadn't previously considered. Whitley and I pondered whether these more insect or reptile-like individuals may not be human at all, but rather, actual insects or reptiles, which have come back from a very, very distant point in the evolutionary future of Earth. In other words, they may hail from a posthuman period where we have been completely replaced by other more enduring species. After all, insects and reptiles have certainly proven their longevity and survivability on this planet.

Arthropods are by far the largest group of animals on Earth, and the class Reptilia also comprises evolutionarily successful animals, which includes turtles, crocodilians, snakes, lizards, birds, and others. As Whitley and I speculated further, we wondered…what if the reptilians and insectoids are actual reptiles and insects, who, in a distant posthuman future, evolve higher intelligence, along with the ability to travel backward in time, to what must be a tremendously distant point in their own past? In fact, they may even stumble upon information about how to build a backward time travel device among the ruins of our earlier human civilizations.

Although it is an interesting thought experiment, and there are aspects of these reports that make it worthy of consideration, because these advanced beings are continually described as bipedal, with a hominin craniofacial configuration, I find Whitley and I's collaborative interpretation of these beings improbable. This is particularly true of the insect varieties, considering that no insect alive today, or at any point in the past, has ever had only two legs.

Reptiles on the other hand are four-limbed animals, so as part of the superclass Tetrapoda, they could potentially stand up to reveal upper arms and lower legs like us. They are also among the oldest form of Tetrapod, and save for some smart birds that evolved from dinosaurs, reptiles are already very well-suited to their respective environments and ecological niches. As such, it is hard to imagine there would ever be selective pressure driving them toward an upright walking hominin form of biocultural evolution, but it isn't impossible either.

The Extratempestrial Model may help explain several aspects of the UFO phenomenon, including physiological variation observable among the visitors, while also providing some insight into why they are here and what they are doing. However, until they fully divulge this information themselves, any interpretation of the visitors' intent based on their observed behaviors is largely speculative. Furthermore, as mentioned previously, abductee and contactee experiences are not yet an officially verified aspect of the UFO phenomenon. While we continue to demonstrate the reality of UFOs, which are most often the same craft observed during abduction encounters, it is likely only a matter of time before these superficially variable contact modalities are all understood as the same side of the same coin.

With this in mind, and while acknowledging the potential for personal bias based on my career as a biological anthropologist, there are numerous indications that at least part of the abduction experience is related to anthropological and biomedical research. This can be seen across abduction accounts. For instance, in the aforementioned case of twin sisters Audrey and Debbie Hewins, the two of them had been taken since they were very young, but they remember a specific point at which experiments started to be carried out on them. According to Audrey Hewins,

> I was probably about five years old or so, and a bright blue light would come into the room and the door would open, and there would be like, a foggy kind of misty blue light, just shining through the whole house. And these two figures would come in… They started doing all kinds of experiments on us when we were 12.[312]

This investigative approach is further indicated by Whitley Strieber's experience, and his description of the procedures he endured.

> I would have said that the nature of my experience indicated that the visitors hadn't been here too long, and that I had been studied by a team of biologists and anthropologists.[313]

In addition to these abductee testimonials, among other markers, this research focus is indicated by the visitors' sampling procedures, major research instrumentation, propensity to sedate or tranquilize their subjects prior to examination, the apparent use of tracking devices, placing abductees on examination tables, a formal doctor/patient type of interaction, their language use and description of procedures, picking up the same subject throughout their lives as one might expect in longitudinal studies, and how their tools and techniques are reminiscent of what modern anthropologists would use while researching past human groups, if we too possessed the capacity for backward time travel.

In addition to gamete extractions, tissue sampling, blood draws, and other biomedical procedures, the extraction of fecal material is commonly reported across contact cases, which is what gave rise to the notorious, and easily ridiculed, "anal probe" aspect of abduction accounts. Whitley Strieber was also subjected to this unpleasant practice. However, unlike many abductees imperiled by the procedure, he was willing to provide details about this uncomfortable and infuriating part of the process.

> … two of the stocky ones drew my legs apart. The next thing I knew I was being shown an enormous and extremely ugly object, gray and scaly, with a sort of network of wires on the end. It was at least a foot long, narrow, and triangular in structure. They inserted this thing into my rectum. It seemed to swarm into me as if it had a life of its own. Apparently, its purpose was to take samples, possibly of fecal matter, but at the time I had the impression that I was being raped, and for the first time I felt anger.[314]

After publishing *Identified Flying Objects* in 2019, I had the privilege of meeting several people who had abduction experiences, including a few lifelong experiencers. One of these was Ellis Martin, who hosts a podcast called the *Ellis Martin Report*, where he interviews financial analysts about commodities, securities, and investing. Given the content of his show, I was surprised when he invited me on as a guest. Although I enjoy trading securities, commodities, and cryptocurrency, admittedly, I am not very good at it, and would likely bankrupt anyone who received my financial advice on his podcast. Fortunately, Ellis was not inviting me on as a financial analyst but instead to discuss the UFO phenomenon, which became clear once he began describing repeated abductions he experienced as a young boy.

A few months later, after finishing a nearby TV shoot in February 2020, just days before Sars-CoV-2 began shutting down the world as we knew it, I had the pleasure of sharing a plate of oysters and some beers with Ellis at a beachside café in Malibu. During the conversation, Ellis expanded on the experiences he divulged in our podcast conversation.[315] One story that stood out in particular involved repeated anal probes he was subjected to beginning at a very young age, which led him to eventually ask his mother "Why all the enemas when I was a kid in Monroe, Mom?"

She was understandably confused by the question and responded that she "didn't know what he was talking about." However, Ellis was wholly convinced of the reality of these incidents, especially considering the frequency with which they occurred throughout his youth. Over time, he pressed the issue and ultimately learned that both he and his mother had experienced a number of odd things in their lives.

I asked Ellis if I could reference his encounter, and naturally offered to use a pseudonym and remove any identifying information, as is standard procedure, to which he replied "I insist you use my name. I've already gone public with it in our segment." This is a great sentiment, and his courage is commendable. Despite the awkwardness of certain procedures endured during abduction events, and most notably those involving things like gamete extractions and anal probes, if more people were brave enough to openly address such occurrences, we could undoubtedly evolve our knowledge of the phenomenon much faster. Also recognizing the importance of speaking openly about these unconventional experiences, Ellis provided me with a short essay describing these childhood encounters, which I published on *The Extratempestrial Model* page of my website to complement this section of the text.[316]

His experience is critical to consider for multiple reasons, but perhaps most notably because, like Whitley Strieber, it adds another detailed explanation of the anal probe aspect of these examinations, which abductees are often uncomfortable discussing. Ellis Martin's report also shows a high degree of consistency with other contact cases, particularly as they pertain to childhood abductions, screen memories, UFO apathy, multiple generation abductions within the same family, parent-child relationships concerning perinormal occurrences, and changes throughout an abductee's lifetime regarding how they conceptualize their own experiences, and those of others.

In addition to anal probes, abductees are often subjected to other invasive and uncomfortable procedures. As discussed previously, the extraction of sperm, egg, and gestating fetuses is frequently reported, and physical implants are often inserted into abductees' bodies. This was also the case for Whitley Strieber, who endured the "taken trifecta" of sperm extraction, anal probe, and an implant. As mentioned in the Terry Lovelace case study, Strieber had a relatively small device placed in his ear in 1989, by "two people, they were not aliens."[317]

In a March 25, 2020, conversation with Rhys Darby, Leon Kirkbeck and Ethan Edenberg, on the podcast *Aliens Like Us*, Strieber provided more information about this implant procedure.[318] He states that these decidedly human-looking surgeons pushed the device through his skin without making a scar, which was also a baffling aspect of Terry Lovelace's leg implant. Strieber's apparatus is also interesting because when a modern human doctor attempted to remove it, the device migrated autonomously from the top of his ear down to his earlobe. Two days later, after feeling a burning sensation in his ear, the implant returned from his earlobe back up to the top of his ear once again.

In *Communion*, and throughout his life, Strieber refers to the beings he interacts with as "The Visitors." This nomenclature is used to avoid making assumptions about who they are, or from where or when they may have come. This is admirable, especially considering how often we default to the term *extraterrestrial*, which pigeonholes the narrative by implying that they have come from a different planet. Although he opted to keep the term used to describe these visitors as vague as possible, like most abductees attempting to make sense of their experience, in *Communion*, Strieber mulls over several theories that could explain their origins, which includes a time-travel interpretation.

The visitors could be:
- From another planet or planets.
- From Earth, but so different from us that we have not hitherto understood that they were even real.
- From another aspect of space-time, in effect another dimension.
- From this dimension in space, but not in time. Some form of time travel may not be impossible, only unlikely and probably very energy-intensive.[319]

Although Whitley Strieber categorized the time-travel model as "unlikely," he also acknowledges how it may help explain certain aspects of the phenomenon. One of these relates to how time travelers would be observed and interpreted in different terms by people spread throughout their past, even if it is the same people visiting each of these different periods. In other words, the visitors would see us evolve along the path to becoming them, but to us, as primitive humans occupying the earlier times they dip into and out of, each group would document and describe the same events in highly variable ways, depending on where they sit along the temporal continuum.

This might mean that they could be here only a short time—say a few weeks or months—but are carrying out a study that would seem to us from our position in sequential time to have extended over our entire recorded history. Of all the theories, this one alone explains why creatures in 1986 would seem so unaware of our languages, nature, and even our clothing, and yet possibly have a history as fairies and gods going back thousands of years....

Even to approach the idea of the visitors, it is necessary to study a whole history of tall stories, bizarre tales, and—just possibly—truths....

Perhaps the keepers of these secrets across the world ought to reflect on the ageless nature of this experience....

As the ages roll along, it could be that what changes is not our visitors, but our way of installing them in the culture.[320]

Strieber considered the above scenario in the context of time-traveling extra*terr*estrials, who arrive on Earth in the future, then make their way back through time to observe our evolution. Though regardless of their origins on Earth or elsewhere, in this scenario, Strieber eloquently asserts how the visitors' presence would be perceived differently as they venture deeper into the past, possibly giving rise to legends of fairies, gods, and other abstruse entities. Naturally, the farther back in time the visitors go, the more advanced they seem to us, and the more primitive we seem to them. However, if they are us from the future, as we approach the earliest point from which our descendants begin voyaging into their past, our technology and physical form will inevitably converge, becoming similar enough that we will eventually begin to recognize ourselves in them—and our shared biocultural history here on Earth.

# Case Study 12

~

# 1992
# Jerry
# Missouri, USA

*Why would they do this? I don't understand this. I'm too little to have a baby.*
*They just told me 'not to worry. I don't have to take care of it.' I think*
*they made me feel it's not mine. It's theirs. It's a part of them.*[321]

– JERRY

Dr. John E. Mack was a pioneering psychiatrist and professor at Harvard Medical School. Among his many accomplishments, Mack was a Pulitzer Prize-winning biographer and author of the acclaimed books *Passport to the Cosmos: Human Transformation and Alien Encounters*,[322] and *Abduction: Human Encounters with Aliens*,[323] which details the accounts of numerous clients he counseled regarding their experiences with the visitors. Along with his colleague, Dominique Callimanopulous, Dr. Mack also traveled to the Ariel school in Ruwa, Zimbabwe, shortly after a famous UAP encounter occurred on September 16, 1994, which was witnessed by over 60 schoolchildren.

Regrettably, Mack was researching this phenomenon at a time, and while part of an institution, where it was not yet acceptable to study UFOs and abduction accounts. Despite these stifling temporal, institutional, and academic limitations, Mack pushed on and succeeded in producing a mind-opening and paradigm-shifting collection of books and papers, which added deep insight into the UFO phenomenon. It would be great if Dr. Mack could see the incredible paradigm shift happening now regarding how research into this subject is conducted and perceived, which, to some extent, we owe to his pioneering efforts and early bravery in investigating this topic decades ago. Sadly, John Mack suffered an untimely death when he was killed by a drunk driver in London, England, on September 27, 2004.

Mack was fascinated by the UFO phenomenon, particularly the astonishing accounts of contactees and abductees. He was also struck by how common it was for experiencers to continue having some form of contact throughout their lives and the high frequency with which they are given warnings about sociopolitical and environmental calamities. One particular client, who Mack referred to simply as Jerry, was given both types of warnings. Among the many encounters Jerry had throughout her life, she was once taken to the top of a large structure by "taller, more human-looking, fair-skinned, blond beings," where she was shown scenes of missiles and other weapons. Remarkably, unlike many abductees who have their memories of an abduction erased, Jerry was assured that she would never forget what they revealed to her on that occasion.[324]

Jerry was the second of four children and lived in a rural area outside Kansas City, Missouri. Her experience with UFOs, like many other abductees, began as a young child and persisted throughout her life. Jerry's older brother Ken recalls seeing unusual lights outside his bedroom window, along with memories of someone entering his room. Jerry also remembers instances of being abducted with her little brother Mark, who was only an infant during Jerry's first encounter when she was seven years old.

Being taken with siblings, children, and other family members often induces additional trauma, which was no different for Jerry, who suffered through the agony of being abducted with her younger brother early in life, then with her own children later in life. Post-traumatic stress is understandable in situations where abductees are taken with younger family members, given our innate altruistic drive to protect those with whom we share alleles identical by descent. Jerry was burdened by lasting emotional scars stemming from these abductions, where she felt powerless to stop her siblings and offspring from being taken and was unable to help them in any way while in the presence of their captors.

Jerry was also forced to endure scorn, ridicule, and persistent sentiments of dismissal and disbelief. The relationship that troubled her most was the way she was treated by her censorious in-laws, who impugned her experiences and largely dismissed her as crazy. Even her empathetic husband Bob struggled with the reality of these events. It is easy to understand how it would be difficult for an abductee's partner to come to grips with an unusual situation like this, especially if they are lying next to the abducted when they are taken but have no memory of seeing or hearing anything happen. This experiential disconnect can also make it harder for abductees, who are understandably cantankerous toward their bed partner for not waking up, despite their desperate screams and cries for help from only inches away.

> Bob accompanied Jerry to our first hypnosis session. He came as a skeptic, but said that either 'she's lying to me or it's really happening, and she is not a liar at all. She's the most honest person I've ever met in my entire life.' Nevertheless, some measure of Bob's resistance was suggested when he said that he 'fell asleep' through much of the *intruders* miniseries, which contained some blood-curdling abduction scenes.[325]

In addition to suffering through the trauma of being abducted with family members, throughout her lifelong interaction with the visitors, Jerry was subjected to numerous invasive medical and gynecological procedures. At the age of 13, Jerry became aware of unwanted touching and probing in her vaginal area. These took place late at night, sometimes at home in her bed, but most often on an examination table in a circular dome-shaped room onboard a UFO. Like the experiences of Lynda Jones and Donna Lee, Jerry claims to have been impregnated, and endured having the fetus removed during gestation, which she estimates happened as many as 50 times throughout her life, beginning soon after her body was physically able to bear children.[326] Further indication of the reality and high frequency of these fertility events can be seen in the fact that recently declassified U.S. Pentagon documents describe cases of 'apparent abduction and unaccounted for pregnancies' in association with UFOs.[327]

In 1992, Jerry underwent several hypnotic regression sessions conducted by Dr. John Mack. During one of these visits, she started to remember more details about what took place when she was 13 years old, just before starting the eighth grade. One night, Jerry woke up to find a bright white light illuminating her bedroom. She could also see two beings standing there, who, despite her protests, said she must go with them. Jerry remembered feeling paralyzed as the beings levitated her out of bed, up through the window and wall, and into a ship hovering above her house.

> They grabbed me by my arms... I was just kind of going with them. Slow. Slow. Going up. It's weird. I don't know how they can do that... how they can manipulate matter, solid matter. Out the window, like the wall. It's like it's not there... I don't think I'll ever get used to their way of doing things, I don't ever get to where I feel comfortable going through the window.[328]

Once inside the ship, Jerry met a taller being who she recognized from previous encounters, having seen him repeatedly since her earliest abduction at age seven. Jerry referred to him as the "leader" and noted that he was the only one who ever spoke to her. In a later session, she provided more detail about this individual, who, like in so many other lifetime abduction accounts, seems to have been specifically assigned to her case, and who, once again, was of the opposite gender from her.

> He looked older, 'wrinkly and tight,' with 'a nice face, and a 'permanent type of smile,' wore a one-piece, goldish-yellow suit, and had a little bit of stringy yellowish-white hair. His hands were 'long and skinny.' This being communicated her name, 'Jerry' to her, as if he knew her, which she found frightening, especially as she realized he seemed familiar to her as well.[329]

In spite of the leader's calm and reassuring demeanor, Jerry didn't necessarily like or trust him, since he was impatient and occasionally short with her, and because he was often poking and prodding her with strange devices, "like they think they're doctors or something."[330] Under hypnosis, Jerry remembered more about her encounter at age 13. She recalled feeling embarrassed and fearful as they took off her pajamas, and she could see that one of them was holding a shiny curved object with a handle, which from the description she provided, sounds similar to a vaginal speculum.

Next, one of the other examiners bent her knees upward while spreading her legs apart. Jerry felt pressure inside her vagina, along with a pinched cramped feeling, and got the sense that something was placed deep inside her body, beyond her vagina and through the cervix. Later, as an adult, Jerry had an abortion, and she compared the associated dilation and curettage (D&C) procedure to what she experienced as a 13-year-old child.

Under hypnosis, Jerry struggled with the memory of what she saw next. As the visitors slowly drew the speculum-like instrument out from her body, Jerry could plainly see a tiny, skinny baby at the end of the device. She noted that it was about 10-inches long, had small hands, and its head seemed overly large compared to the rest of its body. She also noticed that the ones who removed the baby seemed very content with their efforts, as they placed it in a clear cylindrical object where it floated in fluid. This is reminiscent of other reports where incubating fetuses were seen floating in a liquid substrate inside partitioned incubators. In fact, like these other abduction accounts, Jerry also recalls seeing long rows of incubating fetuses on one occasion.

Jerry was naked on a table, unable to move her arms and legs, in a room lined with 'lots and lots and lots and lots' of rectangular-shaped containers, 'like drawers in a cabinet… Inside of these drawers, or 'incubators' as she called them later, were hundreds of 'I don't know if you can call it babies or not, but little just I guess fetuses.'[331]

As mentioned previously, variation in the size and shape of UFOs may be related to the various purposes they serve, in a "form follows function" capacity. For instance, the structure and observed attributes of the metallic disc-shaped craft suggest they possess the ability to manipulate spacetime and are likely capable of traveling through time. Conversely, the exceptionally large triangular craft may have been built in our time, and from numerous abduction accounts, it appears to have some fertility function. This is indicated by the high incidence of gamete extraction, and where incubating fetuses are seen lining the walls of the ship, as indicated by the accounts of Jerry Wills, Terry Lovelace, and Jerry, who all may have been on the same aircraft at different times.

From the 1992 hypnotic regression sessions conducted by John Mack, and another session that took place on March 4, 1993, Jerry started to make sense of the unexplained loss of fetuses that her, her sister, and her mother had all experienced. This insight, along with an awareness that her siblings and children also endured multiple abductions in their lives, led Jerry to conclude that the visitors don't just choose individuals, but oftentimes, they pick entire families. Jerry also pointed out that both her and her son, Colin, have distinctive deformities on one of their toes. She goes on to state that she occasionally felt pain in that toe when she was abducted, and sometimes saw blood on Colin's toe as well. Additionally, as a two-year-old toddler, her son Colin would occasionally complain that "owl people with big eyes bit him on the toe."[332] Even at a very young age, the visitors' eyes are among the most memorable aspects of these encounters, which was no different for Jerry, though she had a stark aversion to them.

> 'They're just really odd-looking. Their eyes. I just hate 'em. I hate 'em. It's like they just look right through you . . . they go inside you,' which gave her 'a really weird, unnerving feeling.' She avoided looking at them, because 'it's hard to put in words. It's as if I'd lose myself, and don't feel like I have any control… I don't know, it's like someone just crawled right inside you and knew everything about you … I just kinda lose myself, and he kinda just gets in there and I just don't like it.'[333]

Although Jerry's encounters began at an early age, most of her more impactful interactions took place during the late 1980s and early 1990s. For instance, during the 1987 abduction when Jerry was unable to wake her husband Bob as two small beings wearing shiny uniforms hovered over her bed, she recalled feeling "deeply moved when twin girls were shown to her, which she feels were her own hybrid offspring."[334] Also, in 1990, soon after Jerry and her husband Bob bought a duplex in Plymouth, Massachusetts, she was abducted and taken into a shiny, metallic, circular room where she once again encountered "the leader."

Of all her abductions, this one was the most traumatic, largely because of the pain Jerry endured throughout the procedure, which may have been to place a tracking device or some other observational tool in her head, since she was told a tiny object was left inside to monitor her.[335] Jerry described the pain she endured throughout this procedure as "even worse than childbirth." In fact, most of Jerry's memories of that 1990 abduction are conscious memories, since the horror of reliving the event kept her from being able to explore it with John Mack while under hypnosis.

At first, Jerry was not frightened during this episode and was pleased that she was able to converse with the beings. The leader asked, 'how the medication has been so far,' and she made the mistake of saying 'fine.' For after this, a procedure was done to the back of her head above the neck that caused the most excruciating pain she had ever experienced, 'even worse than childbirth.... I thought they were killing me.'... In addition to the raw pain, Jerry felt muscle spasms that were out of her control and extended in rapid succession from her legs to her facial muscles. She screamed for them to stop and was filled with hate and rage. 'Here I thought they were somehow perfect and loving beings. How could they have done that to me? I was so terrified. I blanked out after that. The next thing I was back in bed, waking up.'[336]

This traumatic incident in 1990 was the beginning of something of a UFO flap for Jerry, since she would go on to have three encounters in 1991, and even more in the months leading up to her first hypnosis session with John Mack in August 1992. It was during one of these 1991 encounters that Jerry was taken by the "taller, more human looking, fair skinned, blonde beings" who showed her scenes of weapons and missiles. Following this encounter, Jerry began writing profusely, and in a way that many said far exceeded her level of education and poetic abilities. Jerry also felt that "many of her ideas did not come from within herself, but from some other source."[337]

The information transmission that occurred during her 1991 interaction with these more human-looking beings was particularly poignant. Indeed, Jerry was so disturbed by the images and knowledge she received that she burned her first notebook after the encounter. Not long after that, Jerry recalls having vivid dreams of nuclear war and seeing widespread panic as an apocalyptic spectacle unfolded. In one of her dreams, Jerry "looked out into this vast nothingness and saw a UFO, and it was slowly moving along with a beam of some sort shooting down onto the land."[338]

If the visitors are future humans, they would be expected to know what transpires between now and then, assuming they are from a relatively proximate period, with historic records at their disposal. We would also expect them to be aware of major conflicts that occur between now and whatever time they return from, especially ones involving deadly and destructive events like a nuclear holocaust. However, the question of whether they would, or could do anything to avert a global cataclysm is a separate matter, which relates back to the issue of how we conceptualize the Extratempestrial Model, in the context of Block Time, or the Everett interpretation with bifurcating timelines.

In either scenario, it is reassuring to know that if the visitors are future humans, then evidently some percentage of our species persists long enough to become them, and perhaps the lights Jerry saw shining down upon the land during this period of immense destruction are a part of what ensures that outcome. Although this is wildly speculative, in addition to the other potential purposes discussed previously, the visitors' obstinate focus on gamete extraction could be in response to the genetic bottleneck that would inevitably accompany a global catastrophe, where only a small percentage of the population survives or is saved.

For as long as human civilization has existed, every generation thinks it's the last, thinks it's the end of the world,[339] where throughout the ages, each cohort espouses auguries of eminent annihilation. Some even claim such things have already happened, like in the biblical story of Noah and the great flood, which would have been the most dramatic bottleneck imaginable, with insurmountable incest occurring among every species on Earth, even surpassing in scale the original Adam and Eve apologue. However, it is only recently that humans have come to possess the means with which to actually destroy large swaths of the human population, along with most other lifeforms on this planet.

Considered in conjunction with a recent and radical rise in tribalism, nationalism, and ideological polarization within and among nations, these Armageddon-like scenarios no longer seem so farfetched. Could these craft, if piloted by a more intelligent and benevolent future human race, be selecting from an otherwise doomed stock those deemed worthy of contributing to a new creation, an irenic society built on a foundation of respect for each other and the planet we all call home? Or could the widespread practice of gamete extraction be an attempt to collect a diverse set of genes from the last period in history where broad genetic variability exists prior to a conflict-induced bottleneck in the human genome?

The regularity with which abductees and contactees espouse warnings of a coming cataclysm was one of the things that most intrigued Dr. John Mack, and I agree that these end-times prophesies are fascinating, but also frightening. I do not personally subscribe to the idea that there is a coming environmental or nuclear apocalypse. In part because I don't think the visitors would let it happen, but also because these notions are commonly conveyed to people powerless to do anything about it—and often children.

Considering the frequency with which UFOs are seen near nuclear installations, including instances where they took control of bases and disarmed warheads, there may be cause for concern about our near-term future.[340] [341] [342] Or, looking at it the other way, this could be seen as calming, since it might mean if the visitors are capable of preventing a nuclear annihilation event, they would. If a sensible adult saw an eight-year-old child preparing to juggle butcher knives to amuse their friends, said adult would likely intervene. If more primitive and easily agitated humans in possession of weaponry that could destroy the planet were ever gearing up to do so, one would think our more rational human descendants, as stakeholders in Earth's future, would do the same.

While I am hopeful we will not implode our civilization by exploding each other, there are objectively ominous aspects of Jerry's conversations with the visitors, which are echoed across contactee and abductee accounts. These could be concerning when considered in conjunction with the visitors' persistent presence in and around nuclear installations; enduring prophecies of end-time scenarios; their pervasive focus on gametes, genes, and reproduction; our combative nature; and their incessant insistence that we "take care of the Earth." From Jerry's exchanges at least, it should be noted that the visitors view what they are doing as a good thing, which they speak about using words like "beautiful," "wonderful," "new creation," and other terms with an innately positive valence.

'The leader person told me that it was beautiful, and that one day I would understand, but it was about creation.' Creation of what, I asked. 'I guess, like a new being. A new race, or a new—I don't know. He didn't really say specifically. He just said that at a point in time of their own she would know. They said it was beautiful. It was wonderful, and just to trust that it had to do with creation.'

'I think what they are doing is somehow necessary.' It has to do, she said, with 'races, beings or whatever, coming together to make another creation.' This 'was very important,' she said, and 'as a single person, compared to this big huge thing going on, I should look beyond myself and know that it's for the greater good.'

There's a reason they're doing this, she added. She feels that they are 'making – whatever you want to label it–another whole civilization.' She does not know 'whether they're going to take it and place it somewhere else, or it's going to be introduced here.' Jerry, like many abductees, has dreams of the world as we know it coming to an end and relates her breeding role to this eventuality.[343]

Again, I don't necessarily subscribe to these "sky is falling," "the end is nigh" divinations, or the notion that Armageddon or the biblical "rapture" involves UFOs beaming up the saved while the damned suffer a deluded self-imposed fate of fire and brimstone in their home time on Earth below. Nevertheless, given the frequency with which such stories are proffered as prophecy throughout the ages, it is interesting to ponder how such claims could converge, especially considering the visitors' eternal concern with the health of the Earth. What if, to save said Earth from us rough-hewn humans, stricken with acute affluenza and eschatological ideologies, some of us, and clearly some of our genes, are to be transported through time, to begin anew once Mother Earth has healed herself from the scars of past human conflict and the underlying causes of it?

It is concerning how often images of nuclear war and environmental catastrophe are shown to experiencers. However, the visitors' demonstrated ability to shut down nuclear installations, like in September 1966 at Minot Air Force Base in North Dakota,[344] and in March 1967 at Malmstrom Air Force Base in Northwest Montana,[345] for example, indicates they could potentially do it again if deemed necessary. If these are future humans, as stakeholders in maintaining the sanctity of this planet, we might expect them to intervene prior to us strewing eternal radiation upon our shared Earth, or perhaps to gather and transport people and genes deep enough into the future, to a time when these ill effects are no longer felt, if they are unable to intercede in time.

When talking about backward time travel, we must also ask whether they could ever "change" the past to prevent a catastrophe from occurring in the first place. Considering inherent self-consistency in the Block Universe model, this may not be an option, but it raises an important question: Are warnings about war and ecological destruction meant to help prevent it from happening, or are they to prepare us for this near-term inevitability, and the negative implications of our oblivious actions?

Under the block time model of the universe, if modern humans were ever able to sneak nuclear missiles past the watchful eye of our anxious descendants, and an Armageddon-like scenario were to unfold, it will always have been a part of our future and their past, and there is nothing either of us can do about it. As such, the common contactee claim of death and destruction may suggest more of a warning of what's to come, rather than an effort to avert it; unless that is, these efforts were successful, and they had always warned us, and we had always avoided catastrophe in the first place. However, if they are "interdimensional" humans who hail from a different timeline under the many worlds interpretation of quantum mechanics (MWI), they could potentially "change" the past, or at least in the timeline that results from their pre-Armageddon intervention.

Recently, there have been discussions that purportedly originated with informed members of the intelligence community, which seem to conform to the latter MWI scenario. This abstract narrative even involves talk of waring timelines, the Mandela Effect, and future human groups with conflicting intentions, each vying for control of our future reality.[346] Like most others, I still favor the Block Universe model, but it is essential to consider other alternatives, especially since we do not yet fully understand the fundamental aspects of our universe, which time, and potentially space, emerge from, as they appear to be the product of some deeper physics.

One reason I and others favor the block time model is that while it prevents change, it also precludes paradox. However, in the multiverse, if a new reality springs forth from an intentional intervention, to mitigate malfeasance or for some other outcome, numerous paradoxes arise. This includes consistency paradoxes, where our future human descendants could not have known to stop an event from occurring unless it actually happened. That is, if everyone from the previous post-apocalyptic timeline suddenly shifted into the new one where no cataclysm ever occurred, how would they know they needed to go back in time to stop something that never happened?

Unlike the block universe where everything remains self-consistent, logical contradictions are prevalent in scenarios where changing the past is permitted. Additionally, if time-travel technology exists in the future, and if it were possible to change the past, we would likely be bombarded with future humans attempting to right all the wrongs of their past, and we would constantly see them doing it, as opposed to the "do not engage," "prime directive" protocol that seemingly surrounds the phenomenon. That is, unless they are returning to change what went wrong, and with each successful attempt we shift into a new timeline where the bad thing never happened, but now other things that didn't happen do, which may also require correcting, and so it goes.

No one now can know what is going to happen in the future, though I am hopelessly optimistic that we will not destroy this planet and a large percentage of the lifeforms that inhabit it. Still, it gives me pause to acknowledge the number of abductees and contactees who espouse notions of death, destruction, and environmental calamity. Perhaps we should heed these warning, or in the very least, consider the potential implications of our actions and what could be done to avert such a catastrophe. The images, dreams and premonitions Jerry and other experiencers are shown represent further facets of a mysterious, multifarious UFO phenomenon, especially considering what our more omniscient and omnipresent descendants may know of our future, and their more lucid past.

Jerry often felt as though the visitors were being selfish and violating her in abusive ways. However, as indicated in the above quote, she also had the sense that she was a "tool for their design" and that she was participating in something much bigger than herself, or any of us alive at this time. Furthermore, Jerry felt that the people doing these things were participants in something that was being directed at a much higher level and that was all for the greater good. It is also important to note that while many conscious memories of these distressing events were hidden to shield her from trauma, once Jerry became able to see the bigger picture, she was allowed to remember her lifelong experiences and suddenly felt compelled to talk about them.

> My feeling is it's not just them. She also got the sense that she was not meant to remember anything that had happened to her while she was a child, or throughout her teens and 20s, but now she was meant to consciously recall all the events that had taken place throughout her life, stating, 'I was supposed to tell somebody, and they initiated that process.'[347]

Dr. John Mack's representation of Jerry's experiences, like numerous other cases, is consistent with the Extratempestrial Model. This is indicated by the visitors' knowledge of and warnings about future events, their slightly more derived but entirely human appearance, their similar but more advanced toolkit, their apparent ability to produce viable offspring with us, and most notably, because they told Jerry they were us from the human future.

In July 1992, only three weeks before her first hypnosis session with John Mack, Jerry consciously recalled being taken into a UFO by humanoid beings, who she described as having an attitude that seemed loving and benevolent. Like previous visits, Jerry could see different shelves that held numerous vials and other types of tools spread throughout the room where she was seated. In that room, she recalls having an in-depth conversation with these beings, who she described as "beyond what we would think is intelligent or even genius." While engaged in this complex conversation, one of them explained to her that they came from "so far into the future that she would not be able to comprehend."[348] This revelation unlocked a tremendous awareness in Jerry, which validated the reality of her lifelong experiences, while also providing her with a sense of both harmony and alienation.

This is great. I can see everything, and I am so aware. I was convinced beyond a shadow of a doubt that what I was experiencing was real, they looked at me with their loving and all-knowing smile and simply said 'yes.' I then said, well, if this is real then I am somehow living a double life... I had a feeling there was a definite reason that I and others like me were not aware of this other reality, at least not as aware as we are about this reality we have here and now.[349]

People often ask me, "If they are us from the future, why do they always say they are from a different planet?" While instances of interplanetary divulgence do exist, such as in the cases of Leo Dworshak and Betty Hill, we should also acknowledge occasions where the visitors proclaim they are us from the future. Like the travelers Jim Penniston encountered in the Rendlesham Forest and the ones the 16-year-old New Zealand boy spoke with, the humanlike beings Jerry knew throughout her life explicitly stated that they are from the future. It remains a possibility that some of the visitors come from other planets, or conceivably other planets in the future as posited by Whitley Strieber in *Communion*. However, if some are from outer space, while others are our future human descendants, then we would expect to see far more variation in their tools, behavior, and physiological form.

Because abductions and other close encounters are so similar across the board, including the case of Jerry, who was told they were from the future, and Betty Hill, who was told they were from a star system that has yet to be identified, it is unlikely that these and other encounters have separate origins. Additionally, when considering the vast consistency across case studies, and prolific parallels with our own modern technology, culture, consciousness, language, behaviors, and morphological form, it is improbable that these abductions are perpetrated by beings who evolved in a remote region of the universe. Instead, their enlightened state, which exists beyond what we would think is intelligent or even genius, may be a human inevitability, as we progress toward becoming these future prodigies of the past.

# Case Study 13

~

# 1994
# Ariel School
# Ruwa, Zimbabwe

*I could see the little man was dressed in a black, shiny suit; that he had long black hair and his eyes, which seemed lower on the cheek than our eyes, were large and elongated. The mouth was just a slit and the ears were hardly discernible.*[350]

– GUY G., STUDENT WITNESS

Most of the case studies examined thus far have looked at abductions, with many focusing on lifetime abductees. However, other types of close encounters can also be revealing, particularly when viewed through time and in a broad cross-cultural context. One key case involves a roughly 15-minute interaction with two visitors and about 60 schoolchildren, comprising different ages and ethnicities, who all witnessed the same event at the same time. This occurred at the Ariel school, a private primary school located in Ruwa, which is approximately 20 km from Harare, the capital of Zimbabwe. At approximately 10:15 a.m. on Friday, September 16, 1994, around 60 children were playing in a field during their midmorning break. Despite the diverse ethnic background of the children and their broad age range, which spanned from 6 up to 12 years old, there was an incredible level of consistency among their reports of what happened and in how they relayed these abstruse events.

During their recess, the children suddenly stopped playing when they noticed something strange happening adjacent to their school. They watched as three large, shiny, silver, disc-shaped craft, with a red stripe circling the outside edge of the airships, descended from the sky in an overgrown field adjacent to the schoolyard.[351] As one student noted, before they landed, the vehicles could be seen appearing and disappearing in the sky, and as soon as the ships faded out, they would suddenly reappear somewhere else nearby, which he said happened about three separate times.[352]

This commonly reported characteristic of UAPs, where they are seen appearing and disappearing in the sky, or occasionally near the ground like in the case of Lynda Jones, is indicative of something moving through time, or perhaps through higher dimensions if they are someday shown to exist. As mentioned in the Pascagoula case study, if something abruptly appears or disappears in our three observable dimensions of space, it is a good indication that it has just changed its position in the fourth dimension of time, which is currently the only other known dimension. This common occurrence is remarkable because it violates our notions of linear time and object permanence. Yet, watching an object fade in and out of existence is exactly what we would expect to see as a time machine comes to rest in our collective four-dimensional frame of reference.

The children watched in awe as a small "man" suddenly appeared on top of one of the airships. Meanwhile, another man could be seen moving swiftly back and forth under the craft. Rather than using his legs to run through in the thick brush, he appeared to be levitating above the ground as he scurried about. To the children, it appeared as though the man who was perched at the top of the first ship was keeping watch, while the man below it, and much nearer to where the children watched in amazement, was hastily carrying out an important task. This description is reminiscent of what was seen in the 1980 Rendlesham Forest encounter, when Penniston, Burroughs, and Cabansag entered the woods and saw a saucer-shaped craft with diminutive but large-headed beings, who were levitating above the ground in a beam of light, while scurrying about busily as if they were making repairs to their ship.[353]

The description of the beings was also similar between the Rendlesham Forest and Ariel school cases, where both were said to have looked like small human men, standing about four feet tall, with thin arms and legs, large heads with big black eyes, small nostrils, and a tiny slit for a mouth. One of few discrepancies in the children's story had to do with the men's hair, where some of the children recalled them being bald, while others remembered one of them having long black hair, stating that he "looked a bit like Michael Jackson."[354]

Being closer to the amassed throng of children, the man outside the ship was easier for them to see. It was clear that he was also keenly aware of their presence, for at one point, he moved closer to them, looked at them with an intense stare, and according to some of the children's reports, he communicated with them telepathically. Once again, the message that was given to the children was a warning about the dangers of environmental degradation and rapid technological development, which, as discussed in the previous case study, is exceedingly common across contactee and abductee accounts, regardless of where, when, or who they are talking to.

The children's recollection of events was remarkably consistent, though considering their diverse cultural background, age range, and individual personalities, there was understandably some variation in their interpretation of the event. For instance, some of the children felt a real connection with these travelers, espousing a sense of love, empathy, and a deep emotional bond that formed during the encounter. In fact, when tracked down and interviewed as an adult, one former Ariel school student remembered this as one of the most impactful moments of his entire life, stating, "If there's one moment I'd like to relive, it would be that one particular moment that day."[355]

However, some of the children, and particularly those indigenous to the region, were utterly terrified of what was taking place, since many thought the beings might have been Tokoloshe,[356] an evil goblin-like creature that sucks out the brains of small children, among other more horrific forms of punishment. The legend of Tokoloshe exists in multiple different cultures throughout southern Africa, and while the beast can take many forms, it is most often depicted in wood carvings as a menacing elephant-like creature with one butt cheek. Tokoloshe is similar to the "boogeyman" in some Western cultures, serving as negative sanctions and a vital parental tool for convincing a rowdy Snicklefritz to toe the line.

The Ariel schoolchildren who weren't running in fear of having their brains sucked out were treated to a unique experience that they, for better or worse, carried with them the rest of their lives. Despite their youth, and our collectively primitive position in human time, the children were able to describe these beings and their craft in exquisite detail. Furthermore, because their recollection of events was brought forth through individual interviews and drawings made independent of the other students, much like a police interrogation of multiple witnesses, their corroborated accounts boasted higher fidelity. This uniformity across their separate narratives was one of the main reasons why even the most skeptical teachers and administrators at the school eventually came to believe what the kids were saying.

The children's reports were also comparable to other accounts of close encounters. Notable consistencies include their description of small men who could move while hovering above the ground, who had large heads and elongated eyes, diminutive noses, mouths, and ears, and who were wearing shiny black uniforms as their style of dress. As we've seen across these case studies and in other accounts, it is common for the visitors to don either one-piece coverall-type uniforms or more tight-fitting, shiny, one-piece bodysuits, with the only real difference being the color and how tightly they fit.

Similarly, a blue, tight-fitting kind of bodysuit was worn by the humans Travis Walton interacted with toward the end of his encounter. Also, as mentioned in the Terry Lovelace case study, abductee Jerry Wills had lifelong interactions with a man named Zo, which represents a rare example of an ambassador who was the same gender as the abductee. One of the first times Jerry Wills met Zo, he was wearing this same type of slim-fitting, one-piece bodysuit, similar to Lycra or spandex.

I open my eyes and here's this man standing there…. He was dressed oddly anyway. Now, we would call it a lycra outfit, but at the time I never heard of anything such as this. His boots and his pants were all the same thing except they got a little heavier where the boot parts would be, the foot covering, the sole anyway. I didn't see any zippers or anything, it conformed right to his body, went right up close around the neck.[357]

Beyond the visitors' clothing and morphological form, we also see marked similarity in reported descriptions of their craft. More specifically, in nearly every case, including the Ariel school encounter, they are described as large, disc, or occasionally triangle-shaped objects, or in the case of what Jim Penniston saw in the Rendlesham Forest, some combination of the two. They are also said to have a seamless exterior, are generally shiny and silver in color, and they almost always have lights around the outer rim and occasionally a few toward the top or bottom. Although they are silent compared to modern aircraft, people often report hearing a low humming noise. Lastly, these craft possess the ability to hover, can accelerate and decelerate at tremendous speed, are transmedium in that they can seamlessly move through and between air and water with ease, and as mentioned above, they are capable of appearing and disappearing in plain sight.

Marked consistency across reports suggests that what is witnessed by so many people throughout the world and through time is part of the same or a related phenomenon. Furthermore, based on vast similarities with modern human physiology and technology, these bipedal pilots, and their sophisticated machinery, likely originate in the human future. Some level of variation is expected among reports, and in depictions of these beings and their craft, which have been described by different people, with variable levels of technological advancement, stretching back thousands, and perhaps tens, or possibly even hundreds of thousands of years.

Despite our collective inability to fully grasp what we're seeing, artistic depictions, as well as oral and written accounts stretching back through the ages, paint a strikingly similar picture. It is a common misconception that UFOs are largely a Western phenomenon, or a relatively recent one dating back to the 1940s. Instead, consistent patterns emerge across modern encounters and those experienced by different cultural groups spread throughout the historic and prehistoric past. According to Jacques Vallée, in the 2018 documentary *Witness of Another World*,

> The phenomenon did not begin in 1947, it did not begin with WWII, you can go back to the 19th century, and as you know, I, with other researchers, we have gathered over 500 cases of UFO phenomena going back to ancient Egypt. So, it seems the phenomenon has always been with us, in this environment, and we are just beginning to recognize it or to acknowledge it. In earlier times it was called angels or demons, or leprechauns, or other forms of life, but we now can recognize that the patterns, the basic patterns are the same; when we have enough data we can do statistical patterns, and the patterns of the ancient cases resemble the patterns we have now.[358]

Myths, legends, petroglyphs, geoglyphs, cave paintings, carvings, and oral traditions exist all over the world. Many of these depict odd encounters with strange ships, lights, and occasionally big-headed, big-eyed, pale-skinned, humanlike beings with seemingly magical abilities. Many of these also bear a striking resemblance to current descriptions of UFOs and "aliens." Today, we are better able to describe what we see using a technological lexicon that has developed over the last 100-200 years, though the general characteristics of the modern UFO phenomenon can also be seen in the artistry, folklore, and oral and written histories of past peoples. One example, also specific to the Zulu culture of southern Africa, may exist in the story of the rain goddess Mbaba Mwana Waresa.

According to legend, the rain goddess lives in the clouds in a round hut made of rainbow arches. She is capable of shapeshifting, and she can influence the dreams of earthly mortals. Unable to find a suitable husband among the sky gods, she scoured the lands of southern Africa in search of a human husband. According to one interpretation of the story, Mbaba Mwana Waresa appeared in the dreams of the man she chose, where she professed her love for him. However, before the two could be together, she first needed to test his devotion to her. To do so, the rain goddess dressed a beautiful young girl in the costume of a Zulu bride to accompany her when she went to the chosen man's marriage hut, to see if he would recognize that this was not the woman from his dreams.

The rain goddess and the fake bride descended from the sky on a glimmering beam of colorful light, where the groom-to-be was anxiously awaiting Mbaba Mwana Waresa's arrival. There, the rain goddess proclaimed, "This is the beautiful being you saw in your dream." The man looked at the girl and back to the rain goddess, recognizing her pale grey skin and piercing eyes from his earlier visions. He said, "No, this girl is not my bride, you are my bride. You are Mbaba Mwana Waresa, the rain goddess." The two lovers then ascended into the sky, as the man returned to live with the rain goddess in her heavenly home.

Stories such as these are certainly open to interpretation, and much like the kid's game "telephone," they are bound to change over time, as they are told and retold across countless generations. However, this narrative, along with other accounts from oral and written history, show similar patterns to modern and historically recent UFO encounters. In fact, if Antonio Villas-Boas had left to live with his intertemporal consort, the storyline would not have been much different from that of the oral, and now written, legend of Mbaba Mwana Waresa.

Another event that is often cited as an early example of UFO contact can be found in Ezekiel 4:28 of the Hebrew Bible, considering it involves descriptions of a fiery, hovering, domed craft with humanoid beings inside.

> A great cloud with brightness around it and fire flashing forth continually, and in the middle of the fire, something like gleaming amber. In the middle of it was something like four living creatures. This was their appearance: they were of human form…. In the middle of the living creatures there was something that looked like burning coals of fire, like torches moving to and fro among the living creatures;

the fire was bright, and lightning issued from the fire.

The living creatures darted to and fro, like a flash of lightning.... I saw a wheel on the earth beside the living creatures... their construction being something like a wheel within a wheel. When they moved, they moved in any of the four directions without veering as they moved.... Over the heads of the living creatures there was something like a dome, shining like crystal, spread out above their heads. And above the dome over their heads there was something like a throne... and seated above the likeness of a throne was something that seemed like a human form.... When I saw it, I fell on my face, and I heard the voice of someone speaking.[359]

The prophet Ezekiel's vision of this "wheel within a wheel" also became an essential tenet of the Nation of Islam, where Elijah Muhammad taught his followers that the vision seen by the prophet Ezekiel, which the Jews call the Merkabah, was a UFO, or The Mother Wheel. The centrality of UFOs for the Nation of Islam was later expanded by Minister Louis Farrakhan, following a visionary experience he had in 1985, in which he claims to have been physically carried into the Mother Wheel, where he encountered Elijah Muhammad and Master Fard Muhammad, the founder of the Nation of Islam. According to Dr. Stephen C. Finley, associate professor of religious studies and philosophy, and inaugural chair in the Department of African & African American Studies at Louisiana State University:

Louis Farrakhan's 1985 visionary experience of being carried onto the Mother Wheel—an unidentified flying object to the world outside the Nation of Islam (NOI)—was the most significant religious event of his life. The Wheel, and its adjectival modifier 'Mother,' is central to understanding cosmology in Farrakhan's NOI. More than a reiteration of the teachings that Farrakhan's mentor and religious leader, Elijah Muhammad, bequeathed to him, the Wheel is encoded with the meaning of black bodies everywhere and with Farrakhan's body in particular...

At the same time, Minister Farrakhan's experience and teaching regarding the Mother Wheel does assimilate Elijah Muhammad's doctrines that he reports receiving from the NOI founder, Master Fard Muhammad (God, Allah), secret knowledge that includes the centrality of Mother Plane or Wheel – a UFO or 'flying saucer.'[360]

Some religions incorporate elements of UFOs into their world-view, while others ardently admonish them. According to a 2021 Pew Research Center survey, highly religious adults in the United States, and particularly White evangelicals, are far more skeptical about the possibility that intelligent extraterrestrial life exists beyond Earth, compared with those who are less religious.[361] From growing up in a religious household, and from talking with numerous religious people about this subject over the years, the hang-up seems to stem from the notion that humans are considered to be a unique creation of God. As such, the idea of a separate creation of other humanlike beings somewhere else in the galaxy doesn't sit well. If this is the snag, one would think that religious people would love the Extratempestrial Model, since it helps explain UFOs but without invoking a separate creation explanation. Instead, there remains only one divine human creation, where these humans going on to develop technology that allows them to go back in time to visit the ones who came before.

In addition to being a principal doctrine of the Nation of Islam, Ezekiel's account is often cited by ufologists and members of the "ancient astronaut" constituency as an example of extraterrestrial contact. However, as with numerous cases like it, if Ezekiel's experience was in fact a product of real events, it might be better understood as intertemporal rather than interstellar interaction. This assertion largely centers on the common physical description of a domed craft, the fire (lights) around its edge, electromagnetic/static energy radiating from it, a wheel within a wheel (like what Udo Wartena saw in the craft he was shown), and most notably, the human form of the individuals inside. Considering how similar this is to modern reports, which describe the same types of things in more up-to-date terms, i.e., metal, lights, electromagnetism, etc., it is easy to see how the patterns of this and other ancient cases resemble the patterns we have now.

Despite Ezekiel's more primitive position along the same accelerating continuum of technological development, what he described seeing is entirely consistent with other contactee accounts, and it's a further testament to the homogeneity apparent across UAP reports, regardless of where, or when, these objects and visitors are observed. Examining his portrayal from the standpoint of more recent encounters, and our existing knowledge of advanced technology, Ezekiel's odd descriptions, metaphors, and primitive references to wheels, domes, fire, amber, and chatoyant minerals become more understandable in a modern context. Relatedly, it is interesting to imagine how future humans may someday critique our contemporary descriptions of their morphology and technology, as the narratives we construct, and the words and metaphors we currently use, are likely to seem just as primitive to them.

Although these are often interpreted in unconventional ways, the seemingly magical qualities of the entities depicted in the past mirror what people see in the present day. Furthermore, certain magical acts may be more easily appreciated as real events when reconsidered in the context of the future technological prowess of our distant descendants. Even today, with our sophisticated computers, fast cars, and toaster ovens, such skills seem miraculous, as we remain primitive compared to those who hail from a more advanced stage of the human future. Though as more time passes, and we inch toward becoming them, the extraneous oddities of these accounts will eventually coalesce into the conventional.

Many tales from religious texts and other chronicles from oral and written history are simply stories, often meant to invoke some life lesson, while not actually representing true events of the past. As with non-religious legends, folklore, and origin myths, we cannot assume that all narratives describing odd occurrences stem from actual events. Though given the frequency with which ethereal experiences are described in these and other oral and written accounts of the past, it is perhaps worthwhile to keep an open mind to the possibility that some may have been inspired by real encounters with the same types of UFOs seen today.

Being children, and from an earlier time, the young witnesses to the 1994 Ariel school event also struggled to comprehend what they were seeing that morning. Even in later life, largely due to our species-wide ignorance of the phenomenon, these former students continue to grapple with what transpired, and particularly the prophetic telepathic warnings they received about the importance of taking care of the Earth. As mentioned in the previous case study, these urgent environmental messages are commonly communicated to experiencers. The frequency with which these notions are espoused was also of great interest to Dr. John Mack, which may have been why he was one of the first researchers to investigate the Ariel school incident, flying to Zimbabwe soon after it occurred to conduct in-person interviews with students about what they saw that morning. In his book, *Passport to the Cosmos: Human Transformation and Alien Encounters*, Mack writes,

> I was astonished to discover that, in case after case, powerful messages about the human threat to the Earth's ecology were being conveyed to the experiencers in vivid, unmistakable words and images. The impact of these communications is often profound…. Indeed, it seems to me quite possible that the protection of the Earth's life is at the heart of the abduction phenomenon.[362]

The eventual reality and prophetic nature of these dire predictions was not lost on one Ariel school student named Sarah, who was witness to the 1994 UFO landing. She is also one of few former students who stayed in the area, stating that, "Everyone's fucked off to Canada or the UK, or died." During a 2014 interview, she reflected on the telepathic message some of them received about environmental change and rapid technological evolution, stating, "They weren't wrong, though, about the environmental shit, were they? If you go out there now, you'll see the Miombo forests have disappeared for firewood."[363] Moreover, one of the original Ariel school investigators later said, "It haunts me to this day that what the kids said about how we are destroying the environment is coming to pass."[364]

In addition to having a vested interest in the survivability of this planet, the fact that many of these warnings are already manifesting in the form of real environmental degradation, climate change, and rising sociopolitical tensions further suggests these travelers know the future and are fearful of, or warning us about, what will transpire between our present and theirs. It should be noted, however, that they don't seem to care as much about us specifically, or at least not to the extent that they show concern for the environment and ecology of the planet we live on. In a 2020 interview with the *Leak Project*, guest Steve Mera, a British investigative researcher, highlighted the ubiquity of this general ET ambivalence toward us and our primitive warring ways, while adamantly espousing the claim that we must take care of the Earth.

> If we look at these so-called messages from ETs over the years, it's always been the same one-liner... 'Look after planet Earth.' They say it to the kids in schools... they say it to contactees, they say it all around the world 'look after the Earth,' 'we're ruining the Earth.' You know, it's never about us though is it, it's like, 'look after yourselves.' I don't' think they care much about us to be honest with you.... There are people out there who have been responsible for killing mass humans, and it's never been stopped, it's never been intervened, it's like 'do what you want, you're all a pack of mad dogs.' But, look after planet Earth. There's something about planet Earth they are interested in.[365]

If these travelers are indeed extratempestrials, then at least some percentage of the current human population carries on into the future to eventually become them. Yet, while the visitors often demonstrate deep empathy and respect for most of the individuals they abduct, that sentiment doesn't necessarily carry through to the whole of humanity. This makes sense from a basic population and resource scarcity standpoint, since it would be impossible for every member of the human race to persist into the future, especially if we continue to extend our life history cycle, mitigate senescence, and live longer lives.

As Steve Mera points out, there have been and continue to be genocides in human society, most often perpetrated by the same states who are meant to protect the people they serve. If these visitors are our future human descendants, it makes sense why they would be inclined to halt a nuclear Armageddon, since they share the same Earth with us in a different time, though it also makes sense why they might not intervene in instances of mass death. Certainly, some of us must die to make room for those who come next, and with our population in check, together with a more recent trend of using resources more efficiently, our impact on the Earth is minimized. So long as some people survive to carry our species into the future, historic deaths from capitalist commodity-driven wars, ideological despots, religious crusades, self-imposed calamities, and mismanaged pandemic responses, to name a few, may benefit our distant descendants and aid in their attempt to maintain the sanctity of this planet, until it becomes theirs entirely.

# Case Study 14

~

# 2001
# Amy Rylance
# Gundiah & Mackay, Australia

*The doctor just kind of pushed on my stomach and they took my blood pressure,*
*they thought I was on drugs to start with. The only thing she did say was that*
*I was dehydrated, and I was malnourished because I hadn't been drinking*
*or had anything to eat for the last week. And hair was growing all over*
*me, and I can't stand being hairy (laughs a little).* [366]

– AMY RYLANCE

I have always been fascinated by abduction and contactee experiences, perhaps in part because I have never had an encounter of my own, though I think it would be fascinating to see firsthand the technology and morphological form of these visitors. I am also particularly drawn to accounts which suggest these "aliens" might be our distant human descendants, returning from the future to investigate their own hominin evolutionary past. One of my favorite contact cases suggestive of time travel is the nighttime abduction of Amy Rylance in Gundiah, Australia, which occurred on Thursday October 4, 2001.

Like so many other abductions, including several examined as part of the current study, Amy Rylance's initial capture was witnessed by others in real time, which helps substantiate her claims. Additionally, Rylance's description of events is similar to countless other reports across the world and through time, which further suggests these are generally the same types of people doing the same types of things. Most notably, in scrutinizing the specifics of this encounter, many factors

243

suggest that these events could not have occurred in the way they were reported without the aid of a time machine.

Amy Rylance was initially abducted from a trailer kept on her Gundiah property near Tiaro, Australia. This was to be the home of a new winery called *Whispering Winds*, which was a joint business venture involving Amy Rylance, her 40-year-old husband Keith, and their business partner Petra Heller, who was 39 at the time.[367] At around 9:30 p.m. on the night of Thursday, October 4, everyone went to separate rooms of the trailer to get some rest. Keith retired to the main bedroom, Petra to a bedroom in an annex of the building, and Amy stayed up to watch TV on the couch in the main lounge.

That evening, a storm moved into the area, which awoke Petra at about 11:15 p.m.[368] She walked out of her bedroom and into the lounge where Amy had been watching TV and was shocked to find Amy still asleep, face down in a prone position, hovering in the air, and being carried toward the window, along with the contents of the coffee table in front of the couch she was sleeping on. Petra reports that Amy was being levitated and taken through the window by a rectangular beam of light, which was emanating from a massive disc-shaped UFO she could see hovering just above the ground outside, near the trailer where they had all been sleeping.

Overwhelmed by what she was witnessing, Petra momentarily fainted. When she came to, she screamed, which woke up Amy's husband Keith. He came running into the lounge to find an inconsolable Petra— and discovered that his wife was gone. By this time, the light beam and UFO were also gone. Keith tried in vain to find out what had happened from Petra, who was petrified with fear and unable to speak. He eventually abandoned this inquest and rushed outside to see if he could find Amy himself. Having no luck in his search, Keith came back in and was finally able to pry some information from Petra. After hearing her story of a UFO and bright light that carried Amy out through the window, Keith dismissed her claim and went back outside to look for his wife again.

Following this second and equally unfruitful search, Keith started to believe Petra's story and decided to call the police to file a missing person's report. At around 11:45 p.m., Keith telephoned the police station in the nearby town of Tiaro. Because they were short-staffed at the time, it took an hour and a half for the police to arrive. Constable Robert Maragna, along with another officer from the town of Maryborough about 30 km northeast of Tiaro, arrived at the scene of the abduction. Later that night they were joined by Sgt. John Bosnjak, the head of the Tiaro police department, who was pulled out of bed to assist in this odd investigation.[369]

While examining the site and looking for signs of any foul play, the officers noticed a torn screen in the lounge and the contents of the coffee table lying on the floor near the window, which corroborated Petra's story. They also noticed that a *Brunfelsia* bush near the window was damaged, as if it had been burnt or affected by heat in some way. Known as a "yesterday, today, tomorrow" bush for the way its flowers slowly change color from spring to autumn, it was clear some of the leaves and branches nearest to the window were affected. Yet, the hibiscus bush to the right of the window showed no signs of heat or other damage.

Naturally, the police officers were skeptical of what Petra and Keith were telling them and remained open to the idea that this was an active crime scene, which may have involved something far more nefarious than flying saucers and mysterious beams of light. However, their notions of reprehensible deeds soon changed, when a call came in from a concerned woman claiming she had just found Amy Rylance, looking weak and disoriented, at a British Petroleum gas station, approximately 90 minutes after she initially disappeared through the window and into a UFO.

It is noteworthy that Travis Walton was also dropped off in a secluded area, but near enough to a petrol station that he could walk there to phone for help. This is a testament to the concern these visitors have for the safety and wellbeing of those they abduct, and to some extent it validates the common calming phrase they utter, in one form or another, during nearly every abduction, "Don't be afraid, we will not harm you." These cases also suggest the visitors are generally aware of our (past) cultural tendency to keep pay phones at or near gas stations.

Service stations also tend to stock food and beverages that can help replenish a body drained of nutrients and fluids during an abduction. This may be critical because extreme dehydration is a common occurrence following events like these, which again includes the case of Travis Walton. It was also a major part of the narrative in the abduction of Terry Lovelace and his friend Toby, who remained unable to quench their intense thirst, regardless of how much of different kinds of fluids they drank. This may indicate that the extraction of bodily fluids over a short timeframe causes a non-life threatening but intense and memorable feeling of extreme thirst.

According to the National Heart, Lung, and Blood Institute, extreme thirst, along with tiredness, weakness, and dizziness, which Amy Rylance also experienced, is a symptom of anemia brought about by a loss of blood and the red blood cells it contains.[370] Any visitors, whether they be extratempestrial, extraterrestrial, or otherwise, would be expected to optimize the amount of fluid they collect during these rare and relatively brief moments they have us in their possession. These procedures, carried out for any number of currently unknown reasons, drain subjects to such an extent that they are unable to replenish fluids fast enough to stave off the brain and body's thirst response, which persists for some time after the abductee is released.

Finding her weak, confused and very thirsty, the nice woman at the petrol station decided to take Amy Rylance to the local hospital in Mackay, where she was examined by doctors. Because this case involved a missing-persons report, the Mackay police department also became involved, which meant a total of three separate jurisdictions were now all working on the same odd abduction case. At the hospital, the Mackay police officers obtained sworn testimony from Rylance, who, by acknowledging the Justice Act, agreed to provide only true statements, which made her liable for prosecution if any aspect of her account was found to be false.

Much like the case of Corporal Armando Valdés in Chile, the initial stages of the Amy Rylance encounter were recounted by those who witnessed it firsthand. Since Amy was asleep, which is seemingly the visitors' preferred method of apprehending people, she retained no memory of what transpired when she was abducted from the trailer in Gundiah. Fortunately, however, her business partner, Petra, had woken up during the storm at just the right moment to witness the abduction in real time. Additionally, despite being asleep when she was taken, Rylance retained clear conscious memories of what happened during her time with these travelers, so a holistic narrative of the entire abduction is available. Research conducted by Bill Chalker and Diane Harrison, shortly after the abduction occurred, sheds more light on what happened after Amy Rylance woke up inside the UAP.

> She next remembered waking up lying on a bench in a strange rectangular room. Illumination came from the walls and the ceiling.... Soon an opening appeared in the wall and 'a guy' about 6 feet tall walked into the room. The man appeared to be slender in build but in perfect proportion, covered head to foot in a full body suit. He had what seemed to be a black covering mask on his face, with a hole for his eyes, nose and mouth. Amy felt she had been there a while. The guy told her they were returning her to a place not far from where they took her from, because the lights were wrong at the property and it wasn't safe.... The next thing she recollects is that she woke up on the ground with trees around her.[371]

This short account of what Amy Rylance observed inside the ship is consistent with what other abductees describe. This is also true of the lights emanating from the walls and ceiling, which is reiterated time and again across abductee accounts. This includes the case of George Van Tassel, who attempted to build a time machine in the Mojave Desert after having been abducted for 20 minutes, on August 24, 1953.

> The interior walls were what looked like Mother of Pearl plastic, like we put on toilet seats and for decorations. The light inside seemed to come from everywhere. The instrument panel wasn't like anything I'd ever seen before in all my years since 1927 in the air game. And they

had a compartment in the wall which both cleans and deodorizes their clothes by some light process, which required no water, or soap, or detergent, or washing machine.[372]

The prevalence of this illumination description is again indicative of similar technology being used by what may be the same or closely related people. Because it is always toward the top of the list of what abductees recall from their time aboard, the advanced lighting technology of these travelers, like their eyes, is quite memorable, perhaps because we also require lighting for interior spaces but do not yet possess the ability to illuminate them in such an innovative and mesmerizing way. Additionally, Van Tassel's description of the way they clean and sanitize their clothes may again suggest they are aware of the dangers of intertemporal disease transmission, as discussed in the Dworshak and Villas-Boas case studies, which occurs more often among conspecifics, or members of the same species.

Amy Rylance's description of the room as rectangular, as opposed to round or oval, may also mean that she was in an observation or holding room toward the outside edge of a large or medium-sized ship. This deduction is gleaned from numerous other accounts, including that of Travis Walton, where upon escaping the rectangular room he was initially held in, he ventured out into a curved hallway where he discovered the control center, in a large circular room at the center of the craft.

Considered alongside other reports, including that of Whitley Strieber as discussed above, we may infer that smaller UFOs have the examination room in the large domed area at the midpoint of the ship, while the control center and other functional spaces are in smaller rooms toward the outside. On the other hand, bigger ships, like the ones Walton and Rylance were taken to—the latter of which was described as "huge" by her friend Petra—would be large enough to allow for a long, circular hallway, with functional spaces like examination rooms off the main hall, toward the outside of the craft. A more detailed study of how room sizes and shapes are described across abduction reports could reveal more about the configuration, form, and function of various spaces within UFOs, especially since there are only so many ways to organize rooms within rounded structures like these disc-shaped craft.

Functional space allocation limitations are also apparent in any large, circular, modern human building. For instance, while I was a senior in high school, I traveled to Athens, Ohio, to visit my older sister who was attending Ohio University. This also happened to be the weekend of what was, at least at the time, one of the biggest Halloween parties in the United States. Because of my sex and gender, I was unable to stay in my sister's all-female dormitory, so she put me up with some of her male friends who lived in the Convocation Center across campus, a massive circular building with dorm rooms, and where basketball games and other sporting events take place.

In many ways, this building reminded me of a giant UFO. It had a wide, segmental, elliptical, domed roof, much like what is so commonly described in close encounters with these craft.[373] After arriving at this temporary place of slumber, while stumbling through the long circular corridor of this massive cylindrical building, I remember being annoyed that I could never see the end of the hallway, as it seemingly went on forever. I was also taken by the shape of the rooms, which were narrower at the hallway entrance, but widened toward the outside edge of the building, much like the front and back yard configuration of houses in a cul-de-sac.

Although sports arenas and UAPs are entirely different structures that serve different purposes, there are commonalities in their configuration, and not just as they relate to space allocation. For instance, going back to the tour given to Mike and Leo Dworshak in the first case study, the boys were shown a dormitory-style bathroom, kitchen, and workspace, with room designs and equipment that were nearly identical to, though slightly more advanced than, what humans use today.

If the intelligent beings that constructed these ships had evolved on a separate planet elsewhere in the universe, we would not expect their rooms, tools, facilities, lighting, and equipment to be so conducive to human use. In other words, if these craft were piloted by beings with tentacles, sloth claws, hippo feet, or they floated in air or swam in water, we would see something fundamentally different. Additionally, other engineering considerations must be given to the way internal spaces are configured for transmedium vehicles like UFOs. Their rapid acceleration and deceleration capabilities, rotation, ability to seamlessly move through and between air and water, and relatedly, their apparent capacity to alter spacetime, likely impose their own set of limitations on how space could be allotted and utilized in and around these ships.

In addition to overt indications that these spaces are developed and occupied by advanced human groups, further support for the idea that the beings who abducted Amy Rylance were human comes from her description of the "guy" who walked into the room through an opening that appeared in the wall. She explained that he was a six-foot-tall "man" with a slender build and perfect proportions. In an interview conducted by Diane Harrison that took place soon after the abduction, Rylance provided more detail about where she was, for how long, and who she interacted with, after Petra saw her being carried through the trailer window.

**Interviewer:** You believe you were on a spaceship?

**Rylance:** I know I was on a spaceship! I recall everything that happened to me while I was there. I remember it all, in my reality. I was there for about seven days before I was returned. My memories are clear and distinct in my mind. I have no conflicts as to what happened to me.

**Interviewer:** Do you recall people? or alien life forms?

**Rylance:** Yes, Yes, there was one man. I call him a man. I don't call him an alien. He looked just like a man to me. He was in a full body suit, and he had a mask over his face. It didn't look like a normal mask. It had large eyes and a small opening for his mouth. He was just like a normal man, exactly in proportion, same human body shape.[374]

Along with his unmistakably human physique, the man was said to have donned the quintessential one-piece bodysuit described in nearly every case study examined thus far. Masks, or occasionally helmets, like the ones worn by Antonio Villas-Boas's captors, are also commonly reported. As mentioned in the Villas-Boas case, considering the visitors' focus on disinfection, health, and hygiene, it is possible these masks represent a form of personal protective equipment (PPE), to help minimize disease transmission between people from different times. Although she couldn't see his entire face because of the mask, Rylance did note that the eye coverings appeared larger than normal. This is consistent with other reports describing the visitors' larger eyes, which, based on past trends in hominin evolution, is a trait we would expect to see in our future human descendants.

Like so many other abductee and contactee accounts, this man spoke calmly to Amy Rylance, and in her native language of English. She also noted that the man showed her kindness and respect, such as in alerting her to the fact that they would not be taking her back home but instead would be "returning her to a place not far from where they took her from because the lights were wrong at the property, and it wasn't safe."[375] This statement is interesting because it begs the question, not safe for whom? Amy Rylance should have been safe at her own property, where she felt secure enough to fall asleep watching TV on the couch in the living room, though she was clearly not safe from abduction, as it turns out.

This statement suggests that the people who took Amy Rylance didn't feel safe returning her to the site of her abduction, and with good reason, since the police were now at the vineyard in that time. Having everyone see Rylance descend from a UFO would have been validating for Petra, since few people believed her, but it also would have exposed the people who kidnapped Amy. It is doubtful these visitors feared being arrested for unlawfully seizing and carrying away a person by force, but were more concerned about having their cover blown and not adhering to the "Prime Directive," which appears to be the status quo across cases.

While there are many indications that the people who took Amy Rylance were from our future, perhaps the most striking indication of this comes from the way the events of that night unfolded, in two very different reference frames. The man who told Rylance they were "returning her to a place not far from where they took her" was undoubtedly speaking in relative terms. This is because the visitors dropped her off near Mackay, Australia, which is nearly 790 Kilometers (490 miles) from her home in Gundiah. Additionally, the woman who telephoned Amy's husband Keith from the petrol station did so less than two hours after Petra saw Amy being carried through the window by a beam of light and shortly after the police arrived to investigate her disappearance.

> Approximately ninety minutes after Petra witnessed the supposed abduction, Amy was found disorientated and covered in mud at Mackay Queensland... about 790 kms from Gundiah. This trip, when driven by car, would usually take at least 8-9 hours. On discovery, Ms. Rylance stated that she had been abducted for several days. When examined by Mackay hospital staff they found that she had in fact not eaten for days, and her usually shaven bodily hair had grown considerably.[376]

Because Amy awoke in a group of trees and had to schlep across bushland for some time before she found a road that led to the gas station where she was found, her total time onboard the UFO, at least in the reference frame of those who stayed behind, was much less than 90 minutes.[377] Realistically, the time between when Amy was abducted near Gundiah, to when she was dropped off near Mackay, 790 km away, was only about one hour, and maybe less. If there is one thing we know about UFOs, it is that they are capable of traveling very fast, so the average UAP could certainly travel 790 km in one hour. However, in the context of how this case study is suggestive of backward time travel, the speed with which Rylance got from Gundiah to Mackay is less important than her assertion that she was gone for an entire week.

When I was returned, I woke up somewhere over there (referring to Mackay). It was all full of bushes and trees and stuff like that. It was somewhere near the ocean. I had no idea where I was, I was disoriented, and I was scared and all I wanted to do was find somebody, so I knew that I was safe and I was all right. I wasn't too far away. I had no idea how long I was gone for in this time, cause to me I was gone for seven days.[378]

Rylance's chronological conjecture was corroborated by nurses and physicians at the Mackay hospital, who noted that her stomach was empty, she was dehydrated, and she exhibited hair growth far in excess of what would occur in 60–90 minutes. This aspect of the case carries even greater weight, since both the time she was missing, and the time her body indicated she was gone, were documented by police officers and medical staff at the time of the incident. When considering the details of this report, and particularly the timing of events, this anomaly indicates that, like in the Corporal Armando Valdés case, time passed differently inside the ship—or that the people who took Amy Rylance possessed technology that allowed them to travel back in time to drop her off closer to the point in time from which she was taken.

If the latter was the case, it is curious they took Rylance back in time at all, since most abductees are not provided this accommodation, and some go missing for multiple days before they're returned. For instance, in the case of Travis Walton, he was gone for five days, and like Amy Rylance, he was last seen in the proximity of a UFO. This suggests that Travis Walton was taken for five days in both "normal time" and ship time. Comparatively, Amy Rylance was gone for seven days of ship time but only for an hour or two in the temporal reference frame of those looking for her.

It is thought-provoking to contrast the Travis Walton, Amy Rylance, and Corporal Armando Valdés case studies. For both Rylance and Valdés, their physical condition, hunger, dehydration, and excess body hair growth indicates they were abducted for multiple days but were returned to a time closer to when they were taken, and in the case of Armando Valdés, only about 15 minutes later. So if multiple days had passed for Rylance and Valdés, despite only being gone for about 60 and 15 minutes, respectively, why was Travis Walton missing for five days, if time travel is in the wheelhouse of these travelers?

I've always thought abductions most often occur at night so the visitors have enough time to carry out their procedures before needing to take the captured back to their cars or beds. However, the Rylance, Valdés, and Jones case studies, and others like them, suggest these travelers possess the ability to freeze time and to travel backward through time. This means they could conduct their research and related tasks while abductees are in their care and still ensure they are tucked back in bed before sunrise. The people who took Amy Rylance might have wanted to return her to the couch before anyone in the trailer woke up the next morning, but due to the storm, and the bright light elevator they shined through the window, their cover was blown, and they were forced to take Rylance somewhere else. Still, even though Amy spent upwards of a week in the ship, they returned her to a time near to when she was abducted, which may have been done to help calm her panicked husband and friend.

With the aid of backward time-travel technology, abductees could spend multiple days with the extratempestrials and still be returned close to the point in time from which they came. As such, the omnipresence of nighttime abductions may have more to do with avoiding detection, the relative ease of capturing someone who is already asleep, and minimizing psychological harm to the taken, since it would be easier to confuse an abduction experience with a dream if they were already asleep when it occurred.

There are many interesting facets to this case. In fact, it has been called the most curious,[379] and most convincing, UFO encounter of the 21st century.[380] Although questions remain, if Amy Rylance's abduction truly happened the way it was described, then one thing is for certain: if someone is abducted and they show physical signs of having been gone for seven days, but they are found nearly 800 kilometers away and only 90 minutes after they were reported missing, then whoever kidnapped them must have a vehicle that can not only move at tremendous speed but which is also capable of traveling backward through time.

# Case Study 15

~

# 2020
# Declassified US Navy Videos

*I'm glad the Pentagon is finally releasing this footage, but it only scratches the surface of research and materials available. The U.S. needs to take a serious, scientific look at this and any potential national security implications. The American people deserve to be informed.*[381]

— Sen. Harry Reid,
Former US Senate Majority Leader

*There is now a growing, still quiet but increasingly vocal consensus among researchers throughout academia, industry, and government that the UFO phenomenon represents something genuinely anomalous that cannot be dismissed as simple mistakes of perception or explained (away) by conventional means, and that therefore merits the kind of serious, systematic investigation that only combined resources would allow.*[382]

— Hussein Ali Agrama

On Monday, April 27, 2020, the US Navy declassified, and shared on their Naval Air Systems Command website, three video clips of unidentified aerial phenomena.[383] The first video, labeled *FLIR* (for the forward-looking infrared camera it was captured with), was recorded on November 14, 2004, by a F/A-18 Hornet fighter pilot named Chad Underwood. At the time the video was captured, Underwood was performing training exercises off the USS Nimitz, stationed about 60 miles off the coast of San Diego, USA.

The other two videos, dubbed *GOFAST* and *GIMBAL*, were also recorded by F/A-18 Hornet fighter pilots who were carrying out military training exercises off the Theodore Roosevelt aircraft carrier. These were captured during a spate of sightings that occurred almost daily, from the summer of 2014 to March 2015, in the skies off the eastern coast of the United States, stretching from Virginia to Florida.[384] According to Navy pilot Lieutenant Ryan Graves, in a *60 Minutes* interview with Bill Whitaker, UFOs were sighted by members of his squadron "Every day for at least a couple years."[385] They followed his strike group up and down the coast for years, and even after the USS Roosevelt deployed to the Arabian Gulf in March 2015, the UAPs followed them to their new location in the Middle East.

As interest in and debate about the videos grew, the Department of Defense (DOD) decided to release them to the public. In a statement issued on April 27, 2020, the US DOD acknowledged the authenticity of these unclassified Navy videos and provided clarity on why they were released.

> The Department of Defense has authorized the release of three unclassified Navy videos, one taken in November 2004 and the other two in January 2015, which have been circulating in the public domain after unauthorized releases in 2007 and 2017. The U.S. Navy previously acknowledged that these videos circulating in the public domain were indeed Navy videos. After a thorough review, the department has determined that the authorized release of these unclassified videos does not reveal any sensitive capabilities or systems, and does not impinge on any subsequent investigations of military air space incursions by unidentified aerial phenomena. DOD is releasing the videos in order to clear up any misconceptions by the public on whether or not the footage that has been circulating was real, or whether or not there is more to the videos. The aerial phenomena observed in the videos remain characterized as 'unidentified.'[386]

The acknowledgment and public release of these videos marks a monumental shift in US policy regarding how the UFO phenomenon is approached, which historically has been immensely draconian.

In 1948, The US Air Force oversaw what was among the first officially sanctioned investigations of UFO-related occurrences. Originally
named Project SAUCER, which was soon changed to Project SIGN,
the formation of this organization followed a high-profile incident involving an alleged UFO crash that occurred near Roswell, New Mexico,
in 1947.[387] In 1949, Project SIGN was succeeded by Project Grudge,
which, as the name may imply, was created with the purpose of cast-
ing doubt on the reality of UFOs and manufacturing synthetic stigma
meant to quell interest in and conversations about the phenomenon.
Project Grudge officials were instructed to explain away these incidents
and convince people that they were instead the result of weather balloons, hallucinations, mass hysteria, weather balloons again, or people
mistaking natural occurrences for UFOs.[388] This proved to be an incredibly effective campaign, as the cultural hangover from this period of
deceit and derision persists into the present day.

Following a series of sightings at Fort Mammoth, New Jersey, in
1951, the US military revamped Project Grudge, putting US Air Force
Captain Edward J. Ruppelt in charge of a new agency called Project
Blue Book, which was based at Wright-Patterson Air Force Base near
Dayton, Ohio.[389] Captain Ruppelt was responsible for overhauling the
entire project, which included developing a standardized form that
could be used to file reports of UFO sightings. Ruppelt also appointed
members of the Battelle Memorial Institute in Columbus, Ohio, to perform statistical analyses of these standardized reports as part of a new
program named Project Stork. Additionally, Ruppelt formed strong
collaborative relationships with prominent scientists, which included
Dr. J. Allen Hynek at The Ohio State University, who had already been
consulting for the US Air Force as part of the earlier Project Sign and
Project Grudge programs.[390]

Although the surface-level objective of these organizations was to
investigate UFO sightings and other odd encounters, their primary
mission was to debunk these reports and offer more conventional explanations for what people were seeing in the sky. However, and despite
their best efforts, out of the 12,618 sightings of "strange phenomena"

the United States Air Force recorded between 1948 and 1969, 701, or 5.6%, remained unidentified.[391] This is a relatively small number, but it is also significant, considering some of the best scientists of the time were working to provide any conceivable explanation for what people were seeing, though they were unable to explicate 5.6% of cases. Additionally, many injudicious explanations proffered to explain the other 94.4% were highly contentious.

Considering the American government's long-standing policy of specious repudiation, the Pentagon's 2020 affirmation of the reality of these cockpit videos was an earth-shattering revelation, though despite what may appear to be an abrupt sea change, some progress had been made in the years leading up to this announcement. For instance, in 2015, the US Navy issued new guidelines for how military personnel were meant to report and investigate aerial objects; and while these Navy protocols were ultimately updated in early 2020 to state that all data associated with the investigation of these anomalous aerial vehicles (AAVs) will remain classified, it marks a critical turning point in how the phenomenon was approached by a historically flippant government.

In addition to direct government divulgence, as mentioned earlier in this text, the UFO conversation was catapulted forward by Helene Cooper, Ralph Blumenthal, and Leslie Kean's 2017 *New York Times* article, "Glowing Auras and 'Black Money': The Pentagon's Mysterious U.F.O. Program," which made the public aware of the US Advanced Aerospace Threat Identification Program (AATIP).[392] This was spearheaded by the late senator and former US senate majority leader, Harry Reid, who secured a 22-million-dollar budget specifically intended for the study of unidentified aerial phenomena.

Other developments have also come to pass since the Pentagon's 2020 acknowledgment of the reality of these objects. For instance, as mentioned in chapter two of the current text, the United State Office of Naval Intelligence oversaw the formation of the Unidentified Aerial Phenomena Task Force (AUPTF), which released their unclassified "Preliminary Assessment of Unidentified Aerial Phenomena" report on June 25, 2021.[393] Additionally, the successor to the UAPTF, the

Airborne Object Identification and Management Synchronization Group (AOIMSG), was established on November 23, 2021.[394]

The creation of these offices, and the findings they have published, help progress the UFO conversation. However, none may be as impactful as what is considered the most significant advancement to date, when on December 27, 2021, President Joseph Robinette Biden Jr. signed into law the National Defense Authorization Act (NDAA). This bill included the Gillibrand Amendment, which "establishes a Formal Office to Carry Out a Coordinated Effort on Collection and Analysis Related to UAPs."[395] This new office will provide scientific, intelligence, and technical assessments related to UAPs, and among other objectives, it will,

> **Establish a Science Plan:** The UAP office will be responsible for implementing a science plan to test scientific theories related to UAP characteristics and performances....
>
> **Report to Congress:** The UAP office will be required to provide unclassified annual reports to Congress and classified semiannual briefings on intelligence analysis, reported incidents, health-related effects, the role of foreign governments, and nuclear security.
>
> **Collection & Analysis of Data into a Central Repository:** The UAP office will supervise the development and execution of intelligence collection and analysis regarding UAPs in order to understand their technical and scientific characteristics. The UAP office will receive relevant data immediately from Intelligence Community agencies.[396]

Given the wide-ranging goals of this newly established government office and the broad scope of their collaborative activities, it has been hailed as the most significant UFO legislation ever passed. Despite these monumental shifts in policy, and the government's new and more inclusive approach to the UFO phenomenon, the general public has remained largely dismissive of the issue. According to Will Dowd, in an article for the *Boston Globe* that looks back at these and other UFO developments in the year 2021,

By any measure, the year 2021 was a turning point in UFO history. In June, the office of the director of national intelligence released a nine-page report disclosing dozens of aerial sightings (most witnessed by US Navy members) that couldn't be explained. In December, the annual defense bill established a new office that will study UAPs and report its findings to Congress — the most significant UFO legislation ever passed.... And yet, in the inundation of 2021 news, these UFO milestones barely registered as a blip on the public's radar. Was the potential reality of ETs too overwhelming — or too frightening — for our human brains to absorb? Or was our attention simply exhausted by political polarization and the raging pandemic?

The lack of attention this subject has received is often attributed to the fact that the 24-hour news cycle was dominated by numerous other issues, not least among them, an attempted overthrow of American democracy by right-wing extremists, ethnic tensions in the US and abroad, and a global viral pandemic. It was arguably tough for any meaningful information to break through in 2020 and 2021, as we were endlessly bombarded with new and often unsettling developments. However, among those who have been paying attention over the last several years, the question has started to shift from "Is this a real phenomenon?" to "What are these things? Who or what is controlling them? Why are they here? And from where, or potentially when, are they coming?"

With official confirmation of exceptionally advanced aeronautic devices in our oceans and skies, it is important to consider what is happening now in the context of what others have observed in the recent, historic, and prehistoric past. After all, "the phenomenon did not begin in 1947, it did not begin with WWII,"[397] and it certainly did not begin with the FLIR video filmed on November 14, 2004. Although these three US Navy videos are unquestionably crucial for advancing our understanding of UFOs, it is regrettable that they carry so much more weight than the experiences of ordinary and often equally credible people.

To a certain extent, it is understandable why our society puts added value on the testimony of police and military personnel in authoritative positions. We are more inclined to accept the deposition of a police officer over a meth head, even if they witnessed the same event from the same perspective at the same time. Part of this is tied to the knowledge and training of the police officer, which is also the case for Navy pilots, as their skills and experience imbue them with a better framework with which to assess the aeronautic eccentricities of what they are witnessing in real time, and to later contemplate and recount these events as they unfolded.

This dichotomy in the way we view eyewitness testimony may also be related to the Western notion of meritocracy, and the value we put on certain occupational positions over others. There is also the issue of drug and alcohol use, which became part of the stigma and shame campaign of the mid and late 20th century. Because pilots and police are subjected to regular mandatory drug tests, it allows us to immediately rule out that nonfactor in assessing the reliability of their accounts.

As we've seen throughout this text, and across UFO reports more broadly, most people who are abducted, or who had any form of close contact, obstinately iterate that they were not drinking or using drugs. When Charles Hickson and Calvin Parker reported their abduction to the police, Hickson insisted that he only smelled like booze because he had a couple drinks to calm his nerves *after* their abduction, but he was adamant that they had not been drinking prior to the encounter. Amy Rylance was also accused of being on drugs by the police and hospital staff in Mackay, Australia, though a blood test proved she had not drunk alcohol or taken any drugs.[398]

Drugs and alcohol can certainly alter one's perception and memories of an event, particularly psychedelic drugs like LSD, ayahuasca, DMT, psilocybin, and others. However, with something as bizarre as robots or humanoid beings taking someone into a hovering ship, stripping them naked, probing and examining them, and often extracting sperm and eggs, a slight change in perception resulting from the ingestion of drugs or alcohol isn't going to make a difference. In fact, I am not aware of any drug that could induce such consistent conscious and subconscious memories of such things without an actual occurrence, or one that would elicit the same experience in each of these people who never took it. The one exception may be DMT, which none of these experiencers could have been on, considering its short-term effects, its tendency to incapacitate those who take it, and because DMT hadn't become widely popular until the late 20th century, and mostly after clinical psychiatrist Dr. Rick Strassman wrote *DMT: The Spirit Molecule*, in the year 2000.[399]

This outmoded idea that those who see aliens and UFOs must be crazy or on drugs is an old, tired stereotype, which is a sad cultural hangover stemming from many decades of intentional institutionalized campaigns aimed at stigmatizing those who had seen something extraordinary. It is high time we change how we view this phenomenon and those who are directly affected by it. We should consider every account, and assess its merits with a skeptical open mind, regardless of who had the encounter or whether they smoked a bowl or had a few beers beforehand.

Reports of aerial phenomena provided by police officers, scientists, military personnel, and government officials may always be held in higher esteem relative to others. When it comes to assessing the credibility of any case, those with more knowledge and experience are always going to be believed above all others. Because military pilots have spent countless hours in flight, have undergone rigorous training to be able to instantly identify threats, and have seen much throughout their careers, they are in a better position to differentiate between the exceptional and conventional. Considering the well-honed skills, knowledge, and experience of Navy pilots, when they see an advanced aerial object doing things that far exceed the abilities of modern aircraft, their testimony is paramount.

This is certainly the case with Navy Strike Fighter Commander David Fravor. On November 14, 2004, he engaged the "Tic-Tac" UFO seen in the FLIR video, which was captured on film by his colleague, Chad Underwood, soon after Fravor's initial encounter. This now-famous, white, oval-shaped, Tic-Tac-looking object was about 40 to 50 feet long and 10 to 15 feet wide.[400] It was pursued by Fravor and Lt. Commander Alex Dietrich, who encountered the object during a training mission with the Nimitz Carrier Strike Group, which was stationed about 60 miles off the coast of San Diego, California.[401 402]

As an experienced Navy fighter pilot with 18 years in the service, the details of Fravor's interaction with the Anomalous Aerial Vehicle are both credible and fascinating. Fravor was the commanding officer of the VFA-41 Black Aces, a US Navy strike fighter squadron of F/A-18 Hornet fighter jets. As commanding officer, he was among the 20 highest-ranking individuals of the 5,500-person crew on the Nimitz aircraft carrier at the time of the encounter.[403] Around 2:10 p.m. on November 14, 2004, Fravor's squadron was conducting training exercises about 100 miles off the Western Coast of the United States, ahead of deployment to the Persian Gulf during the Iraq War. Fravor, like everyone else, was unsure what this craft was or what it was doing as it zigzagged above what he described as "a disturbance in the ocean." Although he was unsure what the object was, Fravor adamantly asserts that "It was a real object, it exists, and I saw it."[404]

On November 10, 2004, four days before the Tic-Tac encounter, Kevin M. Day, a radar operator in the Combat Information Center (CIC) aboard the USS Princeton, began seeing small groups of strange objects flying at about 140 miles per hour at an elevation of 28,000 feet.[405] According to Knuth et al. (2019), in the article "Estimating Flight Characteristics of Anomalous Unidentified Aerial Vehicles in the 2004 Nimitz Encounter,"

The main incident occurred on 14 November 2004, but several days earlier, radar operators on the USS Princeton were detecting UAPs appearing on radar at about 80,000+ feet altitude to the north of CSG11 in the vicinity of Santa Catalina and San Clemente Islands. Senior Chief Kevin Day informed us that the Ballistic Missile Defense (BMD) radar systems had detected the UAPs in low Earth orbit before they dropped down to 80,000 feet. The objects would arrive in groups of 10 to 20 and subsequently drop down to 28,000 feet with a several hundred foot variation, and track south at a speed of about 100 knots.[406]

A thorough analysis of the observed radar tracks of these objects was also carried out by the Scientific Coalition for UAP Studies (SCU) and published in their report, "A Forensic Analysis of Navy Carrier Strike Group Eleven's Encounter with an Anomalous Aerial Vehicle."[407] Based on statements from two Navy personnel who observed these Tic-Tac objects on radar, the CIC equipment indicated the objects moved from 80,000+ feet to 28,000 feet and down to sea level in only 0.78 seconds. According to the SCU's analysis,

> The AAVs, originally at 80,000+ feet, were observed to descend in as little as 0.78 seconds to various altitudes from 28,000 feet to as low as just 50 feet or less above the ocean surface.... Calculations based on these observations, 60,000 vertical feet in 0.78 seconds and an initial and final velocity of zero, and assuming a constant acceleration (linear velocity) changing to a deceleration midway, yield a maximum velocity of 104,895 mph at the midway point, and an acceleration of 12,250 g-forces. If one of the navy's jets of a similar size (F/A-18F at 18 tons) accelerated at this rate, it would need 90 gigawatts of power.
>
> These numbers are nonsensical to any known aircraft; one would expect to see a fireball due to air friction at those speeds and one would not anticipate any known aircraft to remain structurally intact with such large g-forces.[408]

These radar returns continued over the course of the next few days. However, no one was ever in the area when they were observed on radar, at least not until Commander Fravor's squadron happened to be close enough that they could fly in to check it out. When they arrived at the merge point where these radar hits were observed, they saw a white Tic-Tac-shaped object moving rapidly back and forth in a zig-zag motion above a white-water disturbance in the ocean below. Fravor broke to pursue the craft, leaving the other Hornet to maintain a "Gods-eye view" of their interaction below. According to information compiled from multiple sources by the SCU in their forensic report,

> As the 'FastEagles' continued to observe the water disturbance from an altitude of 20,000 feet, all four pilots saw an additional anomaly. CDR Fravor described a white 'Tic-Tac' shaped object, with perhaps two small appendages hanging below its belly, moving just above the water disturbance. The object had no wings or exhaust and its movement had no observable effect on the calm ocean surface such as that of a rotor wash from a helicopter.
>
> It did not need to slow down to make a change in direction; its directional change was instantaneous. Furthermore, the object was moving in a random and erratic motion below him in left, right, forward, and backward directions.[409]

When Fravor broke to pursue the UFO, it initially darted toward his fighter jet, but then rapidly moved behind him. Over the next 5–7 minutes, the two aircraft played a cat-and-mouse game, until the object suddenly accelerated at tremendous speed away from him, disappearing from sight almost instantaneously. An interesting additional detail, which may indicate that the intelligence controlling these objects are capable of knowing the future, or at least knowing things beyond the scope of modern human understanding, is that when the craft Fravor had been following disappeared, it suddenly reappeared at the exact location of their secret coordinate CAP point.

The jets were on their way back to the Nimitz when CDR Fravor received a call back from the Princeton to tell him that, 'You will not believe this but the 'Tic-Tac' is back at your CAP.' The surprise reaction from the Princeton was because the CAP point was a secret coordinate location that was a precise latitude, longitude, and altitude.

The strangeness of this observation was later noted by Senior Chief Day when he stated in his interview:

'They [the 'Tic-Tac'] shouldn't have known where it was. And that was the bizzareness of it. How the hell did it know where the CAP station was? I mean it was right on it. Directly on it. Not close by, but on it. On that point in space.'[410]

The incredible aeronautic capabilities of the Anomalous Aerial Vehicle that Fravor and the three other pilots saw that afternoon, and in particular, their ability to perform almost instantaneous accelerations and decelerations, is one of the most described characteristics of UFOs. In an interview with the UK paper, *The Independent*, Fravor's fellow airman, Chad Underwood, who was able to record the UFO seen in the FLIR video approximately one hour after the initial encounter, described the object as "not behaving within the normal laws of physics."

Because, aircraft, whether they're manned or unmanned, still have to obey the laws of physics. They have to have some source of lift, some source of propulsion. The Tic Tac was not doing that. It was going from like 50,000 feet to a hundred feet in seconds, which is not possible.[411]

With the materials and technology available to us now, this is not possible. However, if it happened, then it is possible, we just don't yet know how to do it. Furthermore, if we consider these craft and their actions in the context of the Extratempestrial Model, and the more evolved toolkit of our distant human descendants, with better materials, engineering, and a deeper knowledge of physics, which appears to include the ability to manipulate spacetime, then how they carry out such seemingly impossible maneuvers becomes more plausible and comprehensible.

Throughout this text, we've examined cases where UFOs appear to alter the rate at which time passes, such as in the cases of Lynda Jones and Jim Penniston, who remembered all movement and sound ceasing as they approached the ship. The visitors' ability to alter time near these objects was also expressed to Leo Dworshak during a nighttime interaction that took place later in his life. Similar spacetime-altering effects are apparent in the 1977 case of Chilean Army Corporal Armando Valdés, who aged by five days during the 15 minutes he was near or on the ship, as experienced in the frame of reference of his men.

These observed outcomes, seen across countless other instances of close contact, suggest these craft are capable of warping spacetime. This is not only a technological advancement that may allow them to travel backward and forward through time, but it could be an important part of how they achieve such remarkable speeds and perform almost instantaneous accelerations and decelerations, as witnessed by outside observers. More specifically, manipulating spacetime may help explain how these objects, and any occupants inside, could survive the insane g-forces generated in association with such a rapid change in direction and velocity.

As mentioned in the Cpl. Valdés case study, what we see as tremendously fast accelerations and decelerations, which would flatten any occupant against the walls of the ship, could be a slow and steady acceleration to those inside, if they are altering the speed of time in and around the aircraft. The perverse g-forces generated, which were estimated by the SCU to be about 12,250g for the Tic-Tac UFO, are often cited by skeptics as a reason why UFOs can't be real. For example, Mick West, a "prominent UFO debunker and villain of the ufologists,"[412] overlooked the ostensive spacetime manipulation capabilities of these craft when he wrote a comment about the physical implausibility of withstanding the g-forces generated during the rapid descent of the Tic-Tac UFOs.

80,000 feet is 15 miles. 15 miles in 2 seconds is avg, 27000 mph, but mid peak 54,000 mph in 1 second if from hover to hover. That's 2,461g. Physically impossible.[413]

The extreme forces associated with a 2,461 g maneuver, and more so with an acceleration generating 12,250 g-forces, as calculated by the SCU, would crush any machine or living thing inside. However, these g-forces are based solely on calculations of what we see happening as observers outside the reference frame of these objects. Inside, it may be a very different story, particularly if Paul Hill and Dr. Hal Puthoff are correct that light and time near these craft are blueshifted, which would further partition temporal perception within and farther from these objects.[414] [415]

Furthermore, if we can consider the testimony of those who claim to have ridden in these ships, their accounts indicate that no amount of acceleration or deceleration is felt on the inside, regardless of how fast they are moving. In fact, it is likely that the propulsion system of these UAPs is integrated with whatever mechanism is used to alter spacetime while in flight, to fully eliminate the sensation of movement, so that no g-forces are felt whatsoever. In an interview with Mark Snider, on the show *Ohio Exopolitics*, guest Jerry Wills, who was mentioned in a few of the above case studies, explains how he was transported in a disc-shaped UFO up to, and back from, a base on the dark side of the moon. During the return trip back to Earth, Wills claims to have seen the moon receding at an exceedingly fast rate, though he reports feeling no sense of motion while speeding away from it.

**Wills:** When inside, it was very nondescript, it wasn't like the bridge of the enterprise. It was really very simple, and during this occasion there was no sensation of movement, but apparently, we went out as far as the dark side of the moon and came back. They wanted to show me something out there. And you know, I was there, saw it, never did anything except, well, 'there ya go, see that?' 'Uhh huh.' And so, nothing happened. It started getting smaller in the distance. The speed was incredible. It truly was. I don't even know how to tell you how fast it was. It was very, very, very fast. And then, right back to exactly the same place where this disc shaped thing had been setting, and it just landed in the same holes, the same footprints.

**Interviewer:** Amazing. You didn't feel any sense of momentum, or anything did you?

**Wills:** No, not a bit.[416]

Reports provided by people who were given the opportunity to travel in these advanced aircraft don't recall feeling movement of any kind while in flight and certainly not of being splattered against the walls during rapid starts and stops. This includes the case of Terry Lovelace, who also claims to have journeyed between the Earth and Moon on different occasions, while in the company of his lifelong abduction ambassador, Betty Rubble. Although they were flying at very high speed, there was never any sense of movement. Instead, like Jerry Wills, Lovelace felt no acceleration at all. These and similar other accounts suggest that, even though UFOs appear to perform maneuvers that defy the laws of physics, if they are manipulating spacetime in their frame of reference, what we perceive as outsiders who exist in a separate reference frame is an irrelevant illusion.

A similar spacetime-altering explanation for how the Tic-Tac and other UFOs can engage in high-speed maneuvers, and potentially achieve backward time travel, has also been expressed by Dr. Jack Sarfatti, who was mentioned in the opening chapter of this book. Sarfatti is an American theoretical physicist who received a PhD in physics from the University of California, Riverside. He also studied at the Cornell Space Science Center, the Max Planck Institute for Physics, the UK Atomic Energy Research Establishment, and the Abdus Salam International Centre for Theoretical Physics in Italy. During a March 2020 interview on the *Hidden Truth Show* with Jim Breslo, Sarfatti offered a potential explanation for how these UFOs work, and how they may be capable of generating enough energy to perform such extraordinary maneuvers, which has long been another stumbling block for skeptics and "debunkers."

> There's this one key idea of how matter couples to gravity in Einstein's equation and there's something called the speed of light.... They think the speed of light has to be the speed of light in vacuum even though it's inside a material. And the point is, you have to use the speed of light in the material. And then once you realize that, everything about Tic Tac is easy to explain.

See the problem is this, if you read any of the standard papers in the field, when they're talking about warp drive or they're talking about time travel through wormholes they say 'well the problem is it requires so much energy to do it.' And that's not true, you can actually do it with a AAA battery.... The Tic Tac going from 80,000 feet down to 50,000 feet in less than two seconds and there's no jet engines no flares, how's it going to do that....? Going maybe thousands of Gs, how's it doing that?

The way it's doing it is because there's a special material that is the fuselage. The fuselage is built of something called a metamaterial.... And what happens is that if you pump electromagnetic energy into the metamaterial it can have a certain kind of, what's called a resonance, and in that resonance the speed of light inside the material can go down to a very small number.[417]

Not everyone in the physics community agrees with Sarfatti's equations, or his explanation for how this process would work using advanced metamaterials. However, because we are all equally limited regarding what we can know about sophisticated futuristic technologies, based on the limited knowledge available to us in the present time, we should consider and test all valid theories about how these craft may operate. The same way we scoff at our inability to understand even simple processes of the past, current discussions of more advanced machinery will always seem rudimentary to those in the more enlightened future. Even the smartest people alive during the Middle Ages would struggle to explain the mobile phone, especially when pressed about where it came from and how it works.

Time will tell whether Sarfatti is right about the specific operational logistics of the Tic-Tac and other UFOs, most of all if these machines are the product of future human research and development, which Sarfatti also believes to be the case. Later in the same interview, he reiterated the above claims that the Tic-Tac makes use of a type of sophisticated metamaterial fuselage, that these objects move at incredible speeds by lowering their energy requirements, and that everything about the Tic-Tac's behavior suggests it came back in time from the human future.

> My best judgement from everything I know, and everything that is happening, is that the most probable scenario is that they are time travelers back from the future. And by the way, there's a bunch of other people independently coming to that conclusion, I'm not the only one. I was on Coast to Coast, there's this guy, Robert Masters (sic), who's not even a physicist... he's some kind of evolutionary anthropologist.[418]

I would tend to agree with Dr. Sarfatti, and certainly this "Robert" Masters guy. For when we reflect on the astounding aeronautic characteristics of the Tic-Tac, in conjunction with countless other reports of UFOs behaving in similar ways, while also considering the humanoid and entirely human-looking beings so often seen in association with them, the most probable scenario is that they are time travelers coming back from the future. Showcasing the incredible achievements of our more advanced descendants, derived from the cumulative culture of their ancestors, spread throughout the whole of future human history.

# Chapter 5

# A Case Study of Case Studies

*I think what the UFO phenomena is teaching us is that we don't understand time and space. Here are objects that are physical, that interact with our environment, that cause effects on the witnesses, on the psychology and physiology of the witness, that leave traces on the ground, and yet appear to be capable of being able to manipulate time and space in ways that go beyond what our physics understands today.[419]*

– Jacques Fabrice Vallée

*The important thing is not to stop questioning; curiosity has its own reason for existing. One cannot help but be in awe when contemplating the mysteries of eternity, of life, of the marvelous structure of reality. It is enough if one tries merely to comprehend a little of the mystery every day. The important thing is not to stop questioning; never lose a holy curiosity.[420]*

– Albert Einstein

## Intent and Intertemporal Inquiry

One of the most common questions I'm asked when discussing the Extratempestrial Model is "Why?" Why would our descendants care what their ancestors were doing in the distant past? My initial reply always involves acknowledging potential biases I might have as an anthropologist, considering our focus on investigating change through time. I then note the vast similarities across abductee accounts and that most descriptions mirror what anthropologists and other scientists would do if we currently possessed time-travel technology.

Considered holistically, the visitors' efforts appear to be tied to knowledge acquisition. This too is intuitive, for if nothing in the physical universe prevents us from traveling backward in time, which is the general consensus among philosophers and physicists alike, then we are sure to eventually figure out how to do it, and we would be expected to use this ability to garner greater knowledge of the past. Aided by the extraordinary tool of time travel, our understanding of Earth history would advance far beyond that which exists today.

There are many ways to view the potential origins and intent of these travelers, though in examining their reported behaviors across cases, at least part of the purpose seems scientific in nature. If modern researchers could travel back to predetermined points in our evolutionary past, to examine earlier groups or conduct ecological investigations, such as what Leo Dworshak observed in the earliest case study considered, we would be granted a much richer understanding of hominin history and the state of our planet through time.

As time-traveling anthropologists of the present, we could pick people up and take tissue, skin, and fluid samples to run any number of studies on population genetics, evolutionary biology, health, or reproduction. We could take fecal samples to understand what types of foods they ate and to examine how our diets changed through time. We could look at the clothing, tool technology, language, and belief systems of past peoples to better understand the cultural process among different geographic and temporal groups. Additionally, if the societies under scrutiny had developed a preservable written language that could be studied before visiting, we could ask questions to gain deeper insight into their symbolic lives, including their views on creation, the afterlife, how they perceive their existence, and how they perceive us, as visitors to their time.

It is interesting to note, however, that this rarely happens. Instead, most information transmission is from them to us, almost as if they already know everything about us. This would be expected if they are our descendants using time-travel technology to study the past. Relatively proximate future humans may also have access to archived records that provide some knowledge of our times. Or perhaps their commonly described telepathic abilities allow them to learn everything they want to know about us during instances of close contact, circumventing the need for direct two-way communication and ethnographic interviews.

Regarding the highly invasive anal probe aspect of the phenomenon specifically, it does seem easier, and much less awkward, to just ask people what they ate, rather than prodding rectums to obtain this information. However, considering the often-panicked condition of the taken, formal discussions about their diet, or any other aspect of their lives, may be better attained using other means. Since most abductees are frightened, and often belligerent, there could also be safety concerns, as well as questions regarding the reliability of information obtained from interviews with study subjects in a decidedly startled state. Additionally, considering the importance of our microbiome as it relates to overall gastrointestinal health, simply asking what we ate might not provide the purview of information they are after.

Modern humans who claim to have been abducted by presumed future humans most often describe a series of events entirely consistent with what anthropologists across all subfields of the discipline would do. Biological anthropologists, and especially paleoanthropologists like myself, would benefit enormously from the novel ability to analyze the soft-tissue anatomy of the long dead, considering we are currently only able to examine the fossilized skeletal and dental remains of our more distant hominin ancestors. Cultural anthropologists would also be major beneficiaries of a time-travel device, as they would be provided the opportunity to conduct real-time analyses of entire societies, taking holistic ethnographic methods used for researching living peoples and extending them deep into the past.

Cultural anthropologists have always been limited by research methods that can only be used with extant groups. Knowledge of earlier societies, beyond what was recorded by anthropologists over the last three centuries, must be obtained through archaeological survey and analyses of the physical culture of past peoples. Still, there is only so much that can be inferred from material remains, so we are left to speculate about the nonmaterial lives of historic and prehistoric groups, including their symbols, belief systems, rituals, religions, and behaviors, which are not preserved in the archaeological record. Though at some point in the future, if we are able to develop the knowledge, materials, and machinery required to return to the past, it would provide a tremendous opportunity to conduct ethnographic analyses on long-extinct groups, at a time when their traditional lifeways were still intact.

Beyond the cultural implications of time travel, we would be afforded the luxury of answering many hotly debated questions in anthropology. Depending on how far back in time we could go, researchers could finally put to rest debates surrounding hominin speciation events, introgression, the advent and proliferation of tool use, the origin of agriculture, and what happened to the Neanderthals, Denisovans, and other extinct groups, among other vexing questions pertaining to past human biological and cultural processes. Presently, we are left to piece together elements of deep history from the fossil, dental, skeletal, and material culture left behind by past people. However, with the ability to travel back in time, we could examine the living tissues and symbolic elements of incarnate entities in ways we can currently only dream of.

## Paradox and the Prime Directive

Although the manifest function of these visits appears largely scientific in nature, it is possible that some UFO occupants are tourists, who have undoubtedly paid a handsome sum of money for the luxury of visiting and observing past periods. Time tourism could be a lucrative venture for anyone capable of bringing people back from the future to observe past ways of life, interesting historic or prehistoric events, or to gawk at plants and animals that went extinct long before their time. In fact, in much the same way Virgin Atlantic, SpaceX, Blue Origin, and other companies are pushing the boundaries of space tourism, the private sector may help drive the development of backward time-travel technology if there is profit potential in the time-tourism industry.

If time travel does ever become a part of the future human toolkit, it will almost certainly be highly regulated and prohibitive for most. Unless someone is operating a sanctioned time tourism company, or conducting vetted scientific research, visiting the past is likely to be restricted for fear of inadvertently changing the future (if the Everett interpretation is correct), or to avoid having rogue travelers go back to get rich from sports betting and equities trading (if the *Back To the Future Part II* interpretation is correct), or from starting a company they know to be lucrative in their home time (if the *Hot Tub Time Machine* interpretation is correct). This could help explain why abductions most often mirror modern biomedical examinations (i.e., researchers) but also why UFOs are commonly seen off in the distance, or lingering amongst the clouds (i.e., tourists), without overtly interjecting themselves into our times.

A desire, or perhaps requirement, to limit explicit contact during backward time-travel missions may help explain why the visitors seem to follow a type of Star Trekian "Prime Directive," where time travelers are forbidden from interfering with the internal and natural development of past peoples.[421] Apart from abductions, which still tend to take place in remote and relatively unpopulated areas, the covert actions of these visitors, and their persistent unwillingness to openly admit their presence, may be further evidence of their extratempestrial rather than extraterrestrial origins.

As stated previously, if an advanced humanoid civilization did happen to locate us among the one hundred thousand million stars in the Milky Way galaxy, then travel hundreds, thousands, or tens of thousands of light years to get here, we would expect them to at least introduce themselves, or kill us and steal all our resources. However, the doggedly secretive and non-threatening actions of these visitors suggests they seek knowledge over assets and their intentions are peaceful and temporally non-disruptive.

Although it is something we should consider, the visitors' apparent emphasis on avoiding ostentatious interactions with their past probably isn't because they fear inadvertently "changing the future" or "messing up the timeline," for reasons discussed below. While that could be an aspect of their intent if they are interdimensional humans traveling through the multiverse, as per the many worlds interpretation of quantum mechanics—since they may return to a fundamentally different future in a new timeline if too much past change were to occur, and perhaps one in which they do not exist—this would not necessarily be the case in the block universe. When considered in the context of the latter, there are no paradoxes in the way they are often thought of, or how they are commonly portrayed in movies and on television, since all cross-temporal connections, past, present, and future, already exist as one entity.

The Block Universe theory considers everything that has and will ever happen, everywhere in the universe, as part of a massive block of four-dimensional spacetime. According to Dr. Kristie Miller, an associate professor of philosophy, and joint director at the Center for Time, School of Philosophical and Historical Inquiry at the University of Sydney in Australia,

> The block universe: it contains everything that has ever happened and will happen at any time and at any place.... Your birth is out there in space-time. Your death, too, is in space-time. Every moment of your life is out there, somewhere, in space-time. So says the block universe model of our world. According to the block universe theory, the universe is a giant block of all the things that ever happen at any time and at any place. On this view, the past, present and future all exist — and are equally real.[422]

Under the Block Universe Model, which is the most conventionally understood explanation for spacetime, there is no reason to believe that any action in the past creates a *change* that did not already exist in the future. Instead, interacting with the past is innately non-disruptive, meaning that anything and everything resulting from someone going back in time had already occurred prior to that person ever leaving to visit the past. In other words, upon returning to their home time in the future, everything will still be the same because whatever that person did while present in the past had already happened, before they ever left to go do it. In a somewhat comical Marvel comics quote from the film *Avengers: Endgame*, Professor Hulk states,

Changing the past doesn't change the future.... If you travel to the past, that past becomes your future, and your former present becomes the past, which can't now be changed by your new future.[423]

Dr. Kristie Miller says something similar in her article, "The Block Universe Theory, Where Time Travel Is Possible but Time Passing Is an Illusion."

Everything is relative: what is past to you, will be future to someone else. So, if I travel back to the past, I'm travelling to what is someone else's future. That means the past won't be any different, in kind, to the present.

What will happen if I travel to the past? I'll get out of my time machine and start walking around. I'll breathe the air and chat to people. Obviously, this will have effects on the time I travel to. I'll tread on ants; I'll talk to people from that time; I'll pat horses, and feed donkeys and so on.

I'll act, in the past, in the sorts of ways I act in the present. But I won't be changing the past. Just as when I eat cornflakes instead of toast tomorrow, I am not changing the future, I'm just making the future the way it is, when I travel to the past I don't change it, I just make it the way it is, and always has been.[424]

Perceived causality violations also aren't problematic in the Block Universe. This is because a future cause and past effect are intrinsically linked, and anything that happens on the bridge that spans these interconnected points in time has always been and will always be. It makes no difference if the cause is in the future or the past, after all, the distinction between past, present, and future is only a stubbornly persistent illusion.[425] According to renowned physicist Igor Dmitriyevich Novikov, who the Novikov Self-Consistency Principle is named after, the future may dictate events occurring in the past because the future, present, and past are all one, and none are ahead of or behind the other in the presence of a time machine.[426]

Consistency paradoxes, like the grandfather paradox,[427] as well as the causal loop paradox (aka the bootstrap paradox), where something from the future aids in its own creation by being a part of its past, despite their names, also aren't paradoxical.[428] The common heuristic device for understanding causal loops typically involves someone creating something, or having an impactful idea, which, through the mechanism of backward time travel, is revealed to an earlier version of themselves. This past person then uses the newly acquired information for some outcome, and later in life, they become the one traveling back through time to convey that information to their younger self, in a sort of infinite, self-consistent, causal loop of creation and dissemination.[429]

This scenario may appear to laugh in the face of causality. However, when understood within the framework of a closed loop of self-consistent events, causality becomes irrelevant, as does the question of who created the original idea or invention taken back through time. The apparent perplexity of these scenarios largely stems from the fact that our perception of time is habitually derived from obstinate observations of linearly organized events, with clearly defined boundaries between a past cause and a future effect. Yet, in the presence of a time machine, events in the future can elicit an effect in the past, because neither comes before the other.

If the Block Universe Model is correct, then disrupting the timeline and changing the past can't be the reason why explicit contact between future and past peoples is eschewed, and some other explanation must exist for why they have not yet fully disclosed their presence in our presents. Other explanations may include our utter indifference to the UFO question, our lack of understanding of time, our ecological and societal immaturity, or their fear that we may react poorly to knowledge of this new reality. After all, in the context of future human history, it wasn't too long ago that we were entirely unnerved by Orson Welles's 1938 broadcast of H.G. Wells's science fiction novel *The War of the Worlds*. The panic that ensued may indicate to them that our collective consciousness, and broad acceptance of the acute other, has not yet fully matured.

It is also possible that our past and current inability to understand who the visitors are, what they are doing, and what it all might mean for a post-contact future, is reason enough for them to carry out their operations in secrecy, at least for the time being. Our recent response to *The War of the Worlds* broadcast, and our enduring inability to recognize their humanness, despite only slight variations in the technology and physiology of these travelers, implies we may still have a long wait before they fully reveal themselves to us, as we remain the persistently primitive people of their past.

## INSTITUTING INTERTEMPORAL INTERACTION

Considering the question of cross-temporal contact, past interactions among previously isolated groups here on Earth may provide some context. According to genetic, morphological, archaeological, and cultural evidence from Asia, Australia, and the Pacific Islands, humans started using boats as early as 60,000–70,000 years ago.[430] Moreover, recent theories about how the Americas were first populated involves early settlers trickling up and down the coasts of northeastern Siberia and northwestern North America on seal-skin boats, as opposed to the previous notion that they walked across the Bering land bridge into what is now Alaska.[431]

Boatbuilding and adept navigational skills allowed east Asian and Polynesian groups to traverse the Pacific Ocean and populate the Western Hemisphere beginning as early as 30,000 years ago. Because humans had not yet stepped foot on these new lands, the question of cross-cultural contact and communication was never an issue. Conversely, when Western Europeans discovered the benefits of open sea voyage in the late 1400s, tens of thousands of years after those in the Far East, the situation was quite different.

The previously unoccupied territories of North, Central, and South America were now widely inhabited by established human groups with their own cultures and languages. As such, this later stage of intercontinental interaction may represent a better metaphor for how past peoples might perceive those visiting from the future. For instance, enduring confusion about the human status of both Europeans and the indigenous inhabitants of the Old and New Worlds is comparable to how past and modern groups struggle to recognize the inherent humanness of these UFO occupants.

Instead of instantly identifying them as human, some indigenous groups mistakenly perceived the pale-skinned European conquistadores as gods. These instances of mistaken identity, much like our misapprehension of the visitors, were largely due to visible differences in their physiology, but also the Europeans' more sophisticated technology. This incorrect ascription of god status proved deleterious to the continued existence of many native leaders, and entire civilizations, since it made them easier to manipulate, kill, and command. This is analogous to how we have viewed, and how some individuals and groups continue to view, the visitors, though fortunately for us, these more technologically advanced pale-skinned humans seem far less malevolent.

An indication of how past peoples perceived the visitors as gods may be seen in the global prevalence of intentional cranial modification. A common, and even scholastic, explanation for this practice was that certain prehistoric groups attempted to look like, or were instructed to modify their skull by, those they perceived as gods. Although there are other ways this could be interpreted, it may suggest that earlier societies also encountered the same travelers we see today, and they demonstrated this by modifying their skulls to look more like them.

Such veneration is still apparent today, as numerous cults and other religious groups worship these visitors as gods. Among the most infamous of these UFO cults was Heaven's Gate, which in March 1997 lost 39 members who committed mass suicide in a high-class suburb of San Diego, California.[432] Though seemingly less common today, similar organizations have inspired the novel nomenclature "UFO Religion," because of their resemblance in faith, worship, and belief to more mainstream religions like Islam, Judaism, and Christianity.

In the 1500s, we had very little knowledge of human variation across geographic races, and certainly no capacity to comprehend the evolutionary forces that contributed to them. In fact, until relatively recently, many in the Judeo-Christian camp considered people with different skin color to be the product of a separate creation by God.[433] Additionally, the term *humanoid,* a common idiom in UFO circles, is thought to have originated during the colonial period, when European merchants were attempting to understand ancestral relationships among those they encountered on different continents, which included intense discussions about whether these "others" should even be classified as human.

Despite slight differences in their technology and physical form, many common features were shared among Europeans and the indigenous people they came across throughout the world. Their communal humanness was made more palpable once the missionaries arrived, when it became clear they could produce viable offspring, which is the gold standard for determining whether two organisms are classified as the same species. Considered in the context of the UFO phenomenon, our apparent ability to reproduce with the visitors, missionaries or otherwise, is also suggestive of common ancestry and our shared species status.

Where this metaphor begins to break down is that, rather than being the result of geographic ancestry, as was the case during European colonialism, observed physical differences between us and our presumed time-traveling descendants is instead the result of temporal ancestry, and the continuation of the same long-term changes that characterize our evolutionary past. Considering how recently we misclassified other humans based on slight differences among us, it is understandable why we still struggle to recognize our precocious progeny as human.

In addition to glaring synapomorphies observable between the visitors and ourselves, other indications of cultural continuity, including our ability to communicate, is suggestive of shared ancestry on this planet. Looking at the 15 case studies highlighted throughout this text, and considered alongside countless other contactee and abductee accounts, it is easy to see how similar they are to us, and we are to them. Beyond the considerable similarities in our culture and biology, numerous other indications of our shared humanity are apparent when examining the technology, actions, and behaviors of these visitors to our times, not to mention their love of this planet we may both call home. Our common origins are increasingly comprehensible when considering the vast consistency across cases, regardless of where or when they occurred throughout the world or through time.

The visitors are nearly ubiquitously described as "human" and "humanoid," but we have long viewed them as distinct enough that they must have come from a different planet. Perhaps someday, if they do ever choose to fully reveal themselves, prior to us becoming them, that is, we will come to understand just how similar we really are—and always were. In the same way our once divisive geographic racial distinctions have largely been erased by time, so too may these intertemporal discrepancies slowly vanish into the future past, as we embrace our shared ancestry and the universal consciousness that appears to permeate all periods of human time.

# Endnotes

## CHAPTER 1 ENDNOTES

1   Vallée, J. (1975) The invisible college: What a group of scientists has discovered about UFO influences on the human race. Dutton.
2   Strieber, W. (1987) Communion: A True Story. Sag Harbor, New York (USA): Beech Tree Books.
3   Tessman, D. (2020) *Future Humans and The UFOs: Time for New Thinking*. Flying Disc Press.
4   Simpson, C. J. (2014) The Chrononaut. CJS Enterprises.
5   https://open.spotify.com/episode/1vmZ3ETD4Er5VHsLC9EddU
6   Staff writer (May 29, 2019)  UFO Expert Weighs In On UFO Sightings. Retrieved June 2021 from: https://www.audacy.com/kdkaradio/articles/ufo-expert-weighs-20142015-ufo-sightings
7   Penniston, J. (2019) The Rendlesham Enigma: Book 1: Timeline. Independent.
8   Bragalia, A. (2010) Renowned U.S. Navy Commander Reveals Stunning Roswell Crash Secret. UFO Explorations. Retrieved December 2020 from: https://www.ufoexplorations.com/us-navy-commander-reveals-roswell
9   Corso, P., & Birnes, W. J. (1998) The Day After Roswell. Simon and Schuster.
10  https://www.coasttocoastam.com/show/2019-06-23-show/
11  Davenport, M. (1992) Visitors from Time: The Secret of the UFOs. Greenleaf Publications.
12  Randles, J. (2001). Time storms: amazing evidence for time warps, space rifts and time travel. Piatkus.
13  Fair, D. (2010) Uninvited Future Observers. Independent.
14  Butler, A. (2012) Intervention: How Humanity from the Future Has Changed Its Own Past. Watkins.
15  Bollio, N. (2018) *Aliens Are Humans from the Future, UFO Is a Time Machine*. Independent.
16  Articles archived at: https://www.bibliotecapleyades.net/ciencia/time_travel/esp_ciencia_timetravel08b.htm?fbclid=IwAR1M_vPsp6rkJwLXtHWjjZxMuupSXz-VwrCiIwBU2qgu8Dq_F1li17MEbYhU
17  https://www.youtube.com/watch?v=XKOfAwXIGaM
18  Zabel, B. (March 11, 2021) What if Aliens are Us from the Future? Retrieved March 2021 from: https://medium.com/on-the-trail-of-the-saucers/official-denial-1097185b018a
19  https://www.imdb.com/title/tt0087995/, for a link to the specific scene referenced (or at least for however long the clip can be found there) see: https://www.imdb.com/title/tt0087995/
20  http://www.abovetopsecret.com/forum/thread1235391/pg1
21  Goode, E., & Vail, D. A. (Eds.). (2008) *Extreme deviance*. Pine Forge Press.

## CHAPTER 2 ENDNOTES

22 Strieber, W., & McDowall, R. (1987) *Communion: A true story* (pp. 223). Sag Harbor, New York: Beech Tree Books. PG. 243.

23 Sagan, C. Druyan, A. (1980) The Shores of the Cosmic Ocean. Cosmos S1, Ep1.

24 Arecibo Message. SETI Institute. Retrieved November 2021 from: https://www.seti. org/seti-institute/project/details/arecibo-message

25 Mera, Steve (April 17, 2020) They're Here: Physical Evidence of UFO Hot Spots & Science Behind Interstellar Travel, Steve Merra (sic). The Leak Project. @30:20. Retrieved January 2021 from: https://www.youtube.com/watch?v=Dy8NaSGq-0HE&feature=youtu.be

26 Skip Newhall, PhD Applied Mathematics, Caltech; Astronomer, JPL, 36 years. Retrieved October 2021 from: https://www.quora.com/How-long-would-it-take-to-travel-across-the-Milky-Way-at-the-speed-of-light

27 Skip Newhall, PhD Applied Mathematics, Caltech; Astronomer, JPL, 36 years. Retrieved October 2021 from: https://www.quora.com/How-much-time-in-light-years-would-it-take-to-go-to-another-galaxy

28 Mahoney, T. (July 20, 2020) Why Time Dilation May Cause Deep Space Exploration to Be Futile. Retrieved November 2020 from: https://medium.com/predict/why-time-dilation-may-cause-deep-space-exploration-to-be-futile-3321a1352397

29 Data obtained from the PHL Exoplanet Catalog of the Planetary Habitability Laboratory at the University of Puerto Rico at Arecibo. CSV Database File: Confirmed Exoplanets: phl_hec_all_confirmed.csv. Retrieved January 7, 2016 from: http://phl. upr.edu/projects/habitable-exoplanets-catalog/data/database

30 Latimer, B. (2005) The perils of being bipedal. *Annals of Biomedical Engineering, 33*(1), 3-6.

31 Carl Sagan (1978) The Quest for Extraterrestrial Intelligence. *Cosmic Search Magazine*, 1(2). Retrieved April, 2015 from: http://www.bigear.org/vol1no2/sagan.htm

32 Vakoch, D. (2014) Reconstructing Distant Civilizations and Encountering Alien Cultures. *Archaeology, Anthropology, and Interstellar Communication* (pp. xiv). Vakoch, D. A. (Ed.). National Aeronautics and Space Administration. Office of Communications, Public Outreach Division.

33 Snyder-Beattie, A. E., Sandberg, A., Drexler, K. E., & Bonsall, M. B. (2020). The Timing of Evolutionary Transitions Suggests Intelligent Life Is Rare. *Astrobiology*. Vol 21(3). Pgs.1-14.

34 Tipler, F. J. (1980) Extraterrestrial intelligent beings do not exist. *Quarterly Journal of the Royal Astronomical Society, 21*, 267.

35 Chick, G. (2014) Biocultural Prerequisites for the Development of Interstellar Communication. *Archaeology, Anthropology, and Interstellar Communication* (pp. 215). Vakoch, D. A. (Ed.). National Aeronautics and Space Administration. Office of Communications, Public Outreach Division.

36 David, L. (January 20, 2020) Are the aliens us? UFOs may be piloted by time-traveling humans, book argues. Space.com. Retrieved January 2021 from: https://www. space.com/aliens-time-traveling-humans-ufo-hypothesis.html

37 Hynek, P. (September 21, 2020) UFO Project Bluebook EXPOSED w/ Paul Hynek,

son of late Dr. J. Allen Hynek, @1:09:30. Dr. J. Radio Live. Retrieved January 2021 from: https://www.youtube.com/watch?v=Kogw_o0TcG4&feature=emb_logo

38  Everett, H. (2015) The theory of the universal wave function. In *The many worlds interpretation of quantum mechanics* (pp. 1-140). Princeton University Press.

39  Ananthaswamy, A. (December 10, 2014) How to think about… Higher dimensions. New Scientist. Retrieved February 2021 from: https://www.newscientist.com/article/mg22429990-400-how-to-think-about-higher-dimensions/

40  Keel, J. A. (1970) UFO's: Operation Trojan Horse. New York: Putnam.

41  Abbott, E.A. (1884) Flatland. A Romance of Many Dimensions. Seeley & Co. Ltd., London. (Reprint 1992, Dover Publications).

42  Costa, C. (June 2, 2017) Contacting Extraterrestrial: The Method. Syracuse New Times. Retrieved November 2021 from: https://www.syracusenewtimes.com/contacting-extraterrestrials-the-method/

43  Bostrom, N. (2003) Are we living in a computer simulation?. *The philosophical quarterly*, 53(211), 243-255.

44  Irwin, K., Amaral, M., & Chester, D. (2020) The Self-Simulation hypothesis interpretation of quantum mechanics. *Entropy*, 22(2), 247.

45  UAP Task Force (June 25, 2021) Preliminary Assessment of Unidentified Aerial Phenomena. Office of the Director of National Intelligence. Retrieved July 2021 from: Prelimary-Assessment-UAP-20210625.pdf (dni.gov)

46  For a brief overview of Project Bluebook see: https://www.af.mil/About-Us/Fact-Sheets/Display/Article/104590/unidentified-flying-objects-and-air-force-project-blue-book/
And for context regarding the new narrative focusing on UFOs as a threat, note this passage: "No UFO reported, investigated and evaluated by the Air Force was ever an indication of threat to our national security"

47  Stieb, M. & Danner, C. (July 5, 2021) What's Inside the Pentagon's Long-Awaited UFO Report. New York Magazine. Retrieved October 2021 from: https://nymag.com/intelligencer/article/pentagon-ufo-report-what-we-know.html

## CHAPTER 3 ENDNOTES

48  Strieber, W., & McDowall, R. (1987) Communion: A true story (pp. 68). Sag Harbor, New York: Beech Tree Books. Pg. 58.

49  Clarke, A. C. (1962) Hazards of prophecy: The failure of imagination. *Profiles of the Future*, 6(36), 1.

50  Clarke, A. C. (1962) Hazards of prophecy: The failure of imagination. *Profiles of the Future*, 6(36), 1.

51  Clarke, A. C. (1973). Clarke's Third Law. Hazards of Prophecy: The Failure of Imagination. *Profiles of the Future*.

52  Moro, P. A. (2018) Witchcraft, sorcery, and magic. *The international encyclopedia of anthropology*, 1-9.

53  Cooper, H, Blumenthal, R, & Kean, L. (December 16, 2017) Glowing Auras and 'Black Money': The Pentagon's Mysterious U.F.O. Program. The New York Times.

Retrieved February 2021 from: https://www.nytimes.com/2017/12/16/us/politics/pentagon-program-ufo-harry-reid.html?action=click&module=RelatedCoverage&pgtype=Article&region=Footer

54 Blumenthal, R. & Kean, L. (July 23, 2020) No Longer in Shadows, Pentagon's U.F.O. Unit Will Make Some Findings Public. *New York Times*. Retrieved February 2021 from: https://www.nytimes.com/2020/07/23/us/politics/pentagon-ufo-harry-reid-navy.html

55 NAVAIR – FOIA. Retrieved September, 2020 from: https://www.navair.navy.mil/foia/documents

56 Cooper, H, Blumenthal, R, & Kean, L. (December 16, 2017) Glowing Auras and 'Black Money': The Pentagon's Mysterious U.F.O. Program. The New York Times. Retrieved February 2021 from: https://www.nytimes.com/2017/12/16/us/politics/pentagon-program-ufo-harry-reid.html?action=click&module=RelatedCoverage&pgtype=Article&region=Footer

57 Mayer, S. (April 27, 2020) @santiagomayer_ Twitter. Retrieved September 2020 from: https://twitter.com/santiagomayer_/status/1254874547817295877

58 Kirkbeck, L., Darby, R., Schreiber, D., Farrier, D. (March 12, 2018) The Decade Issue. *The Cryptid Factor*. Ep. 33 @35:25. Retrieved February 2021 from: https://www.radio.com/podcasts/the-cryptid-factor-45427/033-the-decade-issue-347747117

59 See for instance the sad saga of 19th-century Hungarian physician Ignaz Semmelweis. For reference: Leighton, L.S. (April 14, 2020) Ignaz Semmelweis, the doctor who discovered the disease-fighting power of hand-washing in 1847. *The Conversation*. Retrieved October 2021 from: https://theconversation.com/ignaz-semmelweis-the-doctor-who-discovered-the-disease-fighting-power-of-hand-washing-in-1847-135528

60 Earman, J. (1995) Outlawing time machines: Chronology protection theorems. Erkenntnis, 42(2), 125-139.

61 Earman, J., Smeenk, C., & Wüthrich, C. (2009) Do the laws of physics forbid the operation of time machines?. Synthese, 169(1), 91-124.

62 Clarke, A. C. (1962) Hazards of prophecy: The failure of imagination. *Profiles of the Future*, 6(36), 1.

63 Gray, R.H. (January 29, 2016) The Fermi Paradox Is Not Fermi's, and It Is Not a Paradox. *Scientific American*. Retrieved October 2021 from: https://blogs.scientificamerican.com/guest-blog/the-fermi-paradox-is-not-fermi-s-and-it-is-not-a-paradox/

64 Jones, E. M. (1985) "Where is everybody?" An account of Fermi's question. Los Alamos National Laboratory (LANL). United States Department of Energy.

65 Hawking, S., & Jackson, M. (1993) *A brief history of time*. Dove Audio.

66 Davies, P. (1996) *About time: Einstein's unfinished revolution* (pp. 250-251). Simon and Schuster.

67 Liverpool, J. D., BT and Saatchi & Saatchi advertising agency (1995) *Inspiring British Telecom TV ad featuring Stephen Hawking 1995* [Television Commercial]. Retrieved September 11, 2015 from: http://toptvadverts.com/inspiring-british-telecom-tv-ad-featuring-stephen-hawking-1995/

## CHAPTER 4 ENDNOTES

68   Stothers, R. (2007) Unidentified flying objects in classical antiquity. *The Classical Journal*, 79-92.

69   Vallee, J. (1969) *Passport to Magonia: From folklore to flying saucers*. H. Regnery Company.

70   Stothers, R. (2007) Unidentified flying objects in classical antiquity. *The Classical Journal*, 79-92.

71   Vallee, J., & Aubeck, C. (2010) Wonders in the sky: Unexplained aerial objects from antiquity to modern times. Penguin.

72   Harman, G. H. (1965). The inference to the best explanation. *The philosophical review*, 74(1), 88-95.

73   Bond, S. E. (November 13, 2018) Pseudoarchaeology and the Racism Behind Ancient Aliens. Hyperallergic. Retrieved September 2021 from: https://hyperallergic.com/470795/pseudoarchaeology-and-the-racism-behind-ancient-aliens/

74   Gerszten, P. C., Gerszten, E. (1995) Intentional cranial deformation: a disappearing form of self-mutilation. *Neurosurgery* 37(3)374-382.

75   Baraniuk, C. (October 4, 2021) How Indigenous Stories Helped Scientists Understand the Origin of Three Huge Boulders. Smithsonian Magazine. Retrieved October 2021 from: https://www.smithsonianmag.com/science-nature/how-indigenous-stories-helped-scientists-understand-the-origin-of-three-huge-boulders-180978788/

76   Rondeau, R. M. (2010, March) The wrecks of Franklin's ships Erebus and Terror; their likely location and the cause of failure of previous search expeditions. *The Journal of the Hakluyt Society*. Retrieved November 19, 2015 from http://www.hakluyt.com/PDF/Rondeau_Franklin.pdf

77   Rondeau, R. M. (2010, March) The wrecks of Franklin's ships Erebus and Terror; their likely location and the cause of failure of previous search expeditions. *The Journal of the Hakluyt Society*. Retrieved November 19, 2015 from http://www.hakluyt.com/PDF/Rondeau_Franklin.pdf

78   Woodman, D. C. (2015) *Unravelling the Franklin mystery: Inuit testimony* (Vol. 5). Canada: McGill-Queen's Press-MQUP.

79   Barrera Jorge (2014, September 11) PMO downplayed rich Inuit link to discovered Franklin ship. *APTN National News*. Retrieved September 24, 2015 from: http://aptn.ca/news/2014/09/11/pmo-downplays-rich-inuit-link-discovered-franklin-ship/

80   Watson, Paul (2014, September 9) The Star with the Franklin search: How the Franklin wreck was finally found. *The Star, Canada*. Retrieved September 24, 2015 from: http://www.thestar.com/news/canada/2014/09/09/the_star_with_the_franklin_search_how_the_franklin_wreck_was_finally_found.html

81   Mack, J. E., & Mack, J. E. (1994) *Abduction: Human encounters with aliens* (p. 432). New York: Scribner's.

82   McLeod, C. C., Corbisier, B., & Mack, J. E. (1996) A more parsimonious explanation for UFO abduction. *Psychological Inquiry*, 7(2), 156-168.

83   Marden, K. (2012) The Marden-Stoner Study on Commonalities Among UFO Abduction Experiencers.

84 Appelle, S. (1996) The Abduction Experience: A Critical Evaluation of Theory and Evidence. *Journal of UFO Studies*, 6, 29–78.

85 Bartholomew, R. E., Basterfield, K., & Howard, G. S. (1991) UFO abductees and contactees: Psychopathology or fantasy proneness?. *Professional Psychology: Research and Practice*, 22(3), 215.

86 Newman, L. S., & Baumeister, R. F. (1996) Toward an explanation of the UFO abduction phenomenon: Hypnotic elaboration, extraterrestrial sadomasochism, and spurious memories. *Psychological Inquiry*, 7(2), 99-126.

87 McLeod, C. C., Corbisier, B., & Mack, J. E. (1996) A more parsimonious explanation for UFO abduction. *Psychological Inquiry*, 7(2), 156-168.

88 Appelle, S. (1996) The abduction experience: A critical evaluation of theory and evidence. *Journal of UFO Studies*, 6, 29-78.

89 Holden, K. J., & French, C. C. (2002) Alien abduction experiences: Some clues from neuropsychology and neuropsychiatry. *Cognitive neuropsychiatry*, 7(3), 163-178.

90 Hough, P., & Rogers, P. (2007) Individuals who report being abducted by aliens: Investigating the differences in fantasy proneness, emotional intelligence and the big five personality factors. *Imagination, Cognition and Personality*, 27(2), 139-161.

91 French, C. C., Santomauro, J., Hamilton, V., Fox, R., & Thalbourne, M. A. (2008) Psychological aspects of the alien contact experience. *Cortex*, 44(10), 1387-1395.

92 Hynek, J. A. (1972) *The UFO Experience: A scientific Inquiry*. Chicago, IL. Henry Regnery Company.

93 Hynek, J. A. (1972) *The UFO Experience: A scientific Inquiry*. Chicago, IL. Henry Regnery Company

94 Hernandez, R., Klimo, J., & Schild, R. (2018) Beyond UFOs: The science of consciousness and contact with non-human intelligence,© The Dr. Edgar Mitchell Foundation for Research into Extraterrestrial and Extraordinary Experiences, FREE.

95 Hernandez, R., Klimo, J., & Schild, R. (2018) Beyond UFOs: The science of consciousness and contact with non-human intelligence,© The Dr. Edgar Mitchell Foundation for Research into Extraterrestrial and Extraordinary Experiences, FREE.

96 Hernandez, R., Klimo, J., & Schild, R. (2018) Beyond UFOs: The science of consciousness and contact with non-human intelligence,© The Dr. Edgar Mitchell Foundation for Research into Extraterrestrial and Extraordinary Experiences, FREE.

97 Note: These percentages don't sum to 100%, which is simply an aspect of the way the study results were reported, where the overall percentage of respondents who answered each question were stated, rather than the percentage within each category.

## CASE STUDY 1 ENDNOTES

98 Dworshak, L. (2003) UFOs Are With Us: Take My Word. Dorrance Publishing.

99 Dworshak, L. (2003) UFOs Are With Us: Take My Word. Dorrance Publishing.

100 Dworshak, L. (2003) UFOs Are With Us: Take My Word. Dorrance Publishing.

101  Dworshak, L. (2003) UFOs Are With Us: Take My Word. Dorrance Publishing.

102  Humanoid Contact. 1980 Case Summaries. *Internet Archive*. Retrieved January 2022 from: https://web.archive.org/web/20120114024502/http://www.thelosthaven. co.uk/1980Cont.htm

103  Dworshak, L. (2003) UFOs Are With Us: Take My Word. Dorrance Publishing.

104  Rosalsky, G (February 25, 2020) Why America is Losing The Toilet Race. Planet Money, National Public Radio. Retrieved November 2021 from: https://www.npr. org/sections/money/2020/02/25/808791622/why-america-is-losing-the-toilet-race

105  Mallapaty, S. (February 26, 2021) Where did COVID come from? Five mysteries that remain. *Nature*. Retrieved March 2021 from: https://www.nature.com/articles/ d41586-021-00502-4

106  Lawton, G. (2021). Did covid-19 come from a lab? 250(3337): 10-11. *New Sci.*

107  Bird, J. *Montana UFOs and Extraterrestrials: Extraordinary stories of documented sightings and encounters.* Riverbend Publishing.

## CASE STUDY 2 ENDNOTES

108  Aston, W.P. (1998) Udo Wartena Contact Case in 1940. *UFO Magazine*. March/ April, 1998. Retrieved April 2021 from: http://www.ufoevidence.org/cases/ case1032.htm

109  Udo Wartena's Letter to John Glenn. Published in Bird, J. (2013) *Montana UFOs and Extraterrestrials: Extraordinary stories of documented sightings and encounters.* Riverbend Publishing.

110  Aston, W.P. (1998) Udo Wartena Contact Case in 1940. *UFO Magazine*. March/ April, 1998. Retrieved April 2021 from: http://www.ufoevidence.org/cases/ case1032.htm

111  Aston, W.P. (1998) Udo Wartena Contact Case in 1940. *UFO Magazine*. March/ April, 1998. Retrieved April 2021 from: http://www.ufoevidence.org/cases/ case1032.htm

112  Aston, W.P. (1998) Udo Wartena Contact Case in 1940. *UFO Magazine*. March/ April, 1998. Retrieved April 2021 from: http://www.ufoevidence.org/cases/ case1032.htm

113  Hernandez, R., Klimo, J., & Schild, R. (2018). Beyond UFOs: The science of consciousness and contact with non-human intelligence,© The Dr. Edgar Mitchell Foundation for Research into Extraterrestrial and Extraordinary Experiences, FREE.

114  Aston, W.P. (1998) Udo Wartena Contact Case in 1940. *UFO Magazine*. March/ April, 1998. Retrieved April 2021 from: http://www.ufoevidence.org/cases/ case1032.htm

115  Aston, W.P. (1998) Udo Wartena Contact Case in 1940. *UFO Magazine*. March/ April, 1998. Retrieved April 2021 from: http://www.ufoevidence.org/cases/ case1032.htm

116  Aston, W.P. (1998) Udo Wartena Contact Case in 1940. *UFO Magazine*. March/

April, 1998. Retrieved April 2021 from: http://www.ufoevidence.org/cases/case1032.htm

117 Aston, W.P. (1998) Udo Wartena Contact Case in 1940. *UFO Magazine*. March/April, 1998. Retrieved April 2021 from: http://www.ufoevidence.org/cases/case1032.htm

118 Stemwedel, J. D. (August 20, 2015) The Philosophy Of Star Trek: Is The Prime Directive Ethical? Forbes. Retrieved March 2021 from: https://www.forbes.com/sites/janetstemwedel/2015/08/20/the-philosophy-of-star-trek-is-the-prime-directive-ethical/?sh=50df617d2177

119 Young, N. (2016, March 23) Project Greenglow and the battle with gravity. *BBC News*. Retrieved April 8, 2016 from: http://www.bbc.com/news/magazine-35861334

120 Aston, W.P. (1998) Udo Wartena Contact Case in 1940. *UFO Magazine*. March/April, 1998. Retrieved April 2021 from: http://www.ufoevidence.org/cases/case1032.htm

121 For more information about Udo Wartena's experience, as well as interesting stories about his life, work, and family, see Bird, Joan. (2013) *Montana UFOs and Extraterrestrials: Extraordinary stories of documented sightings and encounters*. Riverbend Publishing.

122 Aston, W.P. (1997) MUFON Annual Symposium. Michigan, U.S., and personal communication.

## CASE STUDY 3 ENDNOTES

123 DEPOSITION BY ANTONIO VILLAS BOAS. This deposition was given in Dr Fontes' consulting room on the afternoon of February 22, 1958, in the presence of a witness, the journalist Joao Martins. From Creighton, G., BRAZIL - The Amazing Case of António Villas Boas. Retrieved June 2020 from: http://www.ignaciodarnaude.com/ufologia/Abduction%20Vilas%20Boas,G.Creighton.htm

124 DEPOSITION BY ANTONIO VILLAS BOAS. This deposition was given in Dr Fontes' consulting room on the afternoon of February 22, 1958, in the presence of a witness, the journalist Joao Martins. From Creighton, G., BRAZIL - The Amazing Case of António Villas Boas. Retrieved June 2020 from: http://www.ignaciodarnaude.com/ufologia/Abduction%20Vilas%20Boas,G.Creighton.htm

125 DEPOSITION BY ANTONIO VILLAS BOAS. This deposition was given in Dr Fontes' consulting room on the afternoon of February 22, 1958, in the presence of a witness, the journalist Joao Martins. From Creighton, G., BRAZIL - The Amazing Case of António Villas Boas. Retrieved June 2020 from: http://www.ignaciodarnaude.com/ufologia/Abduction%20Vilas%20Boas,G.Creighton.htm

126 DEPOSITION BY ANTONIO VILLAS BOAS. This deposition was given in Dr Fontes' consulting room on the afternoon of February 22, 1958, in the presence of a witness, the journalist Joao Martins. From Creighton, G., BRAZIL - The Amazing Case of António Villas Boas. Retrieved June 2020 from: http://www.ignaciodarnaude.com/ufologia/Abduction%20Vilas%20Boas,G.Creighton.htm

127 Creighton, G. (nd) The Amazing Case of António Villas Boas. Retrieved June 2020

from: http://www.ignaciodarnaude.com/ufologia/Abduction%20Vilas%20Boas,G. Creighton.htm

128 Hynek, J. A. (1972) *The UFO Experience: A scientific Inquiry*. Chicago, IL. Henry Regnery Company.

129 Watson, N. (March 23, 1999) Alien Sex 101, The Antonio Villas Boas Account. Retrieved May, 2015 from: http://www.ufocasebook.com/aliensex101.html

130 Strieber, W., & McDowall, R. (1987) *Communion: A true story* (pp. 223). Sag Harbor, New York: Beech Tree Books.

131 Randles, J., Pritchard A., Pritchard D., Mack J., Kasey P., Yapp C. (1994) Why Are They Doing This? *Alien Discussions: Proceedings of the Abduction Study Conference*. Cambridge: North Cambridge Press. pp. 69–70.

Gleiser, M (November 27, 2013) Probing Extraterrestrial Abduction. NPR 13.7 Cosmos & Culture. Retrieved June 2020 from: https://www.npr.org/sections/13.7/2013/11/27/247220595/probing-extraterrestrial-abduction

Garoutte, A. (October 19, 2005) The Antonio Villas Boas Case. UFO experiences. Summarized by the author from two books, Hans Holzers' *UFONAUTS* & Coral and Jim Lorensen's *Encounters with UFO Occupants*. Retrieved June 2020 from: http://ufoexperiences.blogspot.com/2005/10/antonio-villas-boas-case.html

132 Creighton, G. (nd) The Amazing Case of António Villas Boas. Retrieved June 2020 from: http://www.ignaciodarnaude.com/ufologia/Abduction%20Vilas%20Boas,G. Creighton.htm

133 For a detailed discussion of potential reasons for widespread gamete extraction see: Masters, M.P. (2019) Identified Flying Objects: A Multidisciplinary Scientific Approach to the UFO Phenomenon. Pgs. 215-236.

134 Jinek, M., Chylinski, K., Fonfara, I., Hauer, M., Doudna, J. A., & Charpentier, E. (2012) A programmable dual-RNA–guided DNA endonuclease in adaptive bacterial immunity. *science*, 337(6096), 816-821.

135 Ledford, H., and Callaway, E. (October 7, 2020) Pioneers of revolutionary CRISPR gene editing win chemistry Nobel. *Nature*. Retrieved 4-20-2021 from: https://www.nature.com/articles/d41586-020-02765-9

136 Gorvett, Z. (April 14, 2021) The Genetic Mistakes That Could Shape Our Species. *BBC Future*. Retrieved 4-20-2021 from: https://www.bbc.com/future/article/20210412-the-genetic-mistakes-that-could-shape-our-species

137 Marx, V. (November 24, 2021) The CRISPR Children. Nature Biotechnology. https://doi.org/10.1038/s41587-021-01138-5

138 Weizhi, J. (April 16, 2021) China-US scientists create world's first human-monkey 'chimera' embryo amid ethical storm. South China Morning Post. Retrieved, 4-20-2021 from: https://www.scmp.com/video/world/3129903/china-us-scientists-create-worlds-first-human-monkey-chimera-embryo-amid

139 Regalado, A. (April 13, 2021) Gene therapy offers hope to those with ultra-rare genetic illnesses. MIT Technology Review. Retrieved 4-20-2021 from: https://www.technologyreview.com/2021/04/13/1022210/gene-therapy-expensive-treatment-genetic-diseases/

140 Sreenivasan, H. (Apr 25, 2021) Chemicals in plastic, electronics are lowering fertility in men and women. PBS Newshour. Retrieved November 2021 from: https://

www.pbs.org/newshour/show/chemicals-in-plastic-electronics-are-lowering-fertility-in-men-and-women

## CASE STUDY 4 ENDNOTES

141 Audio recording of Barney Hill's hypnosis session with Dr. Benjamin Simon. Retrieved June 2020 from: https://www.youtube.com/watch?v=sXhxgXjcxcI

142 Fuller, J. G. (1966) *The Interrupted Journey: Two Lost Hours" aboard a Flying Saucer."* Dial Press.

143 Booth, B.J. (n.d.) The Betty and Barney Hill Abduction. *UFO Casebook.* Summarized by the author from Fuller, J.G. (1987) *The Interrupted Journey.* Retrieved June 2020 from: https://www.ufocasebook.com/Hill.html.

144 Webb, W. (1961) A Dramatic UFO Encounter in the White Mountains, New Hampshire: The Hill Case—Sept. 19-20, 1961. *Confidential NICAP Report, October, 26.* Retrieved October 23, 2015 from: http://www.nicap.org/reports/610919hill_report2.pdf

145 Webb, W. (1961) A Dramatic UFO Encounter in the White Mountains, New Hampshire: The Hill Case—Sept. 19-20, 1961. *Confidential NICAP Report, October, 26.* Retrieved October 23, 2015 from: http://www.nicap.org/reports/610919hill_report2.pdf

146 Webb, W. (1961) A Dramatic UFO Encounter in the White Mountains, New Hampshire: The Hill Case—Sept. 19-20, 1961. *Confidential NICAP Report, October, 26.* Retrieved October 23, 2015 from: http://www.nicap.org/reports/610919hill_report2.pdf

147 Friedman, Stanton & Kathleen Marden (2007) *Captured! The Betty and Barney Hill UFO Experience.* Franklin Lakes, NJ: New Page Books.

148 Booth, B.J. (n.d.) The Betty and Barney Hill Abduction. *UFO Casebook.* Summarized by the author from Fuller, J.G. (1987) *The Interrupted Journey.* Retrieved June, 2020 from: https://www.ufocasebook.com/Hill.html

149 Testimony of Ben H. Swett. Pease Air Force Base, New Hampshire. 19621966. Retrieved June, 2020 from: http://bswett.com/1963-09BettyAndBarney.html

150 Booth, B.J. (n.d.) The Betty and Barney Hill Abduction. *UFO Casebook.* Summarized by the author from Fuller, J.G. (1987) *The Interrupted Journey.* Retrieved June 2020 from: https://www.ufocasebook.com/Hill.html

151 Booth, B.J. (n.d.) The Betty and Barney Hill Abduction. *UFO Casebook.* Summarized by the author from Fuller, J.G. (1987) *The Interrupted Journey.* Retrieved June 2020 from: https://www.ufocasebook.com/Hill.html

152 Friedman, S. T, Marden, K. (2007) *Captured! The Betty and Barney Hill UFO Experience.* Franklin Lakes, NJ: New Page Books.

153 Friedman, S. T, Marden, K. (2007) *Captured! The Betty and Barney Hill UFO Experience.* Franklin Lakes, NJ: New Page Books.

154 Friedman, S. T, Marden, K. (2007) *Captured! The Betty and Barney Hill UFO Experience.* Franklin Lakes, NJ: New Page Books.

155 Hernandez, R., Klimo, J., & Schild, R. (2018). Beyond UFOs: The science of con-

sciousness and contact with non-human intelligence,© The Dr. Edgar Mitchell Foundation for Research into Extraterrestrial and Extraordinary Experiences, FREE.

156 Swords, M. D. (1990) UFOs as Time Travelers. *International UFO Reporter* (IUR). September/October issue.

157 Swords, M. D. (1990) UFOs as Time Travelers. *International UFO Reporter* (IUR). September/October issue.

158 Booth, B.J. (n.d.) The Betty and Barney Hill Abduction. *UFO Casebook*. Summarized by the author from Fuller, J.G. (1987) *The Interrupted Journey*. Retrieved June, 2020 from: https://www.ufocasebook.com/Hill.html

159 Fuller, J. G. (1966) *The Interrupted Journey: Two Lost Hours" aboard a Flying Saucer."* Dial Press.

160 Dickinson, T. (December, 1974) The Zeta Reticuli Incident. National Investigations Committte on Aerial Phenomena (NICAP). Retrieved June 2020, from: http://www.nicap.org/articles/hillzeta.htm

161 Holman, B. (November 5, 2008) Goodbye, Zeta Reticuli. *Airminded*. Retrieved June 2020 from: http://airminded.org/2008/11/05/goodbye-zeta-reticuli/

162 Johnston, C. (August 19, 2011, Updated June 2013) *The Truth about Betty Hill's UFO Star Map. Armagh Observatory and Planetarium.* Retrieved June 2020, from: https://armaghplanet.com/betty-hills-ufo-star-map-the-truth.html

163 Swords, M.D. (1990) UFOs as time travelers. *International UFO Reporter.* September/October 18-23.

164 Swords, M. D. (1985) Ufonauts: Homo Sapiens of the Future? *MUFON UFO Journal*, 212: 7-13.

165 Hawking, S. W. (1992) Chronology protection conjecture. *Physical Review* D, 46(2), 603.

166 Earman, J., Smeenk, C., & Wüthrich, C. (2009) Do the laws of physics forbid the operation of time machines?. *Synthese*, 169(1), 91-124.

167 Earman, J. (1995) Outlawing time machines: Chronology protection theorems. *Erkenntnis*, 42(2), 125-139.

168 Earman, J., Smeenk, C., & Wüthrich, C. (2009) Do the laws of physics forbid the operation of time machines?. *Synthese*, 169(1), 91-124.

## CASE STUDY 5 ENDNOTES

169 Amy, J. (October 11, 2013) Man says 1973 UFO 'abduction' incident turned life upside down. NBC Science News. Retrieved June, 2020 from: https://www.nbcnews.com/sciencemain/man-says-1973-ufo-abduction-incident-turned-life-upside-down-8C11377316

170 Brown, R. (December 4, 2019) Where is Artificial Intelligence Used Today? Becoming Human: Artificial Intelligence Magazine. Retrieved November 2021 from: https://becominghuman.ai/where-is-artificial-intelligence-used-today-3fd076d15b68

171 Hickey, H. (December 15, 2020) A.I. model shows promise to generate faster, more accurate weather forecasts. University of Washington News. Retrieved November

2021 from: https://www.washington.edu/news/2020/12/15/a-i-model-shows-promise-to-generate-faster-more-accurate-weather-forecasts/

172  UFO Casebook - The 1973 Pascagoula, Mississippi Abduction (Hickson/Parker) Retrieved June 2020 from: https://www.ufocasebook.com/Pascagoula.html

173  Watkins, B. (October 20, 2002) Look Back: Charles Hickson talks of his abduction by a UFO in Pascagoula. Mississippi Clarion Ledger. Retrieved June 2020 from: https://www.clarionledger.com/story/magnolia/2018/08/16/look-back-charles-hickson-tells-his-abduction-ufo-miss/1006116002/

174  Nelson, K. (Reporter) & McCoy, A. (Videographer) (March 27, 2019) Calvin Parker's alien abduction: 'I saw the blue lights reflected across the water.' Sun Herald. Retrieved June 2020 from: https://www.youtube.com/watch?v=99telRuTBg0

175  Watkins, B. (October 20, 2002) Look Back: Charles Hickson talks of his abduction by a UFO in Pascagoula. Mississippi Clarion Ledger. Retrieved June 2020 from: https://www.clarionledger.com/story/magnolia/2018/08/16/look-back-charles-hickson-tells-his-abduction-ufo-miss/1006116002/

176  All They Meant To Do Was Go Fishing. National Investigations Committee on Aerial Phenomena (NICAP). Sourced from: BEYOND EARTH: Man's Contact with UFOs, Ralph & Judy Blum, 29-36. Retrieved June 2020 from: https://www.nicap.org/reports/731011pascagoula_hicksontape.htm

177  Allen, B. (2000) The A70 Abduction Case. Sommerville, H. (Ed.). Retrieved March 8, 2016 from http://www.ufocasebook.com/a70abduction.html. Sources referenced: Allen, B. J. & Mott, M. (2010) Rosslyn, Between Two Worlds. Healings of Atlantis; Allen, B. J. (2007) The View from the Abyss. T. G. S.

178  Nelson, K. (Reporter) & McCoy, A. (Videographer) (March 27, 2019) Calvin Parker's alien abduction: 'I saw the blue lights reflected across the water.' Sun Herald. Retrieved June 2020 from: https://www.youtube.com/watch?v=99telRuTBg0

179  Watkins, B. (October 20, 2002) Look Back: Charles Hickson talks of his abduction by a UFO in Pascagoula. Mississippi Clarion Ledger. Retrieved June 2020 from: https://www.clarionledger.com/story/magnolia/2018/08/16/look-back-charles-hickson-tells-his-abduction-ufo-miss/1006116002/

180  Parker, C. (2019) Pascagoula – The Story Continues: New Evidence & New Witnesses. Independent.

181  Nelson, K. (Reporter) & McCoy, A. (Videographer) (March 27, 2019) Calvin Parker's alien abduction: 'I saw the blue lights reflected across the water.' Sun Herald. Retrieved June 2020 from: https://www.youtube.com/watch?v=99telRuTBg0

182  The National UFO Reporting Center. Retrieved March, 2015 from: http://www.nwlink.com/~ufocntr/

183  Masters, M.P. (2019) Identified Flying Objects: A Multidisciplinary Scientific Approach to the UFO Phenomenon. Pgs. 137-142. Masters Creative. Butte, Montana.

184  Dowd, M. (October 30, 2021) A.I. Is Not A-OK. The New York Times. Retrieved November 2021 from: https://www.nytimes.com/2021/10/30/opinion/eric-schmidt-ai.html

## CASE STUDY 6 ENDNOTES

185 Walton, T. (1997). Fire in the Sky: The Travis Walton Story. *New York, NY: Marlowe & Co.*

186 Booth, B.J. (n.d.) Travis Walton Abduction, Part 1. UFO Casebook. Retrieved July, 2020 from: https://www.ufocasebook.com/Walton.html

187 Speigel, L. (December 6, 2017) UFO-Alien Abduction Still Haunts Travis Walton. Huffpost. Retrieved July, 2020 from: https://www.huffpost.com/entry/travis-walton-still-haunted-by-ufo_n_7119910

188 Peterson, K. (n.d.) The Witnesses. Travis Walton's Website. Retrieved July, 2020 from: http://www.travis-walton.com/witness.html

189 Walton, T. (1997). Fire in the Sky: The Travis Walton Story. *New York, NY: Marlowe & Co.*

190 Speigel, L. (December 6, 2017) UFO-Alien Abduction Still Haunts Travis Walton. Huffpost. Retrieved July, 2020 from: https://www.huffpost.com/entry/travis-walton-still-haunted-by-ufo_n_7119910

191 Bird, Joan. (2013) *Montana UFOs and Extraterrestrials: Extraordinary stories of documented sightings and encounters.* Riverbend Publishing.

192 Walton, T. (1997). Fire in the Sky: The Travis Walton Story. *New York, NY: Marlowe & Co.*

193 Bird, Joan. (2013) Montana UFOs and Extraterrestrials: Extraordinary stories of documented sightings and encounters. Riverbend Publishing.

194 Tsukahara, J.S., Burgoyne, A.P., Engle, R.W. (June 2, 2021) Pupil Size Is a Marker of Intelligence. *Scientific American.* Retrieved December 2021 from: https://www.scientificamerican.com/article/pupil-size-is-a-marker-of-intelligence/

195 Hofman, M. A. (2014) Evolution of the human brain: when bigger is better. *Frontiers in neuroanatomy*, 8, 15.

196 Benito-Kwiecinski, S., Giandomenico, S. L., Sutcliffe, M., Riis, E. S., Freire-Pritchett, P., Kelava, I., ... & Lancaster, M. A. (2021). An early cell shape transition drives evolutionary expansion of the human forebrain. *Cell, 184*(8), 2084-2102.

197 Schultz, A. H. (1940) The size of the orbit and of the eye in primates. Am J Phys Anthropol 26, 389-408.

198 Chau, A., Fung, K., Pak, K., & Yap, M. (2004) Is eye size related to orbit size in human subjects? Ophthal Physl Opt 24, 35-40.

199 Tawfik, H. A., & Dutton, J. J. (2018). Embryologic and fetal development of the human orbit. *Ophthalmic Plastic & Reconstructive Surgery, 34*(5), 405-421.

200 Todd, T., Beecher, H., Williams, G., & Todd, A. (1940) The weight and growth of the human eyeball. *Hum Biol* 12, 1-20.

201 Weale, R. (1982) A Biography of the Eye: Development, Growth, Age. H.K. Lewis & Co.

202 Weiss, K. (2002) How the Eye Got its Brain. *Evol Anthr* 11, 215-219.

203 Masters, M., Bruner, E., Queer, S., Traynor, S., & Senjem, J. (2015). Analysis of the volumetric relationship among human ocular, orbital and fronto-occipital cortical morphology. *Journal of anatomy, 227*(4), 460-473.

204 Miller, E. M. (1992) On the correlation of myopia and intelligence. *Genet Soc Gen*

*Psychol Monogr* 118, 361-383.

205 Mak, M., Kwan, T., Cheng, K., Chan, R., & Ho, S. (2006) Myopia as a latent pheno-type of a pleiotropic gene positively selected for facilitating neurocognitive develop-ment, and the effects of environmental factors in its expression. *Med Hypotheses* 66, 1209-1215.

206 Cheverud, J. (1996) Developmental integration and the evolution of pleiotropy. *American Zoology* 36, 44-50.

207 Collins, P. (1995) Embryology and development. *Gray's anatomy, 38th edn. Churchill Livingstone, London*, 91-341.

208 Darwin, C. (1868). *The variation of animals and plants under domestication* (Vol. 2). O. Judd.

209 Belyaev, D. K., & Trut, L. N. (1989). The convergent nature of incipient forms and the concept of destabilizing selection. *Vavilov's Heritage in Modern Biology*, 155-169.

210 Trut, L., Oskina, I., & Kharlamova, A. (2009). Animal evolution during domestica-tion: the domesticated fox as a model. *Bioessays*, *31*(3), 349-360.

211 Wilkins, A. S., Wrangham, R. W., & Fitch, W. T. (2014) The "domestication syn-drome" in mammals: a unified explanation based on neural crest cell behavior and genetics. *Genetics*, *197*(3), 795-808.

212 Theofanopoulou, C., Gastaldon, S., O'Rourke, T., Samuels, B. D., Messner, A., Mar-tins, P. T., ... & Boeckx, C. (2017) Self-domestication in Homo sapiens: Insights from comparative genomics. *PloS one*, *12*(10), e0185306.

213 Walton, T. (1997). Fire in the Sky: The Travis Walton Story. *New York, NY: Marlowe & Co.*

214 Margaritoff, M. (October 7, 2020) The 9 Most Convincing Alien Abduction Stories In Modern History. The UFO Abductions Of Audrey and Debbie Hewins From Their Childhood Room. *All That Is Interesting*. Retrieved December 2021 from: https://allthatsinteresting.com/alien-abductions/8

215 Walton, T. (1997). Fire in the Sky: The Travis Walton Story. *New York, NY: Marlowe & Co.*

216 Walton, T. (1997). Fire in the Sky: The Travis Walton Story. *New York, NY: Marlowe & Co.*

## CASE STUDY 7 ENDNOTES

217 UFO Casebook – 1977 – The Armando Valdes UFO – Five-Day Ordeal. Retrieved December 2021 from: https://www.ufocasebook.com/2011/armandovaldes.html

218 UFO Casebook – 1977 – The Armando Valdes UFO – Five-Day Ordeal. Retrieved December 2021 from: https://www.ufocasebook.com/2011/armandovaldes.html

219 Puthoff, H. E. (2012) Advanced space propulsion based on vacuum (spacetime metric) engineering. arXiv preprint arXiv:1204.2184.

220 Burton, C. (November 9, 2021) This man ran the Pentagon's secretive UFO pro-gramme for a decade. We had some questions. *GQ Magazine*. Retrieved December 2021 from: https://www.gq-magazine.co.uk/politics/article/luis-elizondo-inter-view-2021

221 Steinbuch, Y. (April 6, 2021) Ex-CIA director believes UFOs could exist after pal's plane 'paused.' New York Post. Retrieved June 2021 from: https://nypost.com/2021/04/06/former-cia-director-says-he-believes-ufos-could-exist-report/

222 Johnson, J. (May 14, 2019) How long can you live without water. Medical News Today. Retrieved December 2021 from: https://www.medicalnewstoday.com/articles/325174

223 Burton, C. (November 9, 2021) This man ran the Pentagon's secretive UFO programme for a decade. We had some questions. *GQ Magazine*. Retrieved December 2021 from: https://www.gq-magazine.co.uk/politics/article/luis-elizondo-interview-2021

224 UFO Casebook – 1977 – The Armando Valdes UFO – Five-Day Ordeal. Retrieved December 2021 from: https://www.ufocasebook.com/2011/armandovaldes.html

225 UFO Casebook – 1977 – The Armando Valdes UFO – Five-Day Ordeal. Retrieved December 2021 from: https://www.ufocasebook.com/2011/armandovaldes.html

## CASE STUDY 8 ENDNOTES

226 Lovelace, T. (2018) *Incident at Devils Den*. Independent. Quoted from the Audiobook version.

227 Hernandez, R., Klimo, J., & Schild, R. (2018) Beyond UFOs: The science of consciousness and contact with non-human intelligence,© The Dr. Edgar Mitchell Foundation for Research into Extraterrestrial and Extraordinary Experiences, FREE.

228 Lovelace, T. (2018) *Incident at Devils Den*. Independent. Quoted from the Audiobook version.

229 Lovelace, T. (2018) *Incident at Devils Den*. Independent. Quoted from the Audiobook version.

230 Marden, K. (2012) The Marden-Stoner Study on Commonalities Among UFO Abduction Experiencers. Retrieved May 2021 from: http://www.noufors.com/Documents/Books,%20Manuals%20and%20Published%20Papers/The%20Marden-Stoner%20Study%20on%20Commonalities%20Among%20Abduction%20Experiencers.pdf

231 Hernandez, R., Klimo, J., & Schild, R. (2018). Beyond UFOs: The science of consciousness and contact with non-human intelligence,© The Dr. Edgar Mitchell Foundation for Research into Extraterrestrial and Extraordinary Experiences, FREE.

232 Lovelace, T. (2018) *Incident at Devils Den*. Independent. Quoted from the Audiobook version.

233 Steiber, W. (March 25, 2020) Interview on Aliens Like Us with Rhys Darby. Season 1, episode 5, Experiencers. Spotify. Retrieved July, 2020 from: https://open.spotify.com/episode/24LVeNNNDsyrWVrlJTqbdF

234 Lovelace, T. (2018) *Incident at Devils Den*. Independent. Quoted from the Audiobook version.

235 Jerry Wills UFO Contactee and Psychic Healer – April 20, 2017. Quote begins

at 41:05 and ends at 41:35. Retrieved September 2020 from: https://www.youtube.com/watch?v=B8dft89abjU&list=PLH3jl6wuwaPFBRxKezpZqy-2WOUGkVEDrf&index=9&t=0s

236 Lovelace, T. (2018) *Incident at Devils Den*. Independent. Quoted from the Audiobook version.

237 Lovelace, T. (2018) *Incident at Devils Den*. Independent. Quoted from the Audiobook version.

238 Eberstadt, N. (2001). The population implosion. *Foreign Policy*, 42-53.

239 Guzman, J. (July 28, 2021) Elon Musk says population collapse 'potentially the greatest risk to the future of civilization.' The Hill. Retrieved December 2021 from: https://thehill.com/changing-america/sustainability/565224-elon-musk-says-population-collapse-potentially-the-greatest

240 Vollset, S. E., Goren, E., Yuan, C. W., Cao, J., Smith, A. E., Hsiao, T., ... & Murray, C. J. (2020) Fertility, mortality, migration, and population scenarios for 195 countries and territories from 2017 to 2100: a forecasting analysis for the Global Burden of Disease Study. *The Lancet*, 396(10258), 1285-1306.

241 Walton, T. (1997). Fire in the Sky: The Travis Walton Story. *New York, NY: Marlowe & Co.*

242 Clip can be viewed at: Larry King, 1994 Barry Goldwater UFO room at Wright Patterson AFB. Retrieved December 2021 from: https://www.dailymotion.com/video/x635hwr

243 Mosher, D. & Brueck, H. (July 19, 2019) Astronauts explain why nobody has visited the moon in more than 45 years — and the reasons are depressing. Retrieved December 2021 from: https://www.businessinsider.com/moon-missions-why-astronauts-have-not-returned-2018-7

## CASE STUDY 9 ENDNOTES

244 Mera, S. (n.d.) The Jones Abduction. Residential Investigation: Case No. 26413. UFO Sighting & Missing Time. Retrieved July 2020 from: http://www.mapit.kk5.org/the-jones-abduction/4535287448

245 Mera, S. (n.d.) The Jones Abduction. Residential Investigation: Case No. 26413. UFO Sighting & Missing Time. Retrieved July 2020 from: http://www.mapit.kk5.org/the-jones-abduction/4535287448

246 Nagaitis, C. & Mantle, P. (1994) Without Consent: A Comprehensive Study of Missing Time and Abduction Phenomena in the United Kingdom. Ringpull Press, UK.

247 AAPC 2021 (June 5 & 6, 2021) Anomalous Aerospace Phenomena Conference (AAPC) 2021, Sponsored by SCU. https://drive.google.com/file/d/1Gej-4SAcddb2HApwe9RVHnL92dc8uJrpV/view

248 Puthoff, H. E. (2012) Advanced space propulsion based on vacuum (spacetime metric) engineering. arXiv preprint arXiv:1204.2184.

249 Hill, P. R., Wood, R. M., & Donderi, D. C. (1995). Unconventional Flying Objects: a scientific analysis (p. 164). Hampton Roads.

250 Puthoff, H. (June 6, 2021) *UAP Studies: Managing the Transition Intelligence Problem*

-> *Scientific Problem*. Anomalous Aerospace Phenomena Conference (AAPC) 2021, Sponsored by the Scientific Coalition for UAP Studies. Available at: https://www.youtube.com/watch?v=PQ5Dobxnw8c

251 Hill, P. R., Wood, R. M., & Donderi, D. C. (1995). Unconventional Flying Objects: a scientific analysis (p. 164). Hampton Roads.

252 Knuth, K. H., Powell, R. M., & Reali, P. A. (2019) Estimating Flight Characteristics of Anomalous Unidentified Aerial Vehicles. *Entropy*, 21(10), 939. https://doi.org/10.3390/e21100939

253 Puthoff, H. ( June 6, 2021) *UAP Studies: Managing the Transition Intelligence Problem* -> *Scientific Problem*. Anomalous Aerospace Phenomena Conference (AAPC) 2021, Sponsored by the Scientific Coalition for UAP Studies. Available at: https://www.youtube.com/watch?v=PQ5Dobxnw8c

254 Dworshak, L. (2003) UFOs Are With Us: Take My Word. Pg. 61. Dorrance Publishing.

255 Speigel, L. (2015, April 23) UFO-Alien Abduction Still Haunts Travis Walton. *Huffpost*. Retrieved July 2020 from: https://www.huffpost.com/entry/travis-walton-still-haunted-by-ufo_n_7119910

256 Mera, S. (n.d.) The Jones Abduction. Residential Investigation: Case No. 26413. UFO Sighting & Missing Time. Retrieved July 2020 from: http://www.mapit.kk5.org/the-jones-abduction/4535287448

257 Houston, D. ( June 23, 2021) Former Cheshire pub and hotel could be demolished for new housing estate. *Cheshire Live*. Retrieved December 2021 from: https://www.cheshire-live.co.uk/news/chester-cheshire-news/former-cheshire-pub-hotel-could-20871895

258 Lee, D. (2006, January 16) *Personal Story: Abducted by Aliens/ Interviewer*: Bill O'Reilly [Transcript]. From: Back of the Book [Television Series Episode]. The O'Reilly Factor: *Fox Noise*. Retrieved June, 2020 from: http://www.foxnews.com/story/2006/01/16/personal-story-abducted-by-aliens.html

259 Longley, S. & W. (n.d.) The Casino Alien Encounter. Retrieved December 2021 from: http://www.auforn.com/Longleys.html

## CASE STUDY 10 ENDNOTES

260 Penniston, J. ( July 10, 2019) Rendlesham Forest UFO encounter pt. 2 / binary code and Jim Penniston. The Basement Office. *New York Post*. @16:22. Retrieved June 2021 from: https://www.youtube.com/watch?v=IaYfsxbiKsM

261 Margaritoff, M. (December 2, 2020) The Rendlesham Forest Incident: Elaborate UFO Hoax Or Government Cover-Up? Ati. Retrieved December 2020 from: https://allthatsinteresting.com/rendlesham-forest-incident

262 The Rendlesham Forest Incident. The Full Report. Retrieved December 2020 from: http://www.therendleshamforestincident.com/The_Full_Report.html

263 UFO Casebook. UFO Landings-Rendlesham Forest, 1980. Retrieved December 2020 from: https://www.ufocasebook.com/Rendlesham.html

264 UFO Casebook. UFO Landings-Rendlesham Forest, 1980. Retrieved December 2020 from: https://www.ufocasebook.com/Rendlesham.html

265 Staff Writer ( July 13, 2015) Rendlesham Forest UFO sighting 'new evidence' claim. BBC. Retrieved June 2021 from: https://www.bbc.com/news/uk-england-suf-folk-33447592

266 The Rendlesham Forest Incident. A1C Edward Cabansag. Retrieved December 2020 from: http://www.therendleshamforestincident.com/A1C_Edward_Cabansag.html

267 UFO Casebook. UFO Landings-Rendlesham Forest, 1980. Retrieved December 2020 from: https://www.ufocasebook.com/Rendlesham.html

268 The Rendlesham Forest Incident. The Full Report. Retrieved December 2020 from: http://www.therendleshamforestincident.com/The_Full_Report.html

269 Hill, P. R., Wood, R. M., & Donderi, D. C. (1995). Unconventional Flying Objects: a scientific analysis (p. 164). Hampton Roads.

270 Penniston, J. ( July 10, 2019) Rendlesham Forest UFO encounter pt. 2 / binary code and Jim Penniston. The Basement Office. *New York Post.* @04:58. Retrieved June 2021 from: https://www.youtube.com/watch?v=IaYfsxbiKsM

271 The Rendlesham Forest Incident. The Full Report. Retrieved December 2020 from: http://www.therendleshamforestincident.com/The_Full_Report.html

272 Penniston, J. ( July 10, 2019) Rendlesham Forest UFO encounter pt. 2 / binary code and Jim Penniston. The Basement Office. *New York Post.* @11:10. Retrieved June 2021 from: https://www.youtube.com/watch?v=IaYfsxbiKsM

273 Jim Penniston Hypnosis (1994, September 10) Retrieved December 2020 from: http://www.therendleshamforestincident.com/Penniston_Hypnosis.html

274 Jim Penniston Hypnosis (1994, September 10) Retrieved December 2020 from: http://www.therendleshamforestincident.com/Penniston_Hypnosis.html

275 Jim Penniston Hypnosis (1994, September 10) Retrieved December 2020 from: http://www.therendleshamforestincident.com/Penniston_Hypnosis.html

276 Jim Penniston Hypnosis (1994, September 10) Retrieved December 2020 from: http://www.therendleshamforestincident.com/Penniston_Hypnosis.html

277 Jim Penniston Hypnosis (1994, September 10) Retrieved December 2020 from: http://www.therendleshamforestincident.com/Penniston_Hypnosis.html

278 Einstein, A. (1905) On the electrodynamics of moving bodies. Annalen der Physik, 17(891), 50.

279 Einstein, A. (1915) Zur allgemeinen Relativitätstheorie. Sitzungsber. Kön. Preuß. Akad. Wiss. zu Berlin, 778–786.

280 Einstein, A. (1915) Zur allgemeinen Relativitätstheorie (Nachtrag). Sitzungsber. Kön. Preuß. Akad. Wiss. zu Berlin, 799–801.

281 Einstein, A. (1915) Die Feldgleichungen der Gravitation. Sitzungsber. Kön. Preuß. Akad. Wiss. Zu Berlin, 844–847.

282 Bonnor, W. B. (2003) Closed timelike curves in classical relativity. *International Journal of Modern Physics D, 12*(09), 1705-1708.

283 Lobo, F., & Crawford, P. (2003) Time, closed timelike curves and causality. *The Nature of Time: Geometry, Physics and Perception* (pp. 289-296). Springer Netherlands.

284 Stein, Leo C. (2010, May 11) *What are Closed Timelike Curves?* Retrieved April, 2015 from: http://www.quora.com/What-are-closed-timelike-curves.

285 Masters, M. (2019) *Identified Flying Objects.* Masters Creative. Butte, Montana.

286 Penniston, J., Osborn, G. (2019) *The Rendlesham Enigma.* First Edition.

287 Penniston, J., Osborn, G. (2019) *The Rendlesham Enigma*. First Edition.

288 For more about how Penniston's transcribed binary was decoded see: The Rendlesham Forest Incident. The Decoded Binary Code. Retrieved December 2020 from: http://www.therendleshamforestincident.com/The_Decoded_Binary_Code.html; also, 1980 Rendlesham Forest Incident Binary Code. Binary Decoder. Retrieved December 2020 from: http://www.binarydecoder.info/main.php

289 See also: Pope, N., Burroughs, J., & Penniston, J. (2014) Encounter in Rendlesham Forest: The Inside Story of the World's Best-documented UFO Incident. Macmillan.

290 The Rendlesham Forest Incident. The Decoded Binary Code. Retrieved December 2020 from: http://www.therendleshamforestincident.com/The_Decoded_Binary_Code.html

291 For an interesting discussion about the potential added significance of the specific locations indicated by the GPS coordinates, see the chapter written by Gary Osborn: *Code within A Code About an Ancient Code*, which can be found in the Epilogue of: Penniston, J., Osborn, G. (2019) *The Rendlesham Enigma*. First Edition.

## CASE STUDY 11 ENDNOTES

292 Strieber, W., & McDowall, R. (1987) *Communion: A true story* (pp. 223). Sag Harbor, New York: Beech Tree Books. Pgs. 24-25.

293 Strieber, W., & Kripal, J. J. (2016). *The super natural: A new vision of the unexplained.* Jeremy P. Tarcher-Penguin.

294 Strieber, W., & McDowall, R. (1987) Communion: A true story (pp. 68). Sag Harbor, New York: Beech Tree Books.

295 Strieber, W. (March 13, 2020) Are the Visitors Time Travelers? A New Approach to the UFO Phenomenon. *Dreamland - Unknown Country*. Retrieved December 2020 from: https://www.unknowncountry.com/dreamland/are-the-visitors-time-travelers-a-new-approach-to-the-ufo-phenomenon/

296 Margaritoff, M. (March 29, 2021) The 9 Most Convincing Alien Abduction Stories In Modern History. The Alien Story Of Marine Veteran Terrell Copeland That Saw Him Abducted While Napping. *All That Is Interesting*. Retrieved December 2021 from: https://allthatsinteresting.com/alien-abductions/9

297 Strieber, W., & McDowall, R. (1987) Communion: A true story (pp. 68). Sag Harbor, New York: Beech Tree Books. Pgs. 28 & 29.

298 Brown. P. (1987) Pleistocene homogeneity and Holocene size reduction: the Australian human skeletal evidence. *Archaeology in Oceania*, 22: 41-67.

299 Henneberg, M. (1988). Decrease of human skull size in the Holocene. *Hum Biol*, 60(3), 395-405.

300 Lahr M., Wright R. (1996) The question of robusticity and the relationship between cranial size and shape in Homo sapiens. *J Hum Evol*, 31(2):157-191.

301 Wu, X., Wu L., Zhang Q., Zhu, H., Norton C. (2007) Craniofacial morphological microevolution of Holocene populations in northern China. *Chinese Science Bulletin*. 52(12) 1661-1668.

302 Cieri, R. L., Churchill, S. E., Franciscus, R. G., Tan, J., & Hare, B. (2014) Craniofacial feminization, social tolerance, and the origins of behavioral modernity. *Current Anthropology*, 55(4), 419-443.

303 Strieber, W., & McDowall, R. (1987) Communion: A true story (pp. 68). Sag Harbor, New York: Beech Tree Books.

304 Watson, N. (March 23, 1999) Alien Sex 101, The Antonio Villas Boas Account. Retrieved December 2020 from: http://www.ufocasebook.com/aliensex101.html

305 Strieber, W., & McDowall, R. (1987) *Communion: A true story* (pp. 246). Sag Harbor, New York: Beech Tree Books.

306 Strieber, W., & Kripal, J. J. (2016). *The super natural: A new vision of the unexplained.* Jeremy P. Tarcher-Penguin.

307 Strieber, W., & Kripal, J. J. (2016). *The super natural: A new vision of the unexplained.* Jeremy P. Tarcher-Penguin.

308 Strieber, W., & Kripal, J. J. (2016). *The super natural: A new vision of the unexplained.* Jeremy P. Tarcher-Penguin.

309 Strieber, W., & Kripal, J. J. (2016). *The super natural: A new vision of the unexplained.* Jeremy P. Tarcher-Penguin.

310 Hernandez, R., Klimo, J., & Schild, R. (2018). Beyond UFOs: The science of consciousness and contact with non-human intelligence,© The Dr. Edgar Mitchell Foundation for Research into Extraterrestrial and Extraordinary Experiences, FREE.

311 Strieber, W. (March 13, 2020) Are the Visitors Time Travelers? A New Approach to the UFO Phenomenon. *Dreamland - Unknown Country*. Retrieved December 2020 from: https://www.unknowncountry.com/dreamland/are-the-visitors-time-travelers-a-new-approach-to-the-ufo-phenomenon/

312 Margaritoff, M. (October 7, 2020) The 9 Most Convincing Alien Abduction Stories In Modern History. The UFO Abductions Of Audrey and Debbie Hewins From Their Childhood Room. *All That Is Interesting*. Retrieved December 2021 from: https://allthatsinteresting.com/alien-abductions/8

313 Strieber, W., & McDowall, R. (1987) *Communion: A true story* (pp. 223). Sag Harbor, New York: Beech Tree Books.

314 Strieber, W., & McDowall, R. (1987) *Communion: A true story* (pp. 223). Sag Harbor, New York: Beech Tree Books. Pg. 30.

315 Martin, E. (November 9, 2019) Ellis Martin Report with Dr Michael Masters-Identified Flying Objects. Retrieved June 2021 from: https://www.youtube.com/watch?v=ybhoDN4AIPY

316 Ellis Martin's essay can be found at: michaelpmasters.com

317 Steiber, W. (March 25, 2020) Interview on Aliens Like Us with Rhys Darby. Season 1, episode 5, Experiencers. Spotify. Retrieved July, 2020 from: https://open.spotify.com/episode/24LVeNNNDsyrWVrlJTqbdF

318 Strieber, W. (March 25, 2020) Experiencers. *Aliens Like Us with Rhys Darby*. Retrieved December 2020 from: https://open.spotify.com/episode/24LVeNNNDsyrWVrlJTqbdF

319 Strieber, W., & McDowall, R. (1987) *Communion: A true story* (pp. 223). Sag Harbor, New York: Beech Tree Books. Pgs. 223 & 224.

320  Strieber, W., & McDowall, R. (1987) *Communion: A true story* (pp. 223). Sag Harbor, New York: Beech Tree Books. Pgs. 225, 239 & 241.


## CASE STUDY 12 ENDNOTES

321  Mack, J. E. (1994). *Abduction: Human encounters with aliens.* Pg. 127. Ballantine Books.
322  Mack, J. E. (1999). Passport to the cosmos: Human transformation and alien encounters. Crown.
323  Mack, J. E. (1994). Abduction: Human encounters with aliens. Ballantine Books.
324  Mack, J. E. (1994). Abduction: Human encounters with aliens. Pg. 120. Ballantine Books.
325  Mack, J. E. (1994). Abduction: Human encounters with aliens. Pgs. 113-114 & 121. Ballantine Books.
326  Mack, J. E. (1994). Abduction: Human encounters with aliens. Pg. 132. Ballantine Books.
327  Rozsa, M. (April 7, 2022) Declassified Pentagon documents discuss UFOs causing "unaccounted-for pregnancies" Retrieved May 2022 from: https://www.salon.com/2022/04/07/ufo-documents-pentagon/
328  Mack, J. E. (1994). Abduction: Human encounters with aliens. Pgs. 126 & 132. Ballantine Books.
329  Mack, J. E. (1994). Abduction: Human encounters with aliens. Ballantine Books.
330  Mack, J. E. (1994). Abduction: Human encounters with aliens. Pg. 126. Ballantine Books.
331  Mack, J. E. (1994). Abduction: Human encounters with aliens. Pg. 132. Ballantine Books.
332  Mack, J. E. (1994). Abduction: Human encounters with aliens. Pg. 115. Ballantine Books.
333  Mack, J. E. (1994). Abduction: Human encounters with aliens. Pgs. 131 & 134. Ballantine Books.
334  Mack, J. E. (1994). Abduction: Human encounters with aliens. Pg. 119. Ballantine Books.
335  Mack, J. E. (1994). Abduction: Human encounters with aliens. Pgs. 123-124. Ballantine Books.
336  Mack, J. E. (1994). Abduction: Human encounters with aliens. Ballantine Books.
337  Mack, J. E. (1994). Abduction: Human encounters with aliens. Ballantine Books.
338  Wilco. You Never Know. https://wilcoworld.net/song/you-never-know/
339  Wilco. You Never Know. https://wilcoworld.net/song/you-never-know/
340  Hastings, R. L. (2015). *UFOs and Nukes. Extraordinary Encounters at Nuclear Weapons Sites.* Independent.
341  For a good overview of historic and recent developments related to UFOs and nuclear facilities See: Hanks, M. (October 20, 2021) UFOs Disabled Weapons at Nuclear Facilities, According to These Former USAF Officers. *The Debrief.* Retrieved December 2021 from: https://thedebrief.org/ufos-disabled-weapons-at-nuclear-facilities-according-to-these-former-usaf-officers/

342 For a deeper discussion of UFOs and nuclear weapons, particularly regarding potential warnings of their dangers see: O'Connor, R. (2021) *UFOS, Nuclear Weapons, and a New Age of Reason*. Independent.

343 Mack, J. E. (1994). Abduction: Human encounters with aliens. Pgs. 127, 131 & 135. Ballantine Books.

344 Ogden, E. (December 31, 2021) Military veterans urge truth told about unidentified aerial phenomena incidents. Minot Daily News. Retrieved January 2022 from: https://www.minotdailynews.com/news/local-news/2021/12/military-veterans-urge-truth-told-about-unidentified-aerial-phenomena-incidents/

345 Klotz, J., Salas, R. (May 15, 2000) The Malmstrom AFB UFO/Missile Incident. Retrieved January 2022 from: https://www.cufon.org/cufon/malmstrom/malm1.htm

346 Some recent conversations where this future human, cataclysm, warring timelines concept was discussed:
- *That UFO Podcast* with Dr. Michael Masters (December 20, 2021) https://www.youtube.com/watch?v=jux_wagpYDI
- *Point of Convergence Podcast* Hosted by ExoAcademian (November 6, 2021) https://www.youtube.com/watch?v=I4b9WN04jVI
- *The Unidentified Celebrity Review* with Franc Milburn (October 25, 2021) https://www.youtube.com/watch?v=C6l-ZtXH880
- *Theories of Everything* with Ross Coulthart (September 24, 2021) https://www.youtube.com/watch?v=JM3kxeU_oDE

347 Mack, J. E. (1994). Abduction: Human encounters with aliens. Ballantine Books.

348 Mack, J. E. (1994). *Abduction: Human encounters with aliens*. Ballantine Books.

349 Mack, J. E. (1994). *Abduction: Human encounters with aliens*. Ballantine Books.

## CASE STUDY 13 ENDNOTES

350 Staff Reporter (September 4, 2014) Remembering Zimbabwe's great alien invasion. Mail & Guardian. Retrieved August 2020 from: https://mg.co.za/article/2014-09-04-remembering-zimbabwes-great-alien-invasion/

351 Mahoney, E. (June 28, 2018) Through Their Eyes: The 1994 Ariel School Encounter. Journal of Abduction-Encounter Research. Retrieved August 2020 from; https://www.jar-magazine.com/encounters/89-through-their-eyes-ariel-school-encounter

352 Hind, C. (1994) UFO AFRINEWS, 1994. Retrieved August 2020 from: https://www.ufocasebook.com/2008b/1994zimbabwe.html

353 UFO Casebook. UFO Landings-Rendlesham Forest, 1980. Retrieved December 2020 from: https://www.ufocasebook.com/Rendlesham.html

354 Staff Reporter (September 4, 2014) Remembering Zimbabwe's great alien invasion. Mail & Guardian. Retrieved August 2020 from: https://mg.co.za/article/2014-09-04-remembering-zimbabwes-great-alien-invasion/

355 Mahoney, E. (June 28, 2018) Through Their Eyes: The 1994 Ariel School Encounter. Journal of Abduction-Encounter Research. Retrieved August 2020 from; https://www.jar-magazine.com/encounters/89-through-their-eyes-ariel-school-encounter

356 Hind, C. (1994) UFO AFRINEWS, 1994. Retrieved August 2020 from: https://www.ufocasebook.com/2008b/1994zimbabwe.html

357 Jerry Wills UFO Contactee and Psychic Healer – April 20, 2017. Quote begins at 29:36 and ends at 30:46. Retrieved August 2020 from: https://www.youtube.com/watch?v=B8dft89abjU&list=PLH3jl6wuwaPFBRxKezpZqy-2WOUGkVEDrf&index=9&t=0s

358 Jacques Vallée, quoted in Stivelman, A. (Director) (2018) Witness of Another World [Motion picture]. United States: 1091 Pictures.

359 Ezekiel 4:28. The Holy Bible, New Revised Standard Version. Grand Rapids: Zondervan House, 1984.

360 Finley, S. C. (2012). The Meaning of Mother in Louis Farrakhan's "Mother Wheel": Race, Gender, and Sexuality in the Cosmology of the Nation of Islam's UFO. Journal of the American Academy of Religion, 80(2), 434-465.

361 Alper, B.A. & Alvarado, J. ( July 28, 2021) Religious Americans less likely to believe intelligent life exists on other planets. Retrieved December 2021 from: https://www.pewresearch.org/fact-tank/2021/07/28/religious-americans-less-likely-to-believe-intelligent-life-exists-on-other-planets/

362 Mack, J. E. (1999). Passport to the cosmos: Human transformation and alien encounters. Crown.

363 Staff Reporter (September 4, 2014) Remembering Zimbabwe's great alien invasion. Mail & Guardian. Retrieved August 2020 from: https://mg.co.za/article/2014-09-04-remembering-zimbabwes-great-alien-invasion/

364 Mahoney, E. ( June 28, 2018) Through Their Eyes: The 1994 Ariel School Encounter. Journal of Abduction-Encounter Research. Retrieved August 2020 from; https://www.jar-magazine.com/encounters/89-through-their-eyes-ariel-school-encounter

365 Mera, Steve (April 17, 2020) They're Here: Physical Evidence of UFO Hot Spots & Science Behind Interstellar Travel, Steve Merra (sic). The Leak Project. Retrieved January 2021 from: https://www.youtube.com/watch?v=Dy8NaSGq0HE&feature=youtu.be

## CASE STUDY 14 ENDNOTES

366 Harrison, D., Chalker, B. (2001) The Gundiah Mackay Abduction Milieu. A preliminary report by Bill Chalker and Diane Harrison, National Director of The Australian UFO Research Network. Retrieved November, 2020 from: http://www.auforn.com/Gundiah.html

367 Staff Writer (November 19, 2020) Amy Rylance Alien Abduction Is The Most Convincing UFO Encounter Of 21st Century With 100% Proof. How and Whys. Retrieved November 2020 from: https://www.howandwhys.com/amy-rylance-alien-abduction/

368 Wells, Lisa (October 5, 2020) The Most Curious Cases of Extraterrestrial Encounters. Herald Weekly. Retrieved December 2020 from: https://www.heraldweekly.com/the-most-curious-cases-of-extraterrestrial-encounters/17/

369 Harrison, D., Chalker, B. (2001) The Gundiah Mackay Abduction Milieu. A preliminary report by Bill Chalker and Diane Harrison, National Director of The Australian UFO Research Network. Retrieved November, 2020 from: http://www.auforn.

com/Gundiah.html

370 Your Guide to Anemia. U.S. Department of Health and Human Services. National Institutes of Health. National Heart, Lung, and Blood Institute. Retrieved December 2021 from: https://www.nhlbi.nih.gov/files/docs/public/blood/anemia-yg.pdf

371 Harrison, D., Chalker, B. (2001) The Gundiah Mackay Abduction Milieu. A preliminary report by Bill Chalker and Diane Harrison, National Director of The Australian UFO Research Network. Retrieved November, 2020 from: http://www.auforn.com/Gundiah.html

372 George Van Tassel CBS Interview, Giant Rock. Retrieved December 2021 from: https://www.youtube.com/watch?v=kfq6ShpcnIM

373 Image of the Ohio University Convocation Center, with link to a map of the dormitory floor plans inside the building. Retrieved December 2020 from: https://www.ohio.edu/housing/convocation-center

374 Harrison, D., Chalker, B. (2001) The Gundiah Mackay Abduction Milieu. A preliminary report by Bill Chalker and Diane Harrison, National Director of The Australian UFO Research Network. Retrieved November, 2020 from: http://www.auforn.com/Gundiah.html

375 Harrison, D., Chalker, B. (2001) The Gundiah Mackay Abduction Milieu. A preliminary report by Bill Chalker and Diane Harrison, National Director of The Australian UFO Research Network. Retrieved November, 2020 from: http://www.auforn.com/Gundiah.html

376 QUFOSR – Australian and Internationals UFO Sightings an Research. The Gundiah Mackay Alien Abduction–Australia. Retrieved August 28, 2018 from: https://qufosr.wordpress.com/2017/01/09/the-gundiah-mackay-alien-abduction-australia/

377 Harrison, D., Chalker, B. (2001) The Gundiah Mackay Abduction Milieu. A preliminary report by Bill Chalker and Diane Harrison, National Director of The Australian UFO Research Network. Retrieved November, 2020 from: http://www.auforn.com/Gundiah.html

378 Harrison, D., Chalker, B. (2001) The Gundiah Mackay Abduction Milieu. A preliminary report by Bill Chalker and Diane Harrison, National Director of The Australian UFO Research Network. Retrieved November, 2020 from: http://www.auforn.com/Gundiah.html

379 Wells, Lisa (October 5, 2020) The Most Curious Cases of Extraterrestrial Encounters. Herald Weekly. Retrieved December 2020 from: https://www.heraldweekly.com/the-most-curious-cases-of-extraterrestrial-encounters/17/

380 Staff Writer (November 19, 2020) Amy Rylance Alien Abduction Is The Most Convincing UFO Encounter Of 21st Century With 100% Proof. How and Whys. Retrieved November 2020 from: https://www.howandwhys.com/amy-rylance-alien-abduction/

## CASE STUDY 15 ENDNOTES

381 Reid, H. (April 27, 2020) Twitter post. Retrieved July 2021 from: https://twitter.com/senatorreid/status/1254836730546384897?lang=en

382 Agrama, H. A. (2021) Secularity, synchronicity, and uncanny science: Considerations and challenges. *Zygon®*, 56(2), 395-415.

383 NAVAIR – FOIA. Retrieved September 2020 from: https://www.navair.navy.mil/foia/documents

384 Cooper, H, Blumenthal, R., & Kean, L. (May 26, 2019) 'Wow, What Is That?' Navy Pilots Report Unexplained Flying Objects. The New York Times. Retrieved September 2020, from: https://www.nytimes.com/2019/05/26/us/politics/ufo-sightings-navy-pilots.html

385 Thebault, R. (May 17, 2021) For some Navy pilots, UFO sightings were an ordinary event: 'Every day for at least a couple years.' The Washington Post. Retrieved January 2022 from: https://www.washingtonpost.com/nation/2021/05/17/ufo-sightings-navy-ryan-graves/

386 Staff writer (April 27, 2020) Statement by the Department of Defense on the Release of Historical Navy Videos. Retrieved July 2021 from: https://www.defense.gov/Newsroom/Releases/Release/Article/2165713/statement-by-the-department-of-defense-on-the-release-of-historical-navy-videos/

387 Haines, G. K. A Die Hard Issue: CIAs Role in the Study of UFOs 1947-90. Retrieved November 2014 from National Investigations Committee on Aerial Phenomena official web site: http://www.nicap.org/ciarole.htm

388 Haines, G. K. A Die Hard Issue: CIAs Role in the Study of UFOs 1947-90. Retrieved November 2014 from National Investigations Committee on Aerial Phenomena official web site: http://www.nicap.org/ciarole.htm

389 Haines, G. K. A Die Hard Issue: CIAs Role in the Study of UFOs 1947-90. Retrieved November 2014 from National Investigations Committee on Aerial Phenomena official web site: http://www.nicap.org/ciarole.htm

390 Haines, G. K. A Die Hard Issue: CIAs Role in the Study of UFOs 1947-90. Retrieved November 2014 from National Investigations Committee on Aerial Phenomena official web site: http://www.nicap.org/ciarole.htm

391 Losey, S. (January 20, 2015) Air Force UFO files hit the web. *Military Times*. Retrieved June, 2015 from http://www.militarytimes.com/story/military/tech/2015/01/17/air-force-ufo-files/21812539/

392 Cooper, H, Blumenthal, R., & Kean, L. (December 16, 2017) Glowing Auras and 'Black Money': The Pentagon's Mysterious U.F.O. Program. The New York Times. Retrieved February 2021 from: https://www.nytimes.com/2017/12/16/us/politics/pentagon-program-ufo-harry-reid.html?action=click&module=RelatedCoverage&pgtype=Article&region=Footer

393 UAP Task Force (June 25, 2021) Preliminary Assessment of Unidentified Aerial Phenomena. Office of the Director of National Intelligence. Retrieved July 2021 from: Prelimary-Assessment-UAP-20210625.pdf (dni.gov)

394 Hicks, K. (November 23, 2021) Establishment of the Airborne Object Identification and Management Synchronization Group. Retrieved January 2022 from: https://media.defense.gov/2021/Nov/23/2002898596/-1/-1/0/ESTABLISHMENT-OF-THE-AIRBORNE-OBJECT-IDENTIFICATION-AND-MANAGEMENT-SYNCHRONIZATION-GROUP.PDF

395 Press Release (December 9, 2021) Gillibrand's Groundbreaking Unidentified Aerial

Phenomena Amendment Included In Final NDAA. Retrieved January 2022 from: https://www.gillibrand.senate.gov/news/press/release/gillibrands-groundbreaking-unidentified-aerial-phenomena-amendment-included-in-final-ndaa

396 Press Release (December 9, 2021) Rubio, Gillibrand, Gallego Applaud Inclusion of Unidentified Aerial Phenomena Amendment in National Defense Bill. Retrieved January 2022 from: https://www.rubio.senate.gov/public/index.cfm/press-releases?ID=300A0260-2D44-4C0E-AED8-0A21D24EA9CE

397 Jacques Vallée, quoted in Stivelman, A. (Director) (2018) Witness of Another World [Motion picture]. United States: 1091 Pictures.

398 Swancer, B. (January 11, 2021) The Strange Alien Abduction of Amy Rylance. Mysterious Universe. Retrieved January 2022 from: https://mysteriousuniverse.org/2021/01/the-strange-alien-abduction-of-amy-rylance/

399 Strassman, R. (2000). DMT: The spirit molecule: A doctor's revolutionary research into the biology of near-death and mystical experiences. Simon and Schuster.

400 Powell, R., Reali, P., Thompson, T., Beall, M., Kimzey, D., Cates, L., & Hoffman, R. (2019) A Forensic Analysis of Navy Carrier Strike Group Eleven's Encounter with an Anomalous Aerial Vehicle. Scientific Coalition for UAP Studies.

401 Cooper, H, Blumenthal, R, & Kean, L. (December 16, 2017) Glowing Auras and 'Black Money': The Pentagon's Mysterious U.F.O. Program. The New York Times. Retrieved September 2020 from: https://www.nytimes.com/2017/12/16/us/politics/pentagon-program-ufo-harry-reid.html?action=click&module=RelatedCoverage&pgtype=Article&region=Footer

402 Dinick, J. (May 16, 2021) Navy pilots recall "unsettling" 2004 UAP sighting. CBS News. Retrieved January 2022 from: https://www.cbsnews.com/news/navy-ufo-sighting-60-minutes-2021-05-16/

403 Powell, R., Reali, P., Thompson, T., Beall, M., Kimzey, D., Cates, L., & Hoffman, R. (2019) A Forensic Analysis of Navy Carrier Strike Group Eleven's Encounter with an Anomalous Aerial Vehicle. Scientific Coalition for UAP Studies.

404 Interview with Lex Fridman. September 8, 2020. Episode #122 - David Fravor: UFOs, Aliens, Fighter Jets, and Aerospace Engineering. Retrieved July 2021 from: https://www.podbean.com/media/share/dir-zehnn-a757628

405 Phelan, M. (December 19, 2019) Navy Pilot Who Filmed the 'Tic Tac' UFO Speaks: 'It Wasn't Behaving by the Normal Laws of Physics.' Intelligencer. New York Magazine. Retrieved September 2020 from: https://nymag.com/intelligencer/2019/12/tic-tac-ufo-video-q-and-a-with-navy-pilot-chad-underwood.html

406 Knuth, K. H., & Powell, R. M. (2019) Estimating Flight Characteristics of Anomalous Unidentified Aerial Vehicles in the 2004 Nimitz Encounter. In Multidisciplinary Digital Publishing Institute Proceedings (Vol. 33, No. 1, p. 26).

407 Powell, R., Reali, P., Thompson, T., Beall, M., Kimzey, D., Cates, L., & Hoffman, R. (2019) A Forensic Analysis of Navy Carrier Strike Group Eleven's Encounter with an Anomalous Aerial Vehicle. Scientific Coalition for UAP Studies.

408 Powell, R., Reali, P., Thompson, T., Beall, M., Kimzey, D., Cates, L., & Hoffman, R. (2019) A Forensic Analysis of Navy Carrier Strike Group Eleven's Encounter with an Anomalous Aerial Vehicle. Scientific Coalition for UAP Studies.

409 Quoted in Powell, R., Reali, P., Thompson, T., Beall, M., Kimzey, D., Cates, L., &

Hoffman, R. (2019) A Forensic Analysis of Navy Carrier Strike Group Eleven's Encounter with an Anomalous Aerial Vehicle. Pgs. 8 & 9. *Scientific Coalition for UAP Studies.*

410 Quoted in Powell, R., Reali, P., Thompson, T., Beall, M., Kimzey, D., Cates, L., & Hoffman, R. (2019) A Forensic Analysis of Navy Carrier Strike Group Eleven's Encounter with an Anomalous Aerial Vehicle. Pg. 11. *Scientific Coalition for UAP Studies.*

411 Phelan, M. (December 19, 2019) Navy Pilot Who Filmed the 'Tic Tac' UFO Speaks: 'It Wasn't Behaving by the Normal Laws of Physics.' Intelligencer. New York Magazine. Retrieved September 2020 from: https://nymag.com/intelligencer/2019/12/tic-tac-ufo-video-q-and-a-with-navy-pilot-chad-underwood.html

412 Seitz-Wald, A. (January 8, 2022) Disclosure or deception? New UFO Pentagon office divides believers. *NBC News.* Retrieved January 8, 2022 from: https://www.nbcnews.com/politics/national-security/disclosure-or-deception-new-ufo-pentagon-office-divides-believers-n1287199

413 West, M. (September 11, 2020) Twitter. Retrieved September 2020 from: https://twitter.com/MickWest/status/1304436298598330368

414 Puthoff, H. E. (2012) Advanced space propulsion based on vacuum (spacetime metric) engineering. arXiv preprint arXiv:1204.2184.

415 Hill, P. R., Wood, R. M., & Donderi, D. C. (1995). Unconventional Flying Objects: a scientific analysis (p. 164). Hampton Roads.

416 Jerry Wills UFO Contactee and Psychic Healer – April 20, 2017. Quote begins at 42:25 and ends at 43:55. Retrieved September 2020 from: https://www.youtube.com/watch?v=B8dft89abjU&list=PLH3jl6wuwaPFBRxKezpZqy-2WOUGkVEDrf&index=9&t=0s

417 Sarfatti, J. (March 9, 2020) SPACE: Dr. Jack Sarfatti: I Know How Tic Tacs Work, the US Does Not. Hidden Truth Show with Jim Breslo. S5 E16. Quote begins at 13:25 and ends at 15:00. Retrieved September 2020 from: https://www.iheart.com/podcast/269-hidden-truth-las-vegas-sho-28980886/episode/s5e16-space-dr-jack-sarfatti-i-58935760/

418 Sarfatti, J. (March 9, 2020) SPACE: Dr. Jack Sarfatti: I Know How Tic Tacs Work, the US Does Not. Hidden Truth Show with Jim Breslo. S5 E16. Quote begins at 1:15:00 and ends at 1:15:55. Retrieved September 2020 from: https://www.iheart.com/podcast/269-hidden-truth-las-vegas-sho-28980886/episode/s5e16-space-dr-jack-sarfatti-i-58935760/

## CHAPTER 5 ENDNOTES

419 Vallée, J.F. (2003) Thinking Allowed. Implications of the UFO Phenomena. Hosted by Dr. Jeffrey Mislove. Cited in Hernandez, R., Klimo, J., & Schild, R. (2018). Beyond UFOs: The science of consciousness and contact with non-human intelligence. The Dr. Edgar Mitchell Foundation for Research into Extraterrestrial and Extraordinary Experiences, FREE. Pg. 105.

420 Einstein, A. Statement to William Miller, as quoted in LIFE magazine (May 2, 1955).

Retrieved March 2022 from: https://www.patheos.com/blogs/soapboxredemption/2018/01/einstein-holy-curiosity/

421 Stemwedel, J. D. (August 20, 2015) The Philosophy Of Star Trek: Is The Prime Directive Ethical? Forbes. Retrieved March 2021 from: https://www.forbes.com/sites/janetstemwedel/2015/08/20/the-philosophy-of-star-trek-is-the-prime-directive-ethical/?sh=50df617d2177

422 Miller, K. (September 1, 2018) The Block Universe Theory, Where Time Travel Is Possible But Time Passing Is An Illusion. *ABC Science*. Retrieved January 2022 from: *https://www.abc.net.au/news/science/2018-09-02/block-universe-theory-time-past-present-future-travel/10178386*

423 Russo, A., Russo, J., (2019) Avengers: Endgame. Marvel Studios.

424 Miller, K. (September 1, 2018) The Block Universe Theory, Where Time Travel Is Possible But Time Passing Is An Illusion. *ABC Science*. Retrieved January 2022 from: *https://www.abc.net.au/news/science/2018-09-02/block-universe-theory-time-past-present-future-travel/10178386*

425 Albert Einstein, in penning a letter to the sister of his best friend, Michele Besso, who had just died. *Time's arrow: Albert Einstein's letters to Michele Besso*. Retrieved January 2022 from: https://www.christies.com/features/Einstein-letters-to-Michele-Besso-8422-1.aspx

426 Novikov, I. D. (1998) The River of Time. Location: Cambridge University Press.

427 Ringbauer, M., Broome, M. A., Myers, C. R., White, A. G., & Ralph, T. C. (2014) Experimental simulation of closed timelike curves. *Nature communications*, 5.

428 Lobo, F., & Crawford, P. (2003) Time, closed timelike curves and causality. In *The Nature of Time: Geometry, Physics and Perception* (pp. 289-296). Springer Netherlands.

429 Deutsch, D. (1991) Quantum mechanics near closed timelike lines. *Physical Review D*, 44(10), 3197.

430 Webb, S. G. (2006) *The first boat people* (Vol. 47). Cambridge University Press.

431 Goebel, T., Waters, M. R., & O'Rourke, D. H. (2008) The late Pleistocene dispersal of modern humans in the Americas. *Science, 319*(5869), 1497-1502.

432 Balch, R. W., & Taylor, D. (2002) Making sense of the Heaven's Gate suicides. In *Cults, religion, and violence* (pp. 209-228) Bromley, D.G., & Melton J.G. (Eds.). Cambridge, UK: Cambridge University Press.

433 Prentiss, C. R. (2003) *Religion and the creation of race and ethnicity*. New York, New York, US. NYU Press.

Printed in Great Britain
by Amazon